GENERATING
CLEAN ELECTRONS

This book was set in Times New Roman and Arial by Cathy J. Boulay, ETG.

Written by Charles J. Brooks and Contributing Industry Experts

Graphics by Luke Johns

ISBN-13:   978-1-58122-112-1
ISBN-10:   1-58122-112-6

6 7 8 9 10

MARCRAFT

Preface

ETG/Marcraft has been producing technical training materials for various facets of the electronics, computer technology, computer networking and professional installer fields since 1975. These fields are being asked to form the technical basis of a new "Green" industry dedicated to managing the world's natural resources and energy in a more efficient manner while allowing for an acceptable standard of living for its inhabitants.

This movement, composed of many different people and organizations, has been deemed the "green movement". Around the world, this movement has taken hold and is growing as it becomes apparent that key natural resources are becoming much less abundant and the demand for them is growing rapidly.

One of the key areas in the green movement is the search for cleaner, more environmentally friendly sources of electrical power. At the forefront of this search are wind power, solar power and fuel cell technologies. While these technologies are not the only source of clean energy being explored, they are the most promising technologies in the field and are generating demand for workers skilled in these areas.

This course is designed to introduce readers to these three technologies and to begin preparing them for job roles in these new technical fields.

Key Features

The pedagogical features of this book have been carefully developed to provide the user with key content information, hands on activities and review and testing opportunities. The book is designed specifically to implement the Science, Technology, Engineering and Math (STEM) initiative developed by the National Science Foundation.

Each chapter begins with a list of learning objectives that establishes the expected outcomes for the chapter. A theory section that explains the technology being explored in the chapter follows the learning objectives. The theory section also contains a discussion of all safety and precautionary information associated with the technology.

One or more guided hands-on procedures follow the main theory section. In these sections, the user is guided through step-by-step installation, configuration, operation and testing procedures for the technology.

The final lab procedures in each chapter are a guided Research Lab followed by a Guide Design Lab. These labs are designed to help the user apply their theoretical knowledge and hands on experiences to engineering research and design applications. When possible, the design labs have been written by special guest authors who are actively involved in the technology being discussed.

Evaluation and Test Material

The course provides an abundance of quiz and test materials. Each chapter concludes with a chapter review quiz composed of open-ended questions. Each hands-on procedure concludes with a set of open ended lab questions that focus on what the user observed in the procedure (not just more theory questions). Additional test materials in the form of multiple choice questions can be found on the CD-ROM test engine available separately.

ORGANIZATION

This section explains the reasons the Green Movement has taken on such importance in a relatively short amount of time. It describes the breath of the green movement and then focuses on the Green Power technology portion of the movement. It also introduces the GT-1500 Clean Electron Generation panel and its accessories.

Chapter 1 – *Alternative Energy Generation* begins with a discussion of the atom and describes why electrons are important to the generation of power that can be used to perform work. It also describes the Ohms Law relationship that exists between the four major quantities of electricity—voltage (push), current (flow), resistance (load) and power (ability to do work).

The second half the chapter deals with making electrical connections and measurements, as well as introducing the National Electrical Code that governs the installation and connection of electrical systems in residential and commercial structures.

Chapter 2 – *Wind Turbines* is dedicated to the installation, operation and understanding of wind turbines used to generate electrical power from wind. The chapter begins with a discussion of the science of winds and the aerodynamics that convert wind movement into mechanical force, and then the technology that converts the mechanical force into electrical current that can be used to perform work.

The second half of the chapter deals with standard installation, configuration and testing of a wind turbine system. The chapter concludes with guided research and design labs that ask the user to apply what they have learned to a particular wind power scenario.

Chapter 3 – *Photovoltaic Panels* deals with the installation, operation and understanding of photovoltaic (solar) cells/panels/arrays used to generate electrical power from sunlight. The chapter begins with a discussion of the science of converting light energy into electrical current that can be used to perform work.

The second half of the chapter deals with standard installation, configuration and testing of a photovoltaic panel system. The chapter concludes with a guided research and design labs that ask the user to apply what they have learned to fulfill a particular solar power design requirement.

Chapter 4 – *Fuel Cells* examines different types of fuel cell technologies and applications. The first half of the chapter deals with the operation, configuration and understanding of fuel cell technology. It also describes the process of electrolysis used to generate hydrogen for the fuel cells' operation.

The second half of the chapter deals with common steps associated with the installation, configuration and testing of fuel cell systems. The chapter concludes with a guided research and design labs that ask the user to apply what they have learned to design a fuel cell power system to meet a particular design requirement.

Teacher Support

A full-featured instructor's guide is available for the course. Answers for all of the end-of-chapter quiz questions are included along with a paragraph reference in the chapter where that item is covered. Sample schedules are included as guidelines for possible course implementations. Answers to all hands-on questions are provided so that there is an indication of what the expected outcomes should be.

ABOUT THE AUTHORS

Charles J. Brooks

Charles J. Brooks is currently co-owner and vice president of Educational Technologies Group Inc., as well as co-owner of eITPrep LLP, an online training company. He is in charge of research and product development at both organizations. A former electronics instructor and technical writer with the National Education Corporation, Charles taught and wrote on post-secondary ETG curriculum, including introductory electronics, transistor theory, linear integrated circuits, basic digital theory, industrial electronics, microprocessors, and computer peripherals. Charles has authored several books, including the first five editions of A+ Certification Training Guide, The Complete Introductory Computer Course, and IBM PC Peripheral Troubleshooting and Repair. He also writes about networking, residential technology integration, and convergence.

George Lister

George Lister is a professional Control Systems Technician skilled in and knowledgeable of pneumatic, mechanical, and electronic instrumentation. Currently, he is an instructor at Texas State Technical College teaching Wind Energy Technology, SCADA & Industrial Networking. As a Wind Turbine Technician, he maintained wind turbine systems to ensure availability for Mitsubishi Power Systems. A Senior Member of the International Society for Automation (ISA), he is a lifetime member of the Electronics Technicians Association – International (ETA-I) and a member of the Certification Committee.

ACKNOWLEDGMENTS

Charles J. Brooks

I would like to mention some of the people and groups who have been responsible for the success of this book. As always, I want to thank the staff here at ETG/Marcraft for making it easy to turn out a good product. Thanks to Gregory Ter-Oganov and Stuart C. Palmer from the Technical Services area for trying things out for me in the lab. Also, thanks to Cathy Boulay, Tony Tonda, and Whitney Freeman from the Product Development department for their excellent work in getting the text and lab books ready to go and looking good. Thanks also to Ray Stroud for his excellent review and feedback.

As always, I want to thank my wife Robbie for all of her understanding, support, and help with these projects, as well as Robert, Jamaica, Michael, and Joshua.

Table of Contents

WHAT IS GREEN?

CHAPTER 1   ALTERNATIVE ENERGY GENERATION

CHAPTER 2   WIND TURBINES

CHAPTER 3   PHOTOVOLTAIC PANELS

CHAPTER 4   FUEL CELLS

What is Green?

It seems that suddenly there are references to "being Green" or going Green" all around us. There are advertisements for green companies and green products everywhere. Power companies are talking about intelligent **Smart Grids** and power saving equipment and techniques for saving energy. But what is "**Green**" and why is it important to you and me?

True Green is actually a moniker used to encourage the hearer to think about nature (the world around us) and the **quality of life** we can rely on. The world is facing a future that is crowded and features people and countries competing for a shrinking supply of natural resources. In addition, the continued traditional usage of those resources threatens the natural elements that provide and support the quality of life we have on Earth.

While there are many individuals and organizations that are touting their green initiatives and making going green sound and appear as something easy to do, Kermit the Frog actually sums up the reality of "green" in his famous quote "*It's not easy being green.*" There is no simple or easy method for getting to a green condition. There is also no single thing we can do to achieve a sustainable green world. Green is actually a collection of ideas that include:

- Generating power from sources that do not produce carbon as a bi-product.

- Limiting energy usage through personal behavior modification and technology.

- Conserving resources through personal behavior modification and technology.

- Creating sustainable energy conservation through improved building techniques, materials and technologies.

- Creating and using transportation systems and techniques that do not rely on carbon-based products.

| Smart Grids |
| Green |
| quality of life |

GREEN POWER

As you will see in the remainder of this chapter and the rest of this book, it is important for everyone to move toward being and living "green". In this book we will concentrate on technologies associated with the "generation of green (non-carbon producing) power". From the preceding list you can see that this is only one facet of going green.

In discussions surrounding green activities and the conservation of resources, you may hear conversations that would lead you to the conclusion that we must all return to medieval ways of living where we conserve our way to a healthy planet with a sustainable population. The problem is that this will never happen short of a worldwide disaster. The power generation bullet point is at the top of the list because it is one of the fundamental steps in moving *forward* as a civilization, while still protecting the source of that civilization.

WHY GO GREEN?

Why does it seem that we are suddenly worrying so much about environmental concerns and looking for advancements in green technologies? The reason is that several facets have come together to force the issue—accumulation of pollutants in our atmosphere, lands and waters, an increasingly crowded planet due to rapid population growth worldwide, a marked increase in the standard of living in many countries of the world, and diminishing resources that have historically been used to advance civilization.

These factors have led to increasingly scarce and more-expensive energy supplies, accelerated extinction of plant and animal types, greater differences between energy have and have-not countries, political balances based on energy relationships (instead of mutual interests and progress), and increasing climate and environmental changes.

In the sections that follow, you will see how these factors have come together to push the green movement to the forefront of political and educational activities. One of the most highly touted advantages of the green movement is the large number of new jobs and job roles expected to be created in the industry.

THE INDUSTRIAL REVOLUTION

Industrial Revolution

work

machines

In the late 1700's a period of innovation and growth called the **Industrial Revolution** began. Prior to this time, manual labor, domesticated animals and waterpower were the predominate methods of performing **work**. During the industrial revolution, these methods began to be replaced by and enhanced through the use of **machines**. At the forefront of the revolution were the European and North American countries. However, the industrialization movement eventually spread throughout the world in varying degrees.

> **NOTE**
> The definition of *work* is the amount of *energy* transferred by a *force*, or from system to another.

This movement created two basic changes in major portions of the world's civilization. It shifted largely agricultural societies in Europe and North America into machine-based manufacturing communities and it changed the world's level of dependency on **energy** and **power**. It also started a long running era of economic growth and inventiveness.

energy

power

> **NOTE**
> The definition of *energy* is the amount (quantity) of *work* that can be performed by a *force*. Energy appears as kinetic, potential, or thermal.

> **NOTE**
> Similarly, the definition of power is the amount (quantity) of *work* that can be done in a given unit of *time*. This can also be stated as the amount of *energy* that can be transferred in a given unit of *time*.

The first major shift is usually linked to the advent of the **steam engine**, as shown in Figure I-1. The steam engine relies on energy derived from **burning fuels**—such as **wood** or **coal**—to heat water into steam. The steam is then used to perform **mechanical work**. Coal eventually emerged as the favorite fuel because it offered twice as much energy output potential as the same amount of wood.

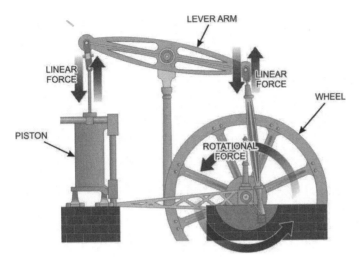

steam engine

burning fuels

wood

coal

mechanical work

Figure I-1: The Steam Engine

Coal, **natural gas**, and **crude oil** were used in the industrial productive processes, as well as to heat homes and buildings. Initially, crude oil replaced whale oil to provide heat and lighting. Its continued refinement eventually lad to its use as fuel for engines used in industry and transportation.

Toward the end of the 1800's (the late 19th century), the **internal combustion engine**, as shown in Figure I-2, was developed. This machine created a major shift in the transportation of goods and people. Internal combustion engines are machines that use **diesel fuel** and **gasoline** for fuel and convert the energy from these fuels into mechanical work.

natural gas

crude oil

internal combustion engine

diesel fuel

gasoline

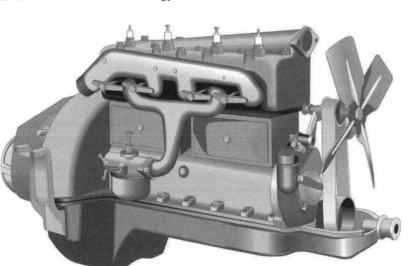

Figure I-2: The Internal Combustion Engine

The development of the modern industrial assembly line by Henry Ford enabled the general public to purchase automobiles. The process made automobile inexpensive enough for individuals to own. This led to a spiraling growth of roads, highways, cities, towns and suburbs, increasing the number of automobiles in use and the average number of miles driven by each car.

electricity

The industrial revolution also produced a commercial power revolution in the form of industrial and residential **electricity**. Electricity emerged as an energy source that could be used to generate heat and light, as well as to produce mechanical and motive forces. The demand for electricity has produced a world full of electrical generation plants. In the year 2000, the worldwide rate of electrical energy consumption was about 13 trillion Watts at any given moment. This amount is expected to double by the year 2050.

fossil fuels

carbon dioxide (CO$_2$)

While there are electrical generation plants powered by water (hydro), wind, sunlight (solar), and nuclear reactions, the majority of the power plants in existence are powered by **fossil fuels** (they burn oil, natural gas, or coal) that produce **carbon dioxide (CO$_2$)** as a byproduct of their processes. The main reasons for using these fuels is that they are cheap, dependable, and occur in relatively abundant amounts.

RISING WORLD POPULATIONS

population increase

The current population of the world is roughly 6.7 billion people. This is up from approximately 2.8 billion people in 1955. The potentially scary part of this math is that the number of people living on Earth is expected to climb to 9.2 billion by 2050. As you can see, the **population increase** in the next forty to fifty years is equal to the total population that was present on the earth just fifty years ago.

infrastructure

According to reports from the United Nations more than half of all people live in cities (as opposed to suburbs and rural locations). The continued increase of people dwelling in cities will place growing stress on urban **infrastructure**—such as roads and streets, electrical supply, and sanitation systems—water, sewage and garbage.

machines

More importantly, most of the population increase predicted is likely to occur in countries that are not capable of handling it. For example, the number of people in African countries such as Ethiopia, Congo, Liberia, and Nigeria are likely to double by 2050. Other countries expecting large population growth include Afghanistan, Niger, and Yemen. In these countries basic resources are already scarce and governing is already difficult. These situations are only likely to deteriorate in the coming years—causing political unrest and a drive to obtain greater access to resources through whatever means necessary.

> **NOTE**
>
> The powers of the world have historically competed for access to the World's natural resources. In the future this competition level can only increase. However, the need for resources will also force poorer countries to compete in whatever ways necessary to obtain the bare minimum in resources and technology.

The only portion of the world currently showing a decrease in population is the Eastern European nations. These nations include Poland, Russia, Romania, Ukraine, Hungary, and the Czech Republic. However immigration onto these countries is expected to reverse this trend as the planet becomes more crowded.

A Rising World Middle Class

While poor countries are struggling to obtain basic resources and technology, several countries with poorer populations are developing a growing **middle class** in their societies. The countries leading the way in this area are China and India, both of which just happen to have huge populations already. These countries are followed closely by growing middle classes in Russia and South East Asian countries. More than 200 million people have moved from the status of "poor" to "middle class" over the past twenty years, in India and China alone.

So what does the growth of middle class populations have to do with green technologies and energy? Well, as people are lifted out of poverty and climb the socioeconomic ladder, they become **consumers** of more resources—in both variety and quantity—as they seek higher levels of comfort and security. Not only do these consumers buy more commodities (things), which require more resources to create, they also become direct consumers of energy.

The "things" that upwardly mobile people add to their lives—such as refrigerators, air conditioners, heaters, computers, microwave ovens, and automobiles—require metals plastics, wood, chemicals and other raw materials to make. However, they all require additional fuel sources to operate. This is the problem—more people are competing for a fixed amount of natural resources at an ever-increasing rate. For example, China is building new power plants to produce an additional billion watts (Giga Watt) of electrical power every two weeks to keep up with the growing demand in that one country.

As you will see in the next section, those fixed amounts of resources are diminishing at an ever-increasing rate.

middle class

consumers

DIMINISHING WORLD RESOURCES

Earlier it was mentioned that one of the reasons for using fossil fuels to power so much of our lives is that they are "cheap, dependable, and occur in relatively abundant amounts". In some cases, there are observations that the supply of many natural resources, including carbon-based fuels, may not be as abundant in the future and may in fact already be in decline. Figure I-3 depicts anticipated production from all hydrocarbon fuel sources.

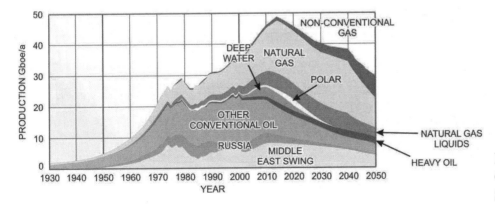

Figure I-3: Carbon-Based Fuel Supplies

Some studies indicate that 90% of all available conventional oil deposits have been found and that global oil production will peak in about 2014. The world is currently consuming 300% of the oil that is being discovered and has already used up as much as 50% of the world's regular oil supply. Coupled with the still increasing demand for oil and oil-based products, a gap has developed between the supply of oil and the demand for it. Without intervention, this gap will continue to grow wider, as illustrated in Figure I-4.

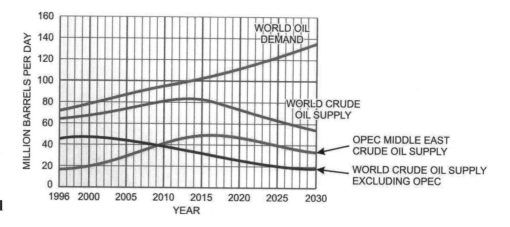

Figure I-4: World Oil Supplies vs. Demand

Natural gas production is expected to peak in about 2030. A gap between supply and demand for natural gas could begin to occur as early as 2012, according to the studies.

Coal remains an abundant source of fuel for the time being. However, by 2050 about 50% of the world's coal supply will have been depleted and could be exhausted by the end of the current century. Using coal with current technology has serious side effects in that it produces emissions of carbon dioxide and other harmful by products in quantities that make it ecologically undesirable. The successful use of coal for fuel is waiting on scientific breakthroughs such as more efficient combustion techniques for burning coal, methods for capturing and storing CO_2 produced by burning coal (referred to as clean coal technology), and coal to liquid conversion techniques.

If these fuels remain the mainstay for the foreseeable future, there are predictions that by the end of the century the world will have used all of the hydrocarbon fuel sources that have ever existed.

ENVIRONMENTAL CONCERNS

In the second half of the 20th century, many groups began to evaluate the affects that modern life was having on the planet Earth. People and organizations began to assess the impact of advanced cultures on the atmosphere, lakes, rivers, streams and aquifers, forestation, climate and wildlife species.

This examination led to awareness of the impact humans in industrialized areas were having on the world. The first waves of understanding were focused on water and air pollution, decreases in bio-diversity and changing world environments.

One of the most pressing issues uncovered in this awakening was the affect created by the fuels and processes underpinning the industrialization of the world. Large amounts of pollutants known as **greenhouse gases** have been accumulating in the atmosphere—out of sight and out of mind. These gases (mainly **carbon dioxide—CO_2**) act as an insulating layer that wraps around the Earth and holds in heat that would normally be radiated into space. Many scientists believe there is a rapidly approaching tipping point where the level of these greenhouse gases may cause irreversible changes in the environment—particularly in the area of **climate change**.

greenhouse gases

carbon dioxide (CO_2)

climate change

Greenhouse gases are mainly the byproduct of industrial, residential and transportation systems in developed countries. However, the accumulation of the greenhouse gases in the atmosphere has been accentuated by an accelerated loss of green areas (forests and prairies) around the globe. These green areas are important in the world's carbon dioxide exchange process. Trees and plants take in CO_2 from the atmosphere and produce oxygen through the **photosynthesis** process.

photosynthesis

The destruction of green areas affect the environment in two ways—first, the reduction in tress and plants means that there are fewer units to carry out the CO_2 to O_2 process, leaving more CO_2 and less O_2 in the atmosphere—second, the removal of the green materials releases carbon stored in the trees and plants back into the atmosphere. As a point of reference, **deforestation** of huge areas in countries such as Brazil and Indonesia has contributed more CO_2 to the atmosphere than all of the transportation devices in the world combined.

deforestation

CO_2 is not the only greenhouse gas piling up in the atmosphere. Other gases include **methane (CH_4)**, a colorless, odorless gas produces by cattle as part of their digestive process.

methane (CH_4)

DIRTY FUELS AND CLEAN FUELS

Historically, the fossil fuels that have been used to provide power for industrialization and life-style advancements have been cheap, abundant and environmentally **dirty**. These fuels (coal, oil and gas) have been produced and used throughout the world. However, the system that supports these fuels cannot continue as they have for so many years. The impact of doing so on the environment, geopolitical relationships, and climate is simply unacceptable.

dirty

Therefore, there is already an accelerated movement into the development and deployment of as many **clean fuel** technologies (wind, solar, hydrogen, hydro, geothermal and nuclear power) as possible, as quickly as possible.

clean fuel

GENERATING CLEAN ELECTRONS

In his book—*Hot, Flat and Crowded*—Thomas Freidman states that: "*No single solution would defuse more of the Energy Climate Era's problems at once than the invention of a source of abundant, clean, reliable and cheap electrons. Give me abundant, clean, reliable and cheap electrons, and I will give you a world that can continue to grow without triggering unmanageable climate change. ... The ability to generate clean electrons is not a solution to every problem, but it is the enabler of solutions to more problems than any other single factor I can think of.*"

It is for exactly this reason that we have produced this first introductory-level Clean Electron Generation Experiment Panel and Text/Lab manual. The three technologies featured in this course—wind turbines, photovoltaic panels, and fuel cells are the leading technologies in clean electron generation. There are other contenders in this category—including hydroelectric systems, geothermal generation systems, and nuclear power generation (it does not produce carbon by products). However, these technologies still represent a second tier of possible clean electron generation.

GT-1500 CLEAN ELECTRON GENERATION PANEL ORIENTATION

The GT-1500 Clean Electron Generation Panel is a training tool to introduce you to the three major alternate energy generation systems. These systems are:

- **Fuel Cells** – Mostly transportation and remote site power applications.

- **Wind Turbines** – Residential and commercial power generation and cogeneration applications.

- **Photovoltaic Panels** – Residential and commercial power generation and cogeneration applications.

Identify and inventory the components that make up the GT-1500 trainer at this point. Figure I-5 depicts the front of the GT-1500 panel in its original delivery state.

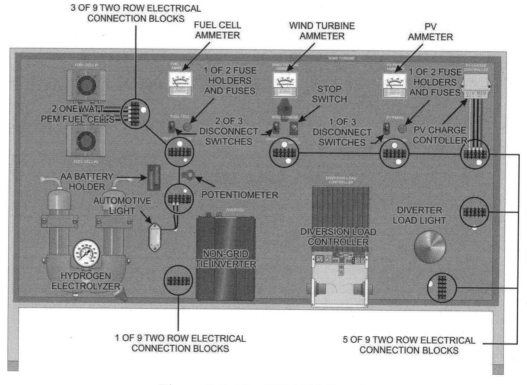

Figure I-5: The GT-1500 Panel

On Board Components

Identify and inventory the following onboard components:

- 12-Watt (11-Cell, 6.6V) PEM Fuel Cells (2)
- Hydrogen Electrolyzer
- Ammeters (3)
- Stop Switch (1)
- Disconnect Switches (3)
- Fuse Holders and Fuses (2)
- Diversion Load Controller (Load Diverter)
- PV Charge Controller

- Non-Grid Tie Inverter
- Two-Row Electrical Connection Blocks (10)
- Diverter Load Light
- Potentiometer
- Electric Motor Assembly
- Automotive Light
- AA Battery Holder

GT-1500 Connection Blocks

Figure I-6 depicts the connection blocks mounted on the front of the GT-1500 panel.

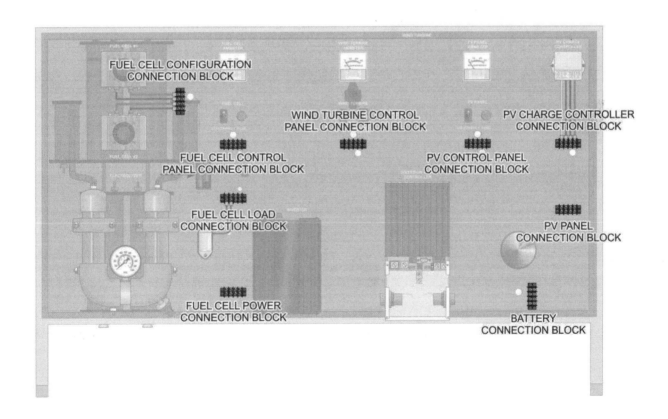

Figure I-6: The Connection Blocks on the Front of the GT-1500 Panel

The Back of The GT-1500 Panel

Identify and inventory the following components located on the back of the panel:

- Hydrogen and Oxygen Bubbler vessels

- Hydrogen and Oxygen Storage vessels

- Hydrogen and Oxygen Overflow vessels

- 50 Amp Breaker

Figure I-7 depicts the components mounted on the back of the GT-1500 panel.

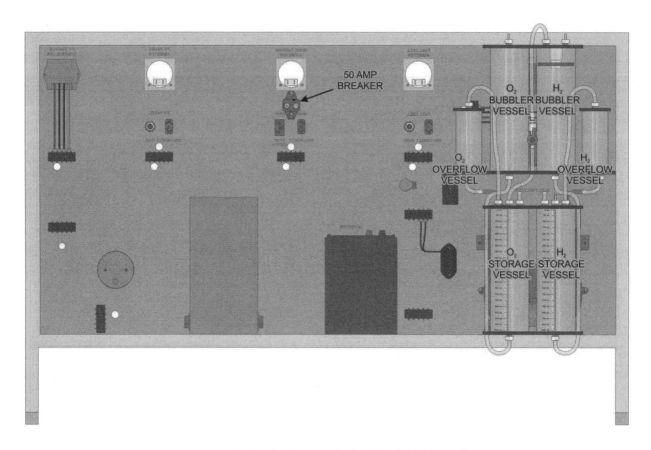

Figure I-7: The Back of the GT-1500 Panel

Accessory Components

Many of the GT-1500 components are not pre-mounted on the GT-1500 panel. These components are mounted and connected in the process of installing and configuring each technology and applying it to an application. Figure I-8 shows the components of the GT-1500 panel that do not come pre-mounted.

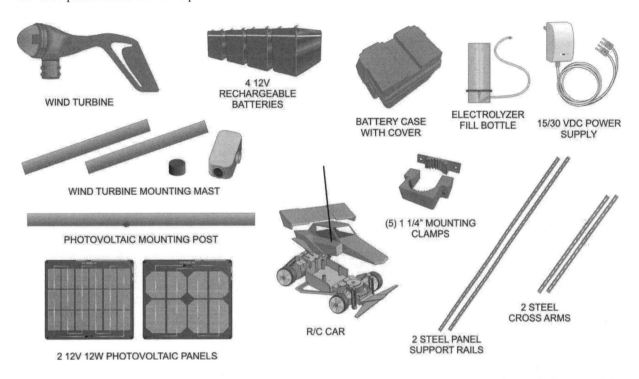

Figure I-8: Non-Mounted GT-1500 Panel Components

Tools

Tools needed to complete the GT-1500 lab procedures are not automatically included with the GT-1500 trainer. Figure I-9 shows the tools needed to complete the GT-1500 lab procedures. If not supplied with the trainer, these tools can be purchased separately from ETG or from your local suppliers.

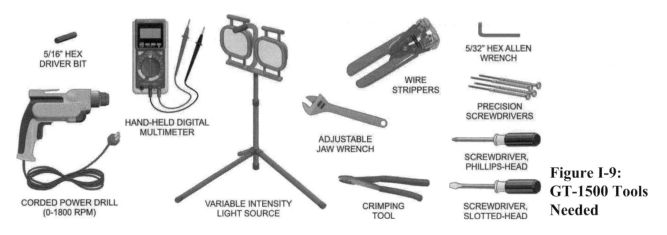

Figure I-9: GT-1500 Tools Needed

Consumables

Consumable items needed to complete the GT-1500 lab procedures are not automatically included with the GT-1500 trainer. Figure I-10 shows the consumables needed to complete the GT-1500 lab procedures. These items are consumed and will need to be replaced periodically. Consumables can be purchased separately from ETG or from your local suppliers.

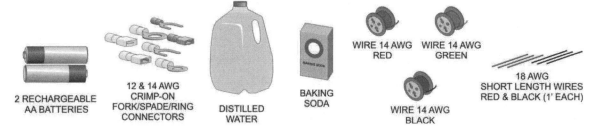

2 RECHARGEABLE AA BATTERIES

12 & 14 AWG CRIMP-ON FORK/SPADE/RING CONNECTORS

DISTILLED WATER

BAKING SODA

WIRE 14 AWG RED   WIRE 14 AWG GREEN

WIRE 14 AWG BLACK

18 AWG SHORT LENGTH WIRES RED & BLACK (1' EACH)

**Figure I-10:
GT-1500 Consumables
Needed**

Non-Mounted GT-1500 Panel Components

Identify and inventory the following non-mounted components. These components should be on hand and available for use at this time:

- Wind Turbine

- Wind Turbine Mounting Mast

- Photovoltaic Panel Mounting Post

- 12V, 12W Photovoltaic Panels (2)

- Mounting Clamps (5)

- DC Power Supply (30V)

- Protective Battery Enclosure and Lid

- 12V Rechargeable Batteries (4)

- 2 Steel Cross Arms

- 2 Steel Panel Rails

- Electrolyzer Fill Bottle

- R/C Car

- Precision Screwdrivers

- Adjustable Jaw Wrench

- Variable Intensity Light Source

- Hand Held Digital Multimeter

- Baking Soda

- Distilled Water

- Wire (Black 12 AWG)

- Wire (Red 12 AWG)

- Wire (Green 12 AWG)

- Wire (Red and Black 18 AWG) - 1' Lengths

- AA Size Rechargeable Batteries (2)

- 12 and 14 AWG Crimp-on Fork/Spade/Ring Connectors

- Corded Power Drill with 5/16 Hex Driver (0-1800 RPM)

CHAPTER 1

Alternative Energy Generation

OBJECTIVES

Upon completion of this chapter, you will be able to perform the following tasks:

1. Create correctly sized connectivity cabling.

2. Demonstrate proper crimping techniques for attaching crimp connectors to cabling.

3. Configure and properly connect a hand held multimeter to perform voltage measurements in a circuit.

4. Configure and properly connect a hand held multimeter to perform resistance and continuity measurements in a circuit – including circuit preparations associated with taking these measurements.

5. Configure and properly connect a hand held multimeter to perform current flow measurements in a circuit – including circuit preparations associated with taking these measurements.

6. Identify common color code for crimp connectors designed to work with different AWG wire sizes.

7. Determine the capabilities of DC sources created by wiring multiple voltage sources in series with each other.

8. Determine the capabilities of DC sources created by wiring multiple voltage sources in parallel with each other.

9. Describe how power consumption is different in AC and DC circuits.

10. Determine which type of power rating is used to determine wire sizes and fusing values for AC circuits.

11. Employ Ohms Law to determine the level of current flowing in a circuit given supply voltage and load resistance.

12. Given a load device with resistance and current requirements, use Ohms Law to determine the size of the voltage source required to meet the specifications.

Alternative Energy Generation

INTRODUCTION

As indicated previously, one of the main components of green technology is the availability of electricity (electrical power) that does not involve or produce carbon-based products or byproducts. However, whether the generation process is based on clean fuels or dirty fuels, the objective is still the same—*push an electron out of its orbit around an atom and use the energy produced from the effort to perform work.*

ATOMIC STRUCTURES

To understand the generation of electricity you must understand the atomic structure of matter and how it can be manipulated. All mater is made up of **atoms**. Atoms are the basic building blocks of all matter and consist of three basic particles—**protons**, **neutrons** and **electrons**. These elements are depicted in Figure 1-1. The protons and neutrons are clustered together in the center of the atom in a structure called the **nucleus**. These particles are relatively large and make up the bulk of the matter in the atom. Electrons are much smaller particles that circle the nucleus in much the same manner as planets orbit the sun.

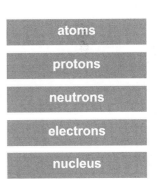

atoms

protons

neutrons

electrons

nucleus

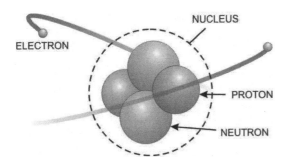

**Figure 1-1:
Atomic Structure**

What makes different types of matter different is the number of protons, neutrons and electrons the atom has. There are over 100 different types of atoms. Each unique atom type is referred to as an **element**. The electrons orbit around the nucleus in elliptical paths called **shells**. The shells of all atoms are organized by nature to accommodate a certain number of electrons:

element

shells

- Shell 1 – 2 electrons

- Shell 2 – 8 electrons

- Shell 3 – 18 electrons

- Shell 4 – 32 electrons

Electrical Charges

positive electrical charge

negative electrical charge

work

resistivity

valence electrons

free electron

ion

conductors

insulators

covalent bonding

Each particle in the atom has energy associated with it and is identified by the type of energy it possesses. Protons possess a **positive electrical charge**, electrons have a **negative electrical charge** and neutrons are neutral and have no charge. What makes the atom interesting for alternative energy is in using its energy to perform **work**, such as providing heat, light or driving an electric motor.

In most alternative energy scenarios we are interested in the number of electrons in the outer shell of the atoms. We typically obtain energy from an atom by causing it to give up an electron from its outer orbit—when the electron leaves its orbit around the atom, energy is given off in the form of heat or light. This is accomplished by applying energy to the electron to *push* (or *pull*) it away from the atom. To free an electron from its atom, enough energy must be applied to the electron to overcome the element's **resistivity** to giving up its electron. Each element has its own resistivity level. Only the electrons in the atom's outer shell (called **valence electrons**) can be separated from the atom.

In this state, the electron is referred to as a **free electron** and represents a negative electrical charge. The atom that gave up the electron is now out of balance and becomes a positive electrical charge. In this state the atom is referred to as an **ion**. When the electron comes into the vicinity of an ion (atom that is missing an electron from its structure), it will fall into an orbit around that atom. This occurs because similar electrically charged particles repel each other while unlike electrical charges attract each other—the positive ion attracts the negative electron. This returns the atom to its normally neutral state (all atoms want to be electrically neutral).

It tends to be much easier to create free electrons with atoms that have three or less electrons in their valence shell. These materials are referred to as electrical **conductors**. Common conductor materials include gold, silver, copper and aluminum. Materials that possess more then three electrons in their outer shell are referred to as **insulators** and do not give up valence electrons easily. Common electrical insulators include rubber, plastics, paper, and glass.

Electrical insulators are typically not a single element (as this list shows). Instead, insulators are most often materials made up of different elements that have joined together to share their valence electrons, as illustrated in Figure 1-2. The sharing of valence electrons is referred to as **covalent bonding** and makes it much more difficult to create a free electron.

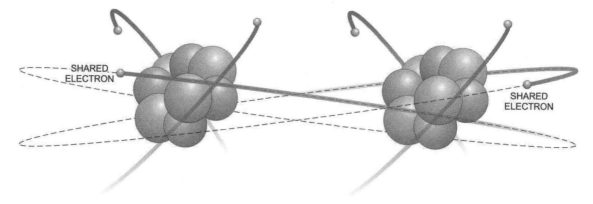

SHARED ELECTRON

SHARED ELECTRON

Figure 1-2: Covalent Bonded Materials

VOLTAGE AND CURRENT

Voltage is the term used to describe the **electromotive force (EMF)** that places the electrical push and pull on the different terminals of a power source. If an acceptable external pathway is provided for the movement of the electrons from the pushing end of the voltage source to the pulling end, an electrical **circuit** is created. This concept is depicted in Figure 1-3. You can envision this as electrons hopping from one atom to the next to move around the circuit from the pushing end of the voltage source to the pulling end. The electromotive force is applied to all of the atoms between the two ends of the conductor, which causes a flow (or **current**) of electrons to move through the circuit.

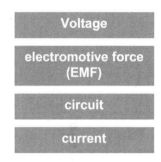

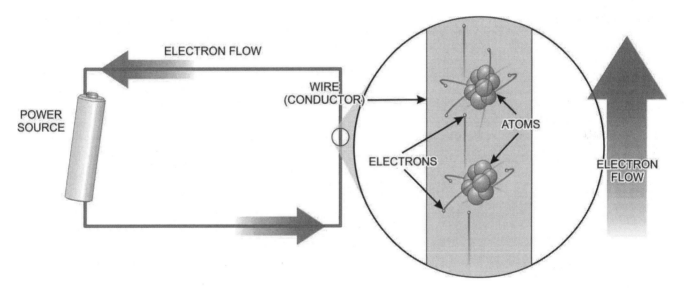

After traveling through the external circuit, the electron reaches the anode (+) side of the source where it recombines with one of the ions that gave up an electron.

Figure 1-3: Electron Current Flow

If the movement of electrons around the circuit is always in one direction, this is referred to as **direct current (DC)**. Direct current is typically associated with batteries. On the other hand, there are electrical generation systems that obtain energy from electrons by causing them to periodically hop back and forth between atoms. This type of electrical current is referred to as **alternating current (AC)** and is usually the product of systems that generate electricity through some type of rotational mechanical system—such as generator and alternators. Direct and alternating currents are depicted in Figure 1-4.

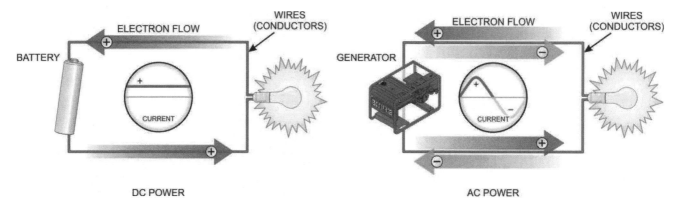

Figure 1-4: Direct and Alternating Current Flows

conventional current
flow

electron current
flow

NOTE

Be aware that technicians and engineers use different methods of describing current flow in circuits. Engineers use a method known as **conventional current flow** to describe the movement of positive charges through the circuit, while technicians employ **electron current flow**, which describes the movement of the electrons through the circuit as moving from negative to positive.

ELECTRICAL LOADS

loads

The reason to generate an electric current is to accomplish something—such as creating heat or light, or performing electrical work. We attach different types of devices to the electrical energy source to perform these activities. Collectively, these devices can be referred to as **loads**.

Loads such as light bulbs and fluorescent tubes convert electrical energy into light, while resistive heating elements convert the same electrical flow into heat. Electric motors are designed to convert electrical energy back into mechanical energy. In each case, the load (or loads) placed between the terminals of the voltage source provides some level of **resistance** to the flow of electrons through the circuit.

resistance

reactance

In an AC circuit the load may also pose a **reactance** to the changing push being applied. Reactance is the opposition to AC current flow from inductance or capacitance instead of resistance.

In a DC circuit the load is strictly resistive. This resistance acts against the current flow being pushed by the voltage and the electrical energy is converted into one of the other energy forms mentioned earlier, as illustrated in Figure 1-5.

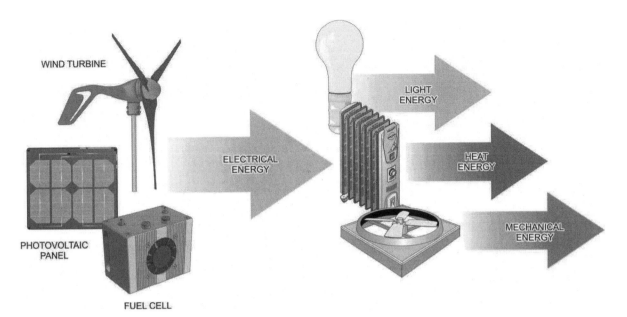

WIND TURBINE

PHOTOVOLTAIC
PANEL

FUEL CELL

ELECTRICAL
ENERGY

LIGHT
ENERGY

HEAT
ENERGY

MECHANICAL
ENERGY

When no external circuit is present, the voltage source pushes against the atoms in the internal wiring, but without a path no current can flow—you still have voltage (push) but no current (flow). This is referred to as an **open circuit**. If a complete path is provided through a material whose atoms offer very little resistance to giving up electrons (called conductors), then the electrical push will provide a very heavy flow of electrons through the material between the terminals. If the amount of resistance provided is too low, this is referred to as a **short circuit**.

Electrical load devices typically provide some level of resistance between these extremes. The relationship between voltage, resistance and current flow in a circuit is expressed in a law called **Ohm's Law**. This relationship simply states that the amount of current that flows in a circuit is directly related to the voltage applied and inversely related to the resistance of the load. This is expressed as:

$$I = \frac{V}{R}$$

where I is current in **Amperes***, V is voltage in **Volts** and R is resistance in **Ohms**.

*An **ampere** is a measure of how many electrons are moving past a point in one second. One ampere equals 6.24 x 10 to the 18th electrons passing a single point in one second. That's a lot of electrons hopping down the wire at one time—nobody wants to count that many electrons or keep track of them, so we just refer to them in terms of amperes.

Figure 1-5: Converting Electrical Energy

open circuit

short circuit

Ohm's Law

Amperes

Volts

Ohms

ampere

Load Calculations

The amount of current flowing in a circuit *increases* directly with the amount of push being applied (double the voltage and the current will double as well). The amount of current flowing also *decreases* directly with an increase in resistance (if the push remains constant but the amount of resistance is doubled, the current flow will be cut in half).

For example: If a 6 Vdc battery is connected to a device that has a total resistance of 1000 Ohm (1kohm), the amount of current that the source would produce should be 0.006 amps (or 6 milliamps—mA). A milliamp is 1/1000th of an amp. In electronics you may also encounter current measurements that occur in the 1/1,000,000 (millionth) of an amp and are specified as microamperes (μA).

The Ohms Law formula demonstrates the relationship between these electrical quantities as follows:

$$I = \frac{V}{R}$$

where:

$$I = \frac{6}{1000}$$

$$I = 0.006 \text{ amp}$$

If the battery is replaced with a 12 Vdc battery, the current flow becomes:

$$I = \frac{12}{1000}$$

$$I = 0.012 \text{ amp} \quad (\text{or } 12 \text{ mA})$$

Likewise, if the load resistance were increased to 2000 Ohms, the current level pulled from the 12-volt source would be cut in half, as follows:

$$I = \frac{12}{2000}$$

$$I = 0.006 \text{ amp} \quad (\text{or } 6 \text{ mA})$$

To recap—current *increases* proportionally when voltage *increases* (they are *directly proportional*) and *decreases* proportionally as resistance *increases* (they are *inversely proportional*)

work

Watts

Ohms Law

Watts

Amperes

Volts

POWER

Power is defined as "the ability to perform **work** over a given period of time". Electrical power is expressed in **Watts**, and is governed by the power formula for **Ohms Law**:

$$P = V \times I$$

where P is power in **Watts**, I is current in **Amperes**, and V is voltage in **Volts** (in some publications, the symbol E—for electromotive force—is used instead of voltage).

Power Math

One of the most common examples of Ohms Law in power relationships would be the common 60 Watt candescent light bulb in a typical 120 Vac residential wiring situation. The amount of current drawn by the light bulb can be calculated as follows:

$$P = V \times I$$

where:

$$60 = 120 \times I$$

$$\frac{60}{120} = \frac{(120 \times I)}{120} \quad \text{(dividing both sides of the equation by the same amount)}$$

$$0.5 \text{ amp} = I$$

NOTE

The 60 Watt designation does not address how much light the bulb produces—this specification is measures in lumens and is dependent on the material producing the light energy—only the amount of power consumed by the bulb to produce the light.

Likewise, a 1300 W space heater operating on a 120 Vac line would draw 10.833 amps of current.

$$P = V \times I$$

$$1300 = 120 \times I$$

$$10.833 \text{ amps} = I$$

As with the light bulb example, the 1300 W rating for the space heater does not address how much heat is produced—this quantity is expressed in terms of **British Thermal Units** (BTUs) and is dependent on several design factors of the heater. The wattage rating simply states how much power the heater consumes to generate the heat.

British Thermal Units

In a final example, 1 **horse power** (hp) pump motor that operates from a 220 Vac line to pump water to a reservoir does not seem to fit into the Ohms Law power formula. However, there is a direct correlation between horsepower (the rating used to describe motors) and Watts—746 Watts equals 1 hp.

horse power

Applying this information to the pump motor scenario gives the following:

$$P = V \times I$$

where:

$$746 \text{ Watts (1 hp)} = 220 \times I$$

$$\frac{746}{220} = \frac{(220 \times I)}{220}$$

$$3.39 \text{ amps} = I$$

The pump motor will draw 3.39 amps of AC current when in operation.

Kilowatt-Hours

Utility companies measure energy in terms of the **kilowatt-hour** (**kWh**). Each **kilowatt-hour** is equal to one thousand watts of power consumed in one hour. Monthly electric utility bills are based on the base rate charged by the local utility per kilowatt-hour.

Wattage ratings for electrical appliances along with their corresponding costs for an assumed rate of 8 cents per kilowatt-hour are presented in Table 1-1. This cost is probably different in your area—consult your residential power bill or call the local electrical utility company for local rates. Electrical installers use tables like this to determine the load of a given scenario.

Table 1-1: Residential Electrical Power Consumption Estimates @ 8 cents/kWh

APPLIANCE	USAGE	RATE
Air cleaner	30 watts per hour	.24 cent per hour (.03 kW/hour x 8 = .24)
Can opener	50 watts per minute	.4 cent per minute (.05 kW/hour x 8 = .4)
Clock	2 watts per hour	.38 cent per day (.002 kW/hour x 8 x 24 = .384)
Electric heating pad	60 watts per hour	.48 cent per hour (.06 kW/hour x 8 = .48)
Fans (ceiling)	100 watts per hour	.8 cent per hour (.1 kW/hour x 8 = .8)
Fax machine	90 watts per hour	17.28 cents per day (.09 kW/hour x 8 x 24 = 17.28)
Home computer	200 watts per hour	1.6 cents per hour (.2 kW/hour x 8 = 1.6)
Iron	1100 watts per hour	8.8 cents per hour (1.1 kW/hour x 8 = 8.8)
Microwave	1500 watts per hour	12 cents per hour (1.5 kW/hour x 8 = 12)
Stereo	100 watts per hour	.8 cent per hour (.1 kW/hour x 8 = .8)
Television	150 watts per hour	1.2 cents per hour (.15 kW/hour x 8 = 1.2)
Toaster	1100 watts per hour	.146 cent per minute (1.1 kW/hour x 8/60 = .1467)
Lights	100-watt bulb	.8 cent per hour (.1 kW/hour x 8 = .8)
Oven (electric)	1500 watts per hour	12 cents per hour (1.5 kW/hour x 8 = 12)
Range top stove	300 watts per hour	2.4 cents per hour (.3 kW/hour x 8 = 2.4)
Refrigerator	220 watts per hour	42.2 cents per day (.22 kW/hour x 8 x 24 = 42.24)

Because some items, such as a bathroom light, will most likely be used for less than 1 hour at a time, this light could be calculated for fractions of a watt-hour usage (i.e., 120-Watt rated light fixture multiplied by 0.25 hours (15 minutes) of usage, would produce a 30 Watt-hours calculated power usage).

Likewise, a vent fan rated at 125 Watts per hour would use 0.125 kilowatt-hours of power each hour. If the utility company charged 8 cents per kilowatt-hour, it would cost 1 cent per hour to operate the fan. The math works as follows:

125W divided by 1000W per kW equals 0.125 kilowatts

$$\frac{125}{1000} = 0.125\text{kW}$$

0.125kW x 1.0h x 0.08cents/kWh = 1 cent/h

When there is a device, such as a water heater, that is used continuously, the kilowatt-per-hour consumption rate for the device must be multiplied by 24 to determine its power consumption and **daily cost of operation**.

daily cost of operation

Real Power and Apparent Power

The Ohm's Law power relationship described earlier is always true for direct current circuits. However, with alternating current circuits the relationship can be altered by the electrical characteristics of the load. If an AC load is purely resistive, such as an incandescent light bulb, the actual power consumption is easily calculated by P = V x I.

However, not all loads in AC circuits are purely resistive. Some load devices, such as electric motors and transformers (ballast) in fluorescent light fixtures operate on the principle of **electromagnetic induction**. The inductive nature in these loads causes the AC current flow to occur at some time after (lag behind) the application of the voltage to the circuit. The amount of delay between the application of the voltage (the push/pull on the circuit) and the actual flow of current is a value based on the amount of **inductance** (measured in *henries*) in the device.

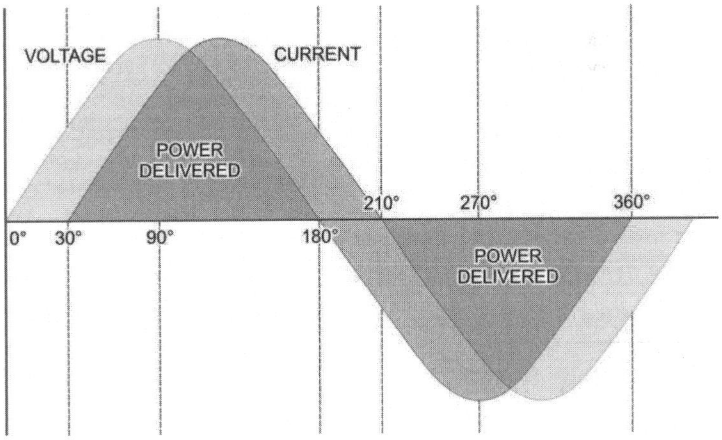

electromagnetic induction

inductance

power factor

Because the values at any given time for current and voltage are at different places in their cycles, as illustrated in Figure 1-6, the simple P = V x I calculation of power must be modified to include a factor for this difference. This factor is a *cosine* trigonometric function relating the phase shift between the current and voltage waveforms and is referred to as **power factor**. In this figure, the phase of the AC current is shown lagging behind the voltage in the circuit.

Figure 1-6: Power Factor

Using the P = V x I power equation on this AC circuit produces an **apparent power** calculation that is expressed in terms of **Volt-Amperes (VA)** instead of Watts. However, the **real power** (or *true power*) that the circuit consumes is expressed in Watts and is calculated using the following formula:

Real Power (watts) = cosine (phase) x Apparent Power (VA)

apparent power

Volt-Amperes (VA)

real power

As the formula indicates, the real power will vary with the value of the cosine function of the phase difference between the voltage and current waveforms.

Apparent power is the easiest to measure and is obtained by multiplying the rms (root mean square) volts and rms amps. The term "rms" refers to the value obtained by measuring AC voltage with a standard voltmeter and ammeter. The result is expressed as volt-amperes (VA) and not watts. The actual power used by the load is expressed in watts. The important point to remember from this discussion is that some loads in an AC circuit can consume more VA power than real power. Therefore, installers must take the sum of all the VA rating for all devices that will used in a circuit to determine wire size and circuit breaker capacity for the circuit and devices.

MAKING ELECTRICAL CONNECTIONS

A common job function of the green technology installer is creating circuitry and making connections to different devices in the system. Cabling is an important part of the clean electron generation program. Incorrect wiring will at best prevent the system from working, and at worst damage equipment or cause injury to personnel. Current levels as low as 0.1 - 0.2 amps can be fatal to humans under certain circumstances. Therefore caution should always be used when working with any electrical circuits or devices.

WARNING
Incorrect wiring will at best cause the system to not work, and at worst damage equipment or cause injury to personnel. Current levels as low as 0. 1-0.2 amps can be fatal to humans under the correct circumstances. Therefore caution should always be used when connecting any type of electrical devices.

burn

fire

conductors

Another danger associated with electrical current flow is the possibility of **burn** or **fire** injuries related to **conductors** (wiring and devices that give up electrons easily) over heating. Even though the conductor materials give up electrons more easily than other substances, their electrons do not just fall off the atom—even conductors have some level of resistance in them. Therefore, some energy is given off as heat when current passes through the conductor.

Heat in wiring systems is often a result of too much current flowing through an undersized wire or through a bad connection. One of the keys to minimizing the amount of heat generated in wiring is to use the proper size wiring and the correct external insulation coating. A wire with a larger cross sectional area carries a given amount of current more easily than a smaller wire of the same material. There are simply more atoms across the face of the larger wire to give up the necessary number of electrons. Therefore, less heat is produced for that level of current.

Qualified, licensed electricians must wire up and connect installations that tie into the commercial power system. However, low-voltage, non-grid tied installations can normally be installed, wired and connected by trained personnel.

National Electrical Code

The **National Electrical Code (NEC)** is a document that describes recommended safe practices for the installation of all types of electrical equipment. The **National Fire Protection Association (NFPA)**, an insurance industry group is responsible for publishing and maintaining the NEC under the official title of NFPA 70. The stated purpose of the NEC is for the "practical safeguarding of persons and property from hazards arising from the use of electricity."

The NEC is not a legal document unless it is so designated by a municipality as its own statute for safe electrical installations. It is revised and published every three years by the NFPA. The NEC is national only in the fact that it is the only document of which all or part is accepted by all states as an electrical guide. It is the only document of its kind written with national input supplied by 20 panels of advisors containing several hundred experts in the electrical field from all parts of the country.

The NEC is organized by subject area in nine chapters. Each chapter contains numbered sections called Articles, which describe specific wiring codes related to the chapter headings.

| National Electrical Code (NEC) |
| National Fire Protection Association (NFPA) |

| American Wire Gauge (AWG) |
| ampacity |

NEC Wire Size and Ampacity Standards

The NEC provides electrical construction standards, including conductor and electrical load requirements. The amount of electrical current that a conductor can carry is measured in **ampacity**, a term for ampere-capacity. The size of electrical wiring is directly related to its capacity to conduct electricity. The larger the wire, the more electricity it can safely conduct.

In the United States, wiring is specified by a measurement standard called the **American Wire Gauge (AWG)**. This standard specifies wire diameter in a descending relationship—larger AWG gauge numbers represent smaller wire diameters. The reason this is important for an installer is because the cross sectional area (diameter) of the wire is directly related to its ability to carry electrical current (referred to as the wire's ampacity).

It is important to follow proper wire-sizing for each application when working with electrical devices and systems to insure a safe electrical system and to help avoid the risk of electrical fire. Due to variables such as wire length, ambient temperature, and connection quality, an important safety practice is to use only 80% of the wire's maximum current carrying capacity. Table 1-2 provides a generic guide to wire sizes used for various current levels in 12 Vdc and 120 Vac circuits.

CAUTION

Always use correct wire sizes to help avoid the risk of an electrical fire.

Table 1-2: Wire Gauge vs. Maximum Current Capacity

AWG	120 Vac	240 Vdc	12 Vdc
22	5A	2.5A	5A
20	7.5A	3.75A	8A
18	10A	5A	10A
16	13A	6.5A	20A
14	17A	8.5A	40A
12	23A	11.5A	60A
10	33A	16.5A	100A
8	46A	23A	150A
6	60A	30A	N/A
4	80A	40A	N/A
2	100A	50A	N/A
1	125A	62.5A	N/A
0	150A	75A	N/A
00	190A	95A	N/A
000	240A	120A	N/A
0000	300A	150A	N/A

Wire gauge size is measured inversely, that is, 14 AWG wire is smaller than 12 AWG wire. A 14 AWG wire is rated at 15 amps, while a 12 AWG wire is rated at 20 amps.

Going up to 10 AWG wire provides an ampacity of 30 amps. Ampacity ratings are stated for copper conductors in "free air" (maximum typical air circulation), as opposed to wires placed in conduit or wire trays.

If electrical wiring is subject to electrical current in excess of its capacity, it will generate heat and eventually cause a fire. Because of this situation, all electrical circuits must be provided with circuit breaker or fuse protection that is rated at not more than the wire's maximum ampacity.

insulation

The type of **insulation** for electrical cabling is also a consideration that must be taken for different environments, operating temperature ranges and locations during installation planning.

Fuses and Circuit Breakers

fuse

circuit breaker

Most alternate energy systems can deliver dangerous amounts of current. If a short circuit occurs in the wiring system, a fire can result or components can be damaged. Likewise, if you are the source of the short circuit you can be injured, burned or killed. In order to avoid these threats, a properly sized **fuse** or **circuit breaker** is required in the lines coming from the electrical source. These devices sense the level of current flowing through them and are designed to interrupt the path of current flow (open circuit) if the current level gets to a certain point (the fuse rating). Use the following fuse sizing information when working with the Marcraft wind turbine circuitry:

- 12-volt model: 50 amps DC

- 24-volt model: 30 amps DC

Making Connections

Crimp connections

PROCEDURE 1 – MAKING CONNECTIONS

In all the hands-on procedures throughout this course you will be asked to make connections between and to different components using different gauges of wire and crimp on connectors. **Crimp connections** involve crushing an insulated connector around a bare length of wire. To create effective, trouble-free connections using crimp connectors requires that there be a relatively tight fit between the sleeve of the connector and the wire, as well as an effective crimp that creates a solid path for current to flow between the wire and the connector body.

<u>**Resources Needed:**</u>

- Crimp connectors
- 12 AWG wire (red and black)
- Crimp tool

For crimping single conductor, multi-strand wiring below AWG 10, a "jaw style" crimp tool is very effective. Simply place the connector into a jaw where one side is concave and the other side contains the tooth, as shown in Figure 1-7. The figure also demonstrates the proper insertion of a crimp connector into the crimp tool.

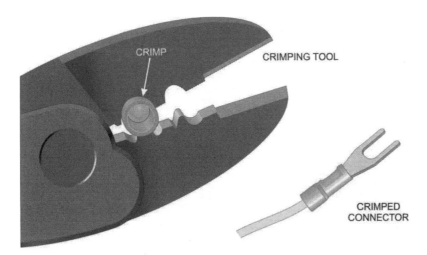

Figure 1-7: Proper Insertion of a Crimp Connector into the Crimp Tool

The jaw presses the connector and causes its soft metal barrel to conform to the shape of the concave side of the tool. The proper method for creating a crimp connection calls for the "seam" of the connector's internal metal barrel to face toward the concave part of the crimp tool (away from the tooth), as shown in Figure 1-8. This will cause the seam to hold together during the crimping process. If the connector is inserted into the crimp tool facing the other way, the jaw will force the seam to open, which creates an opportunity for the connection to separate.

Crimp connectors are color coded according to the wire gauge they are designed to work with. Common crimp connector color codes are:

- Wire sizes between AWG#22 and AWG#18 use Red connectors

- Wire size between AWG#16 to AWG#14 use Blue connectors

- Wire size between AWG#12 to AWG#10 use Yellow connectors

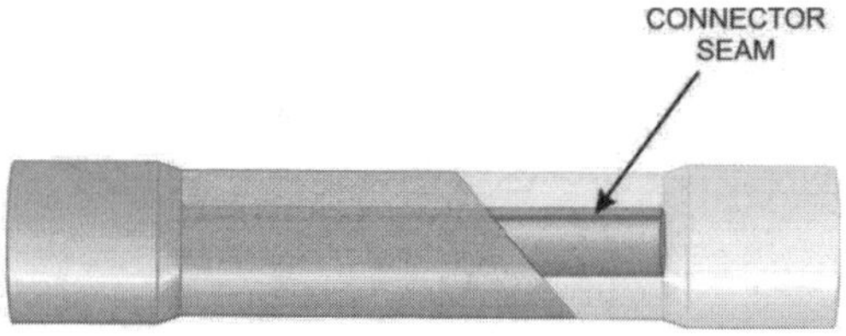

1. Cut 3 pieces each of red and black 12 AWG wire 6 inches in length.

2. Strip 1/2" (one-half inch) from each end of the wire, as illustrated in Figure 1-9.

Figure 1-8: The Internal Metal Seam in the Crimp Connector

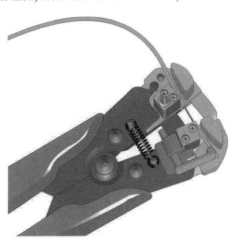

Figure 1-9: Stripping Wire with Squeeze-Handle or Pliers-Style Strippers

3. Repeat Step 2 for the remaining wires.

4. Cut 1 piece each of red and black 12 AWG wire 24 inches in length.

5. Twist the ends of all the wires to keep any stray strands together in a neat, orderly fashion.

6. Using the two 24" wires you just cut and stripped, insert one end of each wire into a Red (18-22 AWG) 0.250" (quarter inch) fork lug connector. Be sure that the wire is fully inserted and the insulation meets the edge of the metal insert of the connector. There should be no exposed wire outside of the connector.

7. Observing the seam of the female .250" fork lug connector, position the jaw of the crimp tool on the bottom of the connector (away from the seam).

8. With the crimp tool in one hand and holding the connector in place with the other, firmly crimp down on the connector. Remember it's important to use enough force to make the connection, but don't over do it, as shown in Figure 1-10.

9. Next, insert the other end of the wire into a Yellow (12-10 AWG) female spade connector, along the bare end of one of the 6 inch pieces you prepared (so both wires share the same connector barrel). The color of both wires in each connector should match so that you have one long/short red wire combination and one long/short black wire combination.

10. Perform the crimp process as described earlier.

11. Insert the free end of the short wire into another Yellow (12-10 AWG) female spade connector, along the bare end of another of the 6 inch pieces you prepared (so that once again, both wires share the same connector barrel). Likewise, the color of both wires in this connector should match.

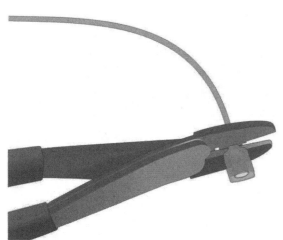

**Figure 1-10:
Crimping the Female
Spade Connector**

12. Repeat Step 11 to add the last sections of short wires to the two wiring harnesses. The results should look similar to the wiring configurations depicted in Figure 1-11.

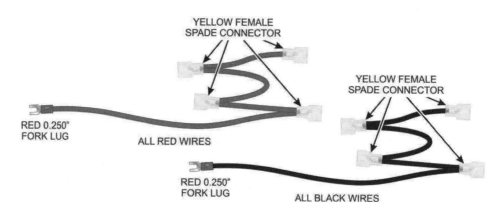

**Figure 1-11:
Completed Wiring
Harnesses**

13. At this point, have your instructor examine the quality of your harnesses.

14. Set these wiring harnesses aside for use later in this procedure.

Procedure 1 Questions

1. What type of tool should be used for crimping single conductor, multi-strand wiring below AWG10?

2. What is the proper method for creating a crimp connection?

3. What is the result of inserting a crimp connector into the crimp tool facing the wrong way?

4. What color are crimp connectors designed for use on wire sizes from AWG#16 to AWG#14?

5. What should be done to keep any stray strands together in a neat, orderly fashion?

MEASURING ELECTRICAL QUANTITIES

One of the most basic pieces of electronic troubleshooting equipment is the **multimeter**. These test instruments are available in both analog and digital readout form and can be used to directly measure values of **voltage (V)**, **current** in milliamperes (mA) or amperes (A), and **resistance** in ohms (Ω). Therefore, these devices are referred to as **VOMs (Volt-Ohm-Milliammeters)** for analog types, or **DMMs (Digital MultiMeters)** for digital types. Figure 1-12 depicts a digital multimeter.

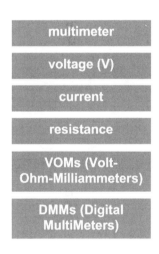

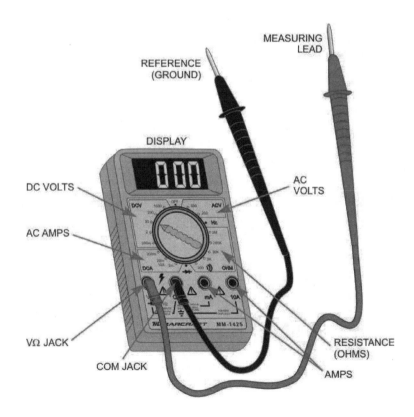

Figure 1-12: Digital Multimeter

With a little practice, you can use this device to check wiring, components, voltage sources, and current flow. Some DMM models contain facilities built into the multimeter to test transistors and diodes. These facilities are in addition to its standard **functions** of current, voltage, and resistance measurement.

In the cases of current and voltage, you will need to select between alternating and direct current measurements. This selection is typically determined through the multimeter's function selection switch.

Measuring Voltages

The multimeter's **DC voltage function** is used to take measurements in live DC circuits. In most troubleshooting applications, fully 99% of the tests made are DC voltage readings.

To take a voltage reading, the multimeter must be connected in parallel with the device being checked. This could mean connecting the reference lead (black lead) to a ground point and the measuring lead (red lead) to a test point to take a measurement, as illustrated in Figure 1-13.

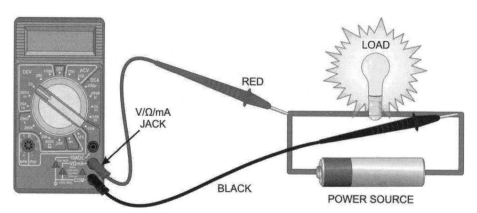

**Figure 1-13:
DC Voltage Check**

As an approximate value is detected, you can decrease the range setting to achieve a more accurate reading. Most multimeters allow for over-voltage protection. However, it is still a good safety practice to decrease the range of the multimeter after you have achieved an initial value.

WARNING

Setting the meter— It is normal practice *to first set the multimeter to its highest voltage range* to make certain that the voltage level being measured does not damage the multimeter.

Only a couple of situations involve using the **AC voltage function**. The primary use of this function is to check the commercial power being supplied. As with any measurement, it is important to select the correct measurement *range*. However, the lethal voltage levels typically associated with these types of measurements call for additional caution. Figure 1-14 depicts a multimeter properly configured to check the power supply from a commercial 120 Vac outlet.

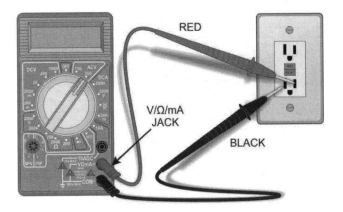

RED

V/Ω/mA JACK

BLACK

Figure 1-14:
Testing an Outlet

DC Voltage Sources

There are several common sources of DC voltage and current. **Batteries** are easily the most widely recognized examples of **DC voltage sources**. Alternative DC sources you will encounter in this course include fuel cells (think of these as hydrogen powered batteries) and photovoltaic cells, or solar cells (think of these as light-powered batteries). The wind turbine featured in this course also produces DC voltage and current at its output terminals, but this is only after manipulation of the alternating current it produces naturally.

Batteries

DC voltage sources

All of the DC voltage sources mentioned come in many sizes and ratings and produce DC electricity through different processes. For example, batteries produce direct current voltage through a chemical reaction process. The chemicals in the battery react with its terminals when an external path for current flow is provided. The process causes free electrons to gather at the negative (-) terminal of the battery while a depletion of electrons occurs at the positive (+) terminal. This provides the push (-) and pull (+) to create current flow through an external circuit, as illustrated in Figure 1-15.

When an external pathway is provided the electrons flow from the negative terminal through the external circuit (and the external load) and back into the positive terminal of the battery. If a very low resistance load is placed across the terminals, a large flow of electron current will occur. Larger resistive loads draw lower levels of current flow from the battery, as described by the basic Ohm's Law formula for current, voltage and resistance.

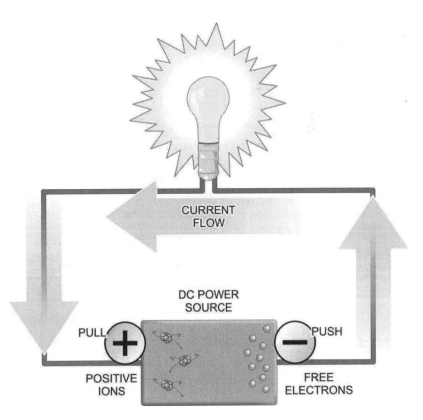

CURRENT FLOW

DC POWER SOURCE

PULL $+$

PUSH $-$

POSITIVE IONS

FREE ELECTRONS

Figure 1-15: Creating DC Current Flow

In cases where a wire or other good conductor is placed across the terminals without a load (referred to as a **short circuit** condition), the electrons flow through the circuit and the inside of the battery as quickly as the internal process can generate more free electrons. The acceleration of the process causes the battery to heat up, which in turn can cause it to overheat and possibly explode.

Some battery types (referred to as **secondary cells** or **storage** batteries) can be recharged by applying a reverse current to them, as illustrated in Figure 1-16. By applying an external voltage source to the battery at a voltage level *slightly higher* than its terminal voltage, a reverse current is forced to flow back into the battery and the internal chemical process is reversed. Under these circumstances, the battery becomes the load in the circuit instead of the source.

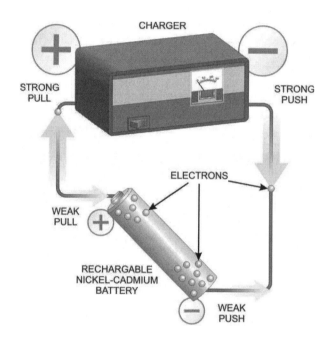

**Figure 1-16:
Recharging a Battery**

Over time, the reverse current flow restores the original chemical configuration inside the battery. The rate at which the battery **recharges** depends on the chemical configuration and the amount of reverse current flowing through the battery. The amount of reverse current is dependent on the voltage difference between the battery and the recharging source.

The recharging option is not available with all battery types (not all chemical current generating processes can be reversed). Applying a reverse voltage to these batteries (**primary cells**) can cause them to overheat and possibly explode.

> ## WARNING
>
> Applying a reverse voltage to non-rechargeable battery types can cause them to overheat and possibly explode.

Voltage Source Configurations

DC voltage sources can be connected together to provide different voltage and current capabilities to fit different load/installation requirements. When DC sources are connected in **series** (positive terminals are connected to negative terminals in a *daisy-chain* connection) as illustrated in Figure 1-17, the voltage level provided to an external load is equal to the sum of all the individual DC source voltages. The current flow is the same through all the sources and the load. This arrangement enables similar DC source devices to be combined to provide power to a piece of equipment that requires a higher voltage source—such as using two 6 volt batteries to provide a 12 Vdc source for a portable lantern.

series

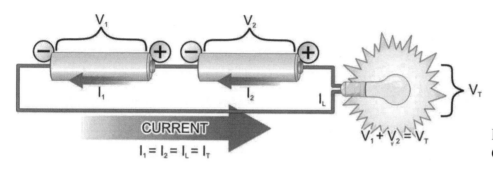

Figure 1-17: Series Connected Batteries

When DC voltage sources are connected in **parallel** (positive terminals are connected to positive terminals) as illustrated in Figure 1-18, the voltage level is the same as the individual sources (all of the sources should have the same voltage ratings). However the current delivery capabilities of parallel sources is equal to the sum of the currents produced by each of the sources. This is helpful in situations where devices that require heavy DC current loads need an acceptable source of power.

parallel

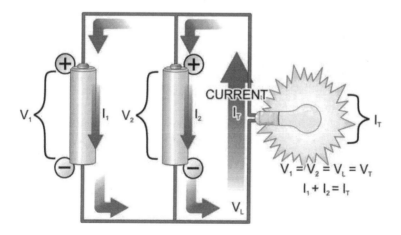

Figure 1-18: Parallel Connected Batteries

**Measuring
Electrical
Quantities**

┌─ **NOTE** ─────────┐
│ The batteries supplied with the │
│ GT-1500 system are Sealed │
│ Lead Acid Batteries. │
└────────────────────┘

PROCEDURE 2 – MEASURING VOLTAGE

In this procedure, you will connect a set of batteries together in different standard configurations to provide different voltage and current outputs. Make sure you are confident with your connections before making them as connecting batteries incorrectly can lead to damage and/or personal injury.

<u>**Resources Needed:**</u>

- 4-Battery Battery Pack (12V, 7 AH, Sealed Lead Acid)

- Hand-Held Digital multimeter

- 12 AWG wire (red and black)

┌──┐
│ ## CAUTION   │
├──┤
│ Be sure not to connect the wires to the battery until everything else has been completed │
│ and you are instructed to do so in this procedure. │
└──┘

1. Locate the protective battery enclosure and verify that there are four matching 12V batteries.

2. Designate each of the batteries with a number identification (i.e., Battery 1, Battery 2, etc.), as illustrated in Figure 1-19.

**Figure 1-19:
Identifying Batteries**

3. Set the multimeter to the 20 DCV setting, and turn the multimeter on, if necessary.

4. Measure the voltage level present at the terminals of each battery and record these values on the following lines:

Battery #1: _____

Battery #2: _____

Battery #3: _____

Battery #4: _____

5. Form a series battery connection by attaching a jumper wire between the positive (+) terminal of battery #1 to the negative (-) terminal of battery #2, as illustrated in Figure 1-20.

Figure 1-20: Connecting Batteries in Series

6. Change the setting on the multimeter to 200 DCV.

7. Connect the black lead of the multimeter to the negative terminal of battery #1 and the red lead to the positive terminal of battery #2. Record the total voltage level provided by the series batteries on the following line:

_____

8. How does this value relate to the individual voltages of batteries #1 and #2 measured in Step 4?

_____

9. Form a parallel battery connection by attaching a jumper wire between the positive (+) terminal of battery #3 to the positive (+) terminal of battery #4.

10. Attach another jumper wire between the negative (-) terminal of battery #3 to the negative (-) terminal of battery #4, as illustrated in Figure 1-21.

11. Change the setting on the multimeter back to 20 DCV to obtain a more accurate reading.

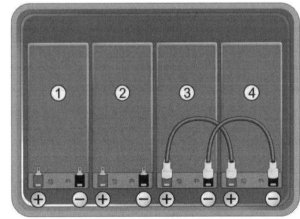

Figure 1-21: Connecting Batteries in Parallel

12. Connect the black lead of the multimeter to the negative terminal of battery #3 and the red lead to the positive terminal of battery #3. Record the total voltage level provided by the parallel batteries on the following line:

_____

13. How does this value relate to the individual voltages of batteries #3 and #4 measured in Step 4?

_____

14. Remove the jumper wires and multimeter leads from batteries #3 and #4.

15. Refer to Figure 1-22 and connect batteries #3 and #4 in series so that they are wired in the same series configuration as batteries #1 and #2.

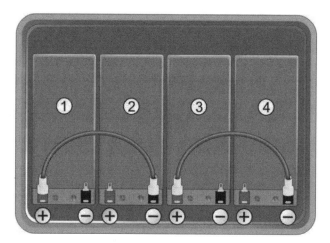

Figure 1-22: Two Sets of Series Connected Batteries

16. Create a parallel battery connection between series batteries #1/#2 and series batteries #3/#4 by attaching a jumper wire between the positive (+) terminal of battery #2 to the positive (+) terminal of battery #4.

17. Attach another jumper wire between the negative (-) terminal of battery #1 to the negative (-) terminal of battery #3, as illustrated in Figure 1-23.

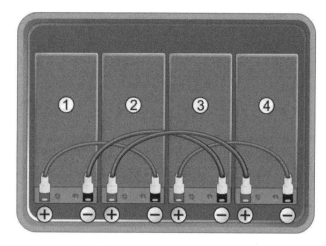

Figure 1-23: Connecting Batteries in Series/Parallel

18. Change the setting on the multimeter to 200 DCV to obtain a more accurate reading.

19. Connect the black lead of the multimeter to the negative terminal of battery #1/#3 and the red lead to the positive terminal of battery #2/#4. Record the total voltage level provided by the series/parallel batteries on the following line:

_____

20. How does this value relate to the individual voltages of all the batteries measured in Step 4?

_____

21. Remove all the jumper wires and multimeter leads from the batteries.

Procedure 2 Questions

1. How many batteries are used in this procedure, and what are their voltage values?

2. What should the multimeter setting be in order to measure the voltage level of each battery?

3. What was the total voltage measured across battery #1 and battery #2 connected in series?

4. What was the total voltage measured across battery #3 and battery #4 connected in parallel?

5. What was the total voltage measured across battery #1/#3 and battery #2/#4 connected in series/parallel?

PROCEDURE 3 – MEASURING RESISTANCE

The second most employed multimeter test is the **resistance**, or **continuity test**.

Measuring Electrical Quantities

resistance

continuity test

WARNING

Power off—Unlike the voltage check, resistance checks are always made with power removed from the system.

Failure to turn off the power when making resistance checks can cause serious damage to the multimeter and can pose a potential risk to the user. Resistance checks also require that you electrically isolate the component being tested from the system. For most components this means de-soldering or disconnecting at least one end from the circuit.

The resistance check is very useful in isolating some types of problems in the system. One of the main uses of the resistance function is to test fuses. You must disconnect at least one end of the fuse from the system to test its continuity. You should set the multimeter on the 1-kilohm resistance setting. If the fuse is good, the multimeter should read near 0 ohms. If it is bad, the multimeter reads infinite.

Measuring Electrical Quantities

The resistance function is also useful in checking cables and connectors. By removing the cable from the system and connecting a multimeter lead to each end, you can check the cable's continuity conductor-by-conductor to verify its integrity.

Resources Needed:

- Marcraft Green Electron Generation Experiment Panel
- Hand-Held Digital Multimeter
- 12 AWG wire (red and black)

1. Place the red (measuring) lead in the multimeter's V/Ω /mA jack and the black (reference) lead in the Ground (GND) jack, as shown in Figure 1-24. Turn the multimeter to the **On** position.

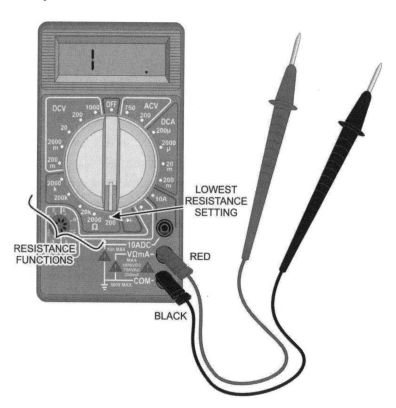

Figure 1-24:
Meter Leads Set for
Measuring Continuity

2. Set the multimeter to its lowest *resistance range* (used for checking Continuity of a device or circuit).

3. Place the multimeter's leads on the opposite terminals of the Wind Turbine's Disconnect Switch. On the following lines, record the reading obtained from the multimeter with the switch in the up and down positions:

    Switch Up: _____

    Switch Down: _____

4. Place the black lead of the multimeter on the center terminal of the Wind Turbine's Emergency Stop switch. Place the multimeter's red lead on the top terminal of the switch. On the following lines, record the reading from the multimeter with the switch in the up and down positions:

    Switch Up: _____

    Switch Down: _____

5. Move the meter's red lead to the bottom terminal of the switch. On the following lines, record the reading from the multimeter with the switch in the up and down positions:

Switch Up: _____

Switch Down: _____

6. Place the multimeter leads on opposite terminals of the Wind Turbine's breaker. Record the resistance measurement on the following lines. Move the leads to the opposite terminals and record the multimeter reading in this direction:

_____

_____

7. Place the multimeter on its lowest resistance range and connect the leads on opposite terminals of the Wind Turbine's ammeter. Record the resistance measurement on the following lines. Move the leads to the opposite terminals and record the multimeter reading in this direction:

_____

_____

8. Make certain that the multimeter leads are configured to measure V/Ω/mA and set the function selector switch to measure resistance—using the 200kΩ range.

9. Verify that there is nothing connected to the potentiometer output at the Fuel Cell Load connection block terminals (the two lower right hand terminals), as illustrated in Figure 1-25.

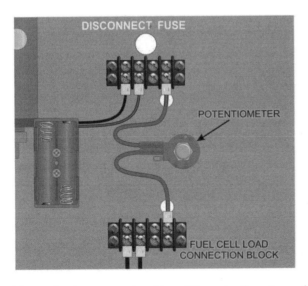

**Figure 1-25:
Potentiometer
Open Circuit**

10. Place the multimeter leads on opposite sides of the potentiometer as depicted in Figure 1-26. This figure shows the proper method of taking a resistance reading of a device or circuit—the multimeter must be placed in parallel with the device or circuit being measured and no current paths can be allowed to exist except the one that runs through the multimeter and the device/circuit.

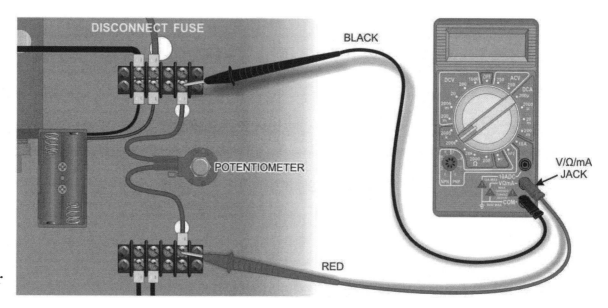

**Figure 1-26:
Checking the
Potentiometer**

┌─ **NOTE** ───
│ To measure resistance with a multimeter, the meter function must be set to measure resistance, the test leads must be across the
│ component being measured and other paths of current must be removed from the component so that only the current supplied
│ by the meter is used and there are no other paths for this current than directly through the component.
└───

11. Adjust the potentiometer to its maximum resistance setting and record the value on
    the following line:

    Maximum Resistance: _____

12. Adjust the potentiometer to its approximate mid range resistance setting and record
    the value on the following line:

    Mid-Range Resistance: _____

13. Adjust the potentiometer to its minimum resistance setting and record the value on
    the following line:

    Minimum Resistance: _____

Procedure 3 Questions

1. What is another name for the measurement of resistance?

2. Why must resistance measurements be conducted only after power to the circuit
   under test has been removed?

3. What must be done to electrically isolate the component being tested for continuity
   from the system?

4. What is the resistance reading for a bad fuse?

5. What is the proper range setting for a multimeter being used to check continuity?

**Measuring
Electrical
Quantities**

PROCEDURE 4 – MEASURING CURRENT

The last major measurement function associated with multimeters is measuring the flow of current through a circuit or device. Unlike voltage and resistance measurements where the multimeter is placed "across" a source or a component, current measurements must be set up so that the current flowing through the circuit or component also flows directly *through* the multimeter. This requires that the multimeter be placed in line (in series) with the circuit or component, as illustrated in Figure 1-27.

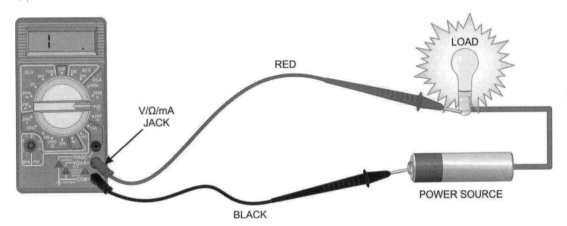

**Figure 1-27:
Measuring
Current**

<u>Resources Needed:</u>

- Marcraft Green Electron Generation Experiment Panel

- Hand-Held Digital multimeter

- 12 AWG wire (red and black)

- AA 1.5V rechargeable batteries (2)

1. Prepare and connect a red 12 AWG jumper wire at the inside left terminal on the upper row of the Fuel Cell Control Panel connection block—adjacent to the positive terminal (red wire) of the battery pack.

2. Connect the other end of the jumper wire to the potentiometer connection at the far right terminal on the upper row of the Fuel Cell Control Panel connection block.

3. Make sure that the multimeter function is set to measure *DC amps* (200 milliamps – mA range).

4. Secure the black (reference) lead of the multimeter under the far-right terminal of the Fuel Cell Load connection block.

5. Secure the red (measuring) lead from the multimeter adjacent to the battery pack's negative (black wire) terminal.

Figure 1-28 shows the complete current path from one side of the battery pack to the other, using the multimeter as the final leg of the circuit. In this way, all of the current that leaves the battery pack must travel through the multimeter to get back to the battery pack.

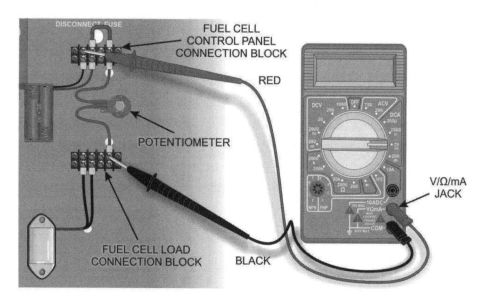

**Figure 1-28:
Configured to
Measure Current**

6. Turn the multimeter **on**.

7. Rotate the potentiometer fully counter clockwise.

8. Place the two AA batteries in the battery holder in the Fuel Cell load area of the panel—observe the polarity markings on the battery to make sure they are installed correctly.

9. Record the current level displayed on the multimeter at this setting on the following line:

   Milliamps: _____

10. Rotate the potentiometer clockwise for one half a turn.

11. Record the current level displayed on the multimeter at this setting on the following line:

   Milliamps: _____

12. Rotate the potentiometer fully clockwise.

13. Record the current level displayed on the multimeter at this setting on the following line:

    Milliamps: _____

14. Remove one of the batteries from the battery holder.

15. Reverse the positions of the multimeter's leads in the circuit, rotate the potentiometer fully counter clockwise, and then reinstall the battery in the battery pack.

16. Repeat Steps 9 through 13 with the multimeter connected in this manner. Record the outcomes on the following lines:

    Milliamps: _____

    Milliamps: _____

    Milliamps: _____

Procedure 4 Questions

1. When measuring current, how must the multimeter be connected?

2. Reversing the multimeter's leads resulted in what changes in outcomes?

3. What is the total voltage supplied to the motor circuit by the batteries?

4. How much current leaving the battery pack must travel through the multimeter?

5. When setting up the circuit, where did the multimeter's red measuring lead connect?

REVIEW QUESTIONS

The following questions test your knowledge of the material presented in this chapter:

1. List four causes for growing emphasis on alternative, renewable energy systems.

2. What is the most important requirement for connecting a multimeter in a circuit to measure current flow?

3. What is the color code for crimp connectors designed to work with a single 18-22 AWG wire?

4. Which direction should the seam be in a crimp terminal in relation to the jaw of the crimp tool?

5. What type of DC source is created by wiring four 12V, 1 amp sources in series with each other?

6. What type of DC source is created by wiring four 12V, 1 amp sources in parallel with each other?

7. What is the most important requirement for connecting a multimeter in a circuit to measure resistance?

8. How is power consumption different in AC and DC circuits?

9. Which power rating is used to determine wire sizes and fusing values for AC circuits?

10. How much current is flowing in a 120 Vac circuit that supplies a 5 kΩ load?

11. What size voltage source would be required to provide 1 amp of current to a 100Ω load?

12. How much electrical power is consumed by a 1/2 hp motor?

Wind Turbines

OBJECTIVES

Upon completion of this chapter, you will be able to perform the following tasks:

1. Identify the major components of a wind turbine electrical generation system.

2. Properly mount the wind turbine.

3. Connect the wind turbine to common protective/control devices.

4. Test the basic operation of the wind turbine.

5. Testing the direct output of the wind turbine.

6. Correlate wind power-to-turbine speed-to-electrical power generation (efficiency) of the wind turbine electrical generation system.

7. Test various battery configuration options.

8. Connect the Marcraft wind turbine circuitry to storage batteries.

9. Supply a DC load with the Marcraft wind turbine system.

10. Document battery charge/discharge rates.

11. Adjust the output of the wind turbine.

12. Implement excess capacity management by driving auxiliary loads.

13. Connect the wind turbine circuitry to an AC inverter.

14. Drive an AC load with the Marcraft wind turbine system.

15. Document battery charge/discharge rates vs. inverter output (system efficiency).

16. Search for wind power services.

17. Research various wind power components and strategies.

18. Locate applicable wind turbine regulations and legislation.

19. Research the elements which determine the amount of energy in the wind.

20. Explain the aerodynamics of wind turbine blades and the concept of Lift.

21. Describe Betz' law and the conversion of energy.

22. List the 10 Steps in building a wind farm.

CHAPTER 2

Wind Turbines

INTRODUCTION

Wind is the movement (or flow) of air—or other atmospheric gas—molecules from one place to another. Wind is created on Earth when a difference in **atmospheric pressure** exists between two geographical points. The air molecules move from the area of higher pressure to the area of lower pressure. The biggest reason for differing atmospheric pressure levels is **differential heating** (different levels of heating) from the sun—some geographical areas receive or absorb more solar energy than others. **High-pressure** areas correspond to cooler, dryer air, while **low-pressure** areas are associated with moister, warmer air.

Another major force at work in varying atmospheric pressures is the rotation of the planet. The Earth's rotation changes the directions of winds in a process known as the **Coriolis effect**. Coriolis forces are created when wind is moving between the pressure centers and the Earth rotates under it. This motion causes the wind, which would prefer to travel in a straight line, to flow in a curve path.

Wind

atmospheric pressure

differential heating

High-pressure

low-pressure

Coriolis effect

INTRODUCTION TO WIND TURBINES

The amount of energy that can be derived from wind depends primarily on the speed it is moving. The speed of wind is a function of the difference between the level of the high-pressure area and the low level area. If the difference between the high-pressure measurement and the low-pressure measurement is relatively small, the intensity of wind (and its speed) will be small. Conversely, if there is a large pressure difference between these two centers, the amount of wind produced—and the amount of energy that can be derived from it—will be large.

The most common way to determine wind movement is to look at a **meteorological** (weather) **map** that shows high-pressure and low-pressure centers, as illustrated in Figure 2-1. The map should also include **isobar** lines that connect points that have equal or constant atmospheric pressures.

meteorological map

isobar

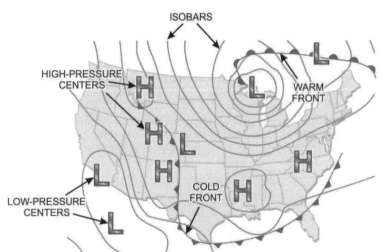

Figure 2-1: Reading a Weather Map

When you examine the map, you can spot the high and low-pressure centers identified by Hs and Ls. Coriolis forces cause the winds to rotate around a high-pressure center in a clockwise direction (in the northern hemisphere of the world). Likewise, wind travels around low-pressure centers in a counter-clockwise direction. These directions are reversed in the southern hemisphere.

As mentioned before, the intensity of winds is primarily determined by the pressure difference between the high- and low-pressure centers. However, the wind speed is also dependent on the distance the centers are separated. When the isobar lines on the map are forced closer to each other by the fact that the centers are physically closer to each other, the greater the wind speed developed between the centers. This concept is illustrated in Figure 2-2.

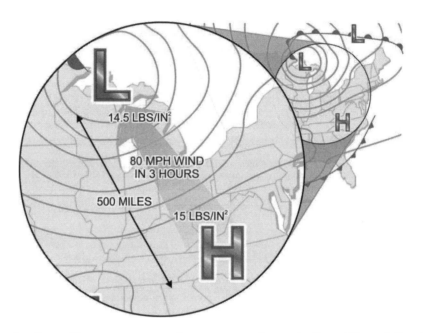

Figure 2-2:
Wind Speeds

The other lines of interest on our weather map example are the frontal lines. A **front** is a boundary where air masses with different temperatures and densities (dry cold air meets warm moist air) meet. Cold fronts are indicated by lines with small triangular pips on one side of the line, while warm fronts are represented by lines with semi-circular pips pointing in the direction of the front's travel. **Cold fronts** are associated with low-pressure areas and tend to move from west to east. **Warm fronts** are associated with high-pressure areas and tend to move toward the Earth's north and south poles.

Other factors that can affect wind speed include geographical structures and obstacles, such as valleys and mountains. These structures cause variations in the wind's speed due to friction and funneling effects. As air moves, it loses energy to friction created between its molecules and between it and the ground it is traveling over.

Wind Turbines

The Marcraft GT-1500 Green Electron Generation panel includes a 400-Watt, 12-volt, three-blade, microprocessor-controlled wind turbine and all the support components required to generate both direct current (DC) and alternating current (AC) electricity from wind power. The Marcraft wind turbine is depicted in Figure 2-3.

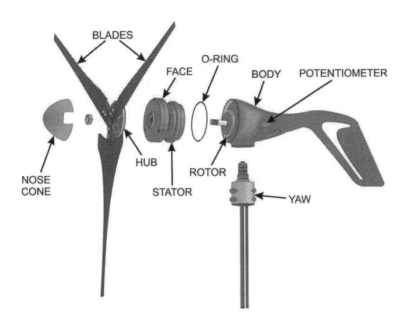

BLADES

FACE — O-RING — BODY — POTENTIOMETER

NOSE CONE

HUB

STATOR — ROTOR

YAW

Figure 2-3: Wind Generator Components

Blades

The wind turbine component fundamentally responsible for converting wind energy into another usable source of energy is the **blade assembly**. This structure is also used as a source of propulsion in aircraft and watercraft, however, in these applications mechanical energy is being applied to the blade assembly to turn it and the blades are referred to as *propellers*.

In a wind turbine, air moves past the blades causing them to move, as illustrated in Figure 2-4. The blades are designed in such a way that when the wind strikes them, it is diverted around the opposite faces of the blades. One side of the blade is curved so that air passing over it takes longer to travel over the surface than the air passing over the opposite surface of the blade. This creates a force on the blade referred to in aerodynamics as **lift**. This action is described in science by a law called **Bernoulli's Principle**. This lifting force on the blades causes the blade assembly to rotate around a central shaft it is attached to.

The amount of force applied to the blade is based on the intensity of the wind, the surface area of the blade and the angle at which the wind strikes the blade. As the wind intensity flowing across the surface area of the blades increases, so does the level of rotational force developed by the blade assembly. The energy potential of a wind turbine is proportional to the square of the length of its blades and to the cube of the speed at which its blades spin.

The energy applied to the blade assembly does not correspond directly to an increase in the angle (**pitch**) at which the wind strikes the blades. Instead, there is an optimum pitch setting for the blades that relates to the wind speed flowing across them. Most wind turbine blade designs actually provide varying pitch angles along the length of the blade to optimize the blade's ability to work efficiently over a variety of wind speeds.

For the most part, wind turbine blades are wider and thicker at the root end (the end closest to the center shaft) than they are at the tip. This design makes it easier for the blade to start turning while providing more power when the blade is moving a higher speeds. The direction the blade assembly will rotate is dictated by the direction of the blade's pitch.

blade assembly

lift

Bernoulli's Principle

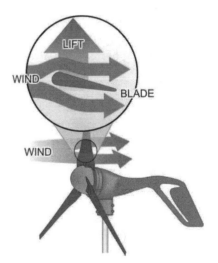

LIFT

WIND

BLADE

WIND

Figure 2-4: Wind Pulling on a Blade

Most wind turbines mount the blades so they are vertical to the ground, which produces a **horizontal axis wind turbine (HAWT)**. However, there are also a number of wind turbine designs that mount the blades horizontally—making the turbine a **vertical axis wind turbine (VAWT)**. Figure 2-5 depicts different wind turbine blade mounting scenarios.

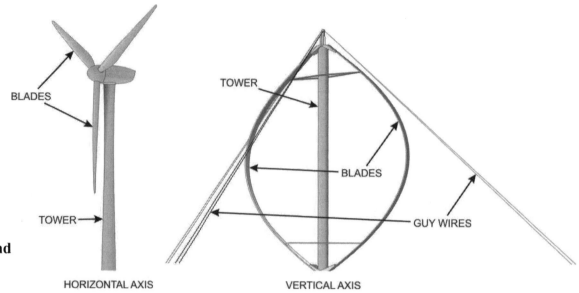

Figure 2-5: Wind Turbine Blade Configurations

Generating Electricity

generators

alternators

direct current (DC)

alternating currents
(AC)

The design intention of a wind turbine is to convert wind energy into mechanical energy and then into electrical energy. We've seen how wind acts on the wind turbine's blades to create rotational mechanical energy. The next step is to use that rotational energy to create electrical energy. There are two common electro-mechanical devices that can be used to accomplish this—electrical **generators** and **alternators**. Both devices convert the mechanical energy provided through the rotating shaft into electrical current. A generator produces **direct** electrical **current** (**DC**) flows, while alternators generate **alternating** electrical **currents** (**AC**) flows. In a DC circuit electrons move from atom to atom in a conductor in a constant direction. In an AC circuit the electrons move back and forth between atoms in the conductor on a regular cycle. Direct and alternating currents are depicted in Figure 2-6.

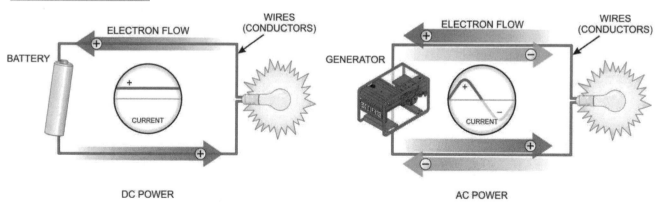

Figure 2-6: Direct and Alternating Current Flows

In both devices, the movement of electrons in the conductor is caused by magnetic fields placing an electrical push and pull on the electrons in one or more coils of wire. This push is referred to as **electromotive force (EMF)** or **voltage (V)**. If an acceptable pathway—referred to as a **circuit**—is provided for the movement of the electrons from the pushing end of the device to the pulling end an electrical circuit is created. This concept is depicted in Figure 2-7. You can envision this as electrons hopping from one atom to the next to move around the circuit from the pushing end of the device to the pulling end. The electromotive force is applied to all of the atoms between the two ends of the conductor, which causes a flow (or current) of electrons to move through the circuit.

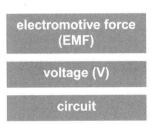

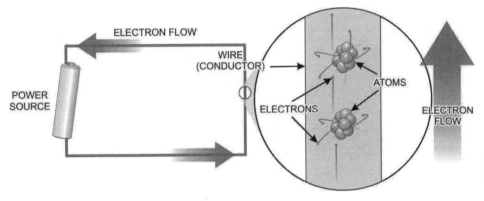

Figure 2-7: Electron Current Flow

The wind turbine's central shaft uses the mechanical energy from the rotating blade assembly to turn a set of magnets housed in a structure called the **rotor**. The rotor turns inside a collection of coiled wires (field coils) called the **stator**. As the magnets turn past the field coils, their magnetic fields push on the atoms in the coil's causing them to give up outer shell electrons.

rotor

stator

The effect that the moving magnet has on the material in the coils is dependent on the strength and polarity of the magnet's field, the angle that the field cuts through the coil and the speed at which the field cuts through the wires.

Figure 2-8 illustrates the effects of magnetic fields cutting through a wire. As each magnet nears a wire, the outermost part of its field begins to exert force on the atoms in the conductor. Its field is very weak in the beginning. However, as the magnet moves closer and closer to the wire, the force its field exerts on the wire increases. As the magnet passes the wire and moves away, its force begins to decrease. This is demonstrated by the rising and then falling waveform. This produces a sine wave output wave form.

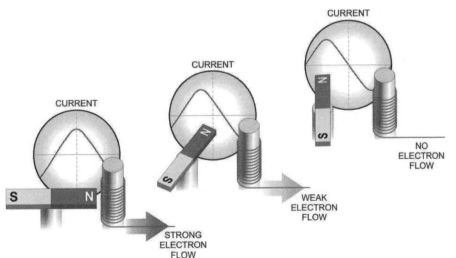

Figure 2-8: Magnetic Fields Generating Current Flow

The direction of electron movement in the wire is determined by the polarity of the magnet. In the figure the **north pole** of the magnet is shown forcing the electrons to flow to the right of the figure—this is illustrated as a positive flow. If the magnet is turned around so that it's **south pole** is moved past the wire, the magnetic field would push in the other direction and the current would flow to the left in the figure. In the figure, this is represented by a waveform that cycles below the zero reference line. These directions are purely arbitrary for this discussion, as positive and negative flow are relative terms determined by the point of reference the measurement is taken from.

In an alternator, the two poles of the magnets create alternating currents in the stator windings. Many alternator designs, including the one in the Marcraft Wind Turbine, include three sets of stator winding that are offset from each other to generate three overlapping current waveforms, as illustrated in Figure 2-9. These currents add and subtract from each other at each point along the waveform to provide a more consistent overall waveform.

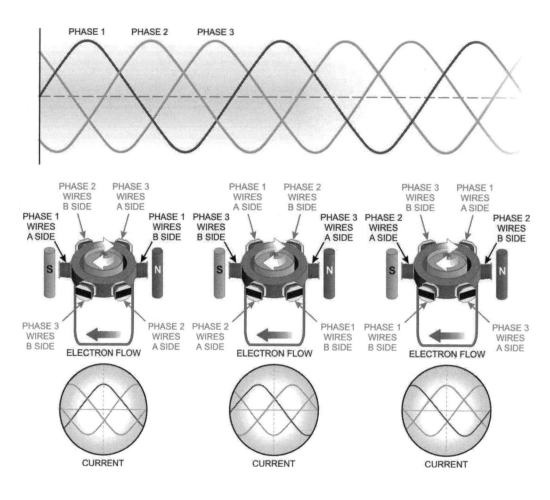

Figure 2-9: Three Phase Waveforms

In a DC generator, the connection from the coils to the outside world is made through a set of split slip rings. The split in the rings, insure that the same polarity of electrical push is applied to the same wires—*as the coils turn inside the magnets*—as illustrated in Figure 1-10. The current flows out of one side of the coil, through a spring-loaded brush contact, into one of the slip ring halves (referred to as commutator bars), into the external wire, through the external circuit, into the other brush and commutator bar, and finally, into the other end of the coil.

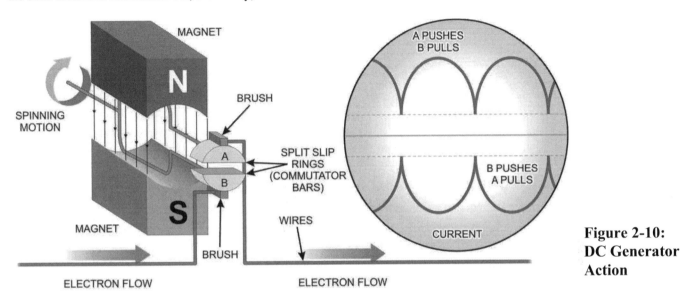

Figure 2-10: DC Generator Action

In a similar **AC generator** (alternator), the same actions occur, except that the slip rings are not split. Therefore, the alternating current being generated in the coil is applied to both sides of the external circuit through spring-loaded brushes and slip rings. This concept is depicted in Figure 2-11. The AC output can either be used as it is generated, or it can be converted to DC current through a device call a **rectifier**. This is the way the alternator in an automobile operates.

AC generator

rectifier

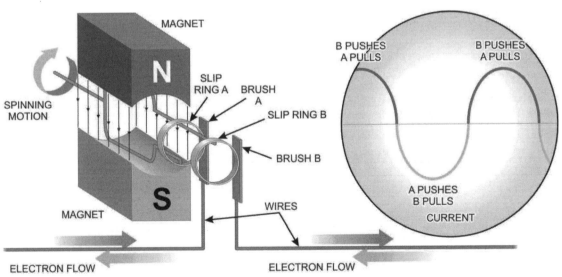

Figure 2-11: Rectifying AC into DC

The AC generator used in the Marcraft wind turbine uses stationary coils and spins permanent magnets inside the windings. This method requires no brushes or slip rings, so there are fewer moving parts to wear out. A rectifier built into the wind turbine's electronic controller board converts the AC current generated in the windings into DC current.

Wind Turbine Housings

nacelle

gear sets

monitoring and control circuitry

YAW shaft

The wind turbine's electrical generation circuitry is generally placed in a housing called the **nacelle** that is mounted on the top of the wind turbine's tower. The nacelle may also hold mechanical **gear sets** to amplify the mechanical force produced by the blades, as well as electrical **monitoring and control circuitry** to manage the output and safe operation of the wind turbine.

The Marcraft wind turbine is designed so that it can swivel on top of the mounting mast. This allows the body and blades of the turbine to swing into the optimum position for the direction of the wind. The turbine employs a freely turning **YAW shaft** connection that securely fastens the body of the turbine to the mounting mast. Electrical current produced by the turbine's generator, is passed to wires running down the mounting mast to the user's control panel mounted near the bottom of the tower. A set of slip rings and brushes in the yaw collar enable the turbine to spin around completely without entangling the three wires that run down the mast.

Wind acting on the tail fin built into the wind turbine's body swings the turbine so that it faces directly into the wind. The slot in the Marcraft turbine's fin gives the turbine good balance so that it tracks with the wind as efficiently as possible.

Safety Precautions

All wind turbines pose mechanical, electrical, and rotor blade hazards. You must be aware of how these three types of hazards are presented by the wind turbine system and take steps necessary to prevent injury or damage from these causes.

Mechanical Hazards

Rotating blades present a very serious mechanical hazard associated with wind turbine. The Marcraft wind turbine's rotor blades are made of very strong thermoplastic. In the field, the blades may be moving at velocities over 275 miles per hour (440 km/hr) at the tip. At this speed, the tip of a blade is nearly invisible and can cause serious injury. Under no circumstances should you install the turbine where a person could come in contact with moving rotor blades.

> ## CAUTION
>
> Never install the blades on the turbine in a location where anyone can approach the path of the blades. Never install the blades in a classroom environment.

Electrical Hazards

The Marcraft wind turbine is a 12-volt system capable of producing up to 400 Watts of power. The relationship between electrical power, current and voltage is an extended part of Ohm's Law and is expressed as:

$$P = V \times I \text{ or } I = \frac{P}{V}$$

where P is power in Watts, V is voltage in Volts, and I is current in amperes (amps)

> ## CAUTION
>
> Current levels as low as 0.1-0.2 amps can be fatal to humans under the correct circumstances. Therefore, caution should always be used when connecting this and other electrical devices.

Therefore, a 12-volt wind turbine operating at the 400-Watt level would be delivering 33.34 amps of current to the load. Current levels as low as 0.1 - 0.2 amps can be fatal to humans under the certain circumstances. Therefore caution should always be used when working with this or any other electrical devices.

Another danger associated with electrical current flow is the possibility of **burns** or **fire** related to **conductors** (wiring and devices that give up electrons easily) heating up. Even though the conductor materials give up electrons more easily than other substances, their electrons do not just fall off the atom—even conductors have some level of resistance in them. Therefore, some energy is given off as heat when current passes through the conductor.

Heat in wiring systems is often a result of too much current flowing through an undersized wire or through a bad connection. One of the keys to minimizing the amount of heat generated in wiring is to use the proper size wiring and the correct external insulation coating. A wire with a larger cross sectional area carries a given amount of current more easily than a smaller wire of the same material. There are simply more atoms across the face of the larger wire to give up the necessary number of electrons. Therefore, less heat is produced for that level of current.

In the United States, wiring is specified by a measurement standard called the **American Wire Gauge (AWG)**. This standard specifies wire diameter in a descending relationship—larger AWG gauge numbers represent smaller wire diameters. The reason this is important for an installer is because the cross sectional area (diameter) of the wire is directly related to its ability to carry electrical current (referred to as the wire's **ampacity**). It is important to follow the wire-sizing chart in Table 2-1 when working with the Marcraft wind turbine to insure a safe electrical system and to help avoid the risk of electrical fire.

| burns |
| fire |
| conductors |

| American Wire Gauge (AWG) |
| ampacity |

Table 2-1: Wire Gauge Sizes

# TURBINES	0-30 FEET	30-60 FEET	60-90 FEET	90-150 FEET	150-190 FEET	190-250 FEET	250-310 FEET	310-390 FEET	390-500 FEET
1	8g/8	6g/13	4g/21	2g/34	1g/53	0g/53	00g/67	000g/85	000g/85
2	6g/13	4g/21	1g/44	00/67	000g/85	0000g/107	*	*	*
3	4g/21	2g/34	0g/53	000g/85	0000g/107	*	*	*	*

*If your system requires this length of wire, consider using additional, parallel wire(s).

CAUTION
Follow the wire gauge sizing chart in Table 2-1 to help avoid the risk of an electrical fire.

fuse

circuit breaker

Wind turbines can deliver a dangerous amount of current. If a short circuit occurs in the wiring system, a fire can result or components can be damaged. Likewise, if you are the source of the short circuit you can be injured, burned or killed. In order to avoid these threats, a properly sized **fuse** or **circuit breaker** is required in the lines coming from the wind turbine (or any other electrical source). These devices sense the level of current flowing through them and are designed to interrupt the path of current flow (open circuit) if the current level gets to a certain point (the fuse rating). Use the following fuse sizing information when working with the Marcraft wind turbine circuitry:

- 12-volt model: 50 amps DC

- 24-volt model: 30 amps DC

CAUTION
FUSE ALL CONNECTIONS. Follow the fuse sizing information to minimize the risk of fire and/or electrical failure.

PROCEDURE 5 – WIND TURBINES

In this lab procedure you will identify the key components of a wind turbine electrical generation system, mount and correctly wire a wind turbine for use, and test the basic operation of the wind turbine system.

Wind

Resources Needed:

- Wind Turbine
- Electric Variable Speed Drill
- 5/16" Hex Key Bit
- 1-1/2" Schedule 80 3-piece mast (approximately 3 ft. long when assembled)
- Marcraft Green Electron Generation Experiment Panel
- Hand-held Digital multimeter
- 1 12V, 7 AH, Sealed Lead Acid Battery

Introduction to Wind Turbines

One of the keys to installing any electrical system—including wind turbines—is to read and understand its documentation. Locate and record the following information from the Owners Manual:

1. Obtain the Wind Turbine's Owners Manual and verify that all of the Wind Turbine's parts are present in your work area.

2. According to the manual, what precaution should be taken when making electrical connections to the wind turbine? What can happen to the Wind Turbine if this warning is ignored?

   _____

   _____

   _____

3. What wire size is recommended for the 12V version of the wind turbine if it is mounted between 60 and 90 feet from the battery system?

   _____

4. What action should be taken to protect the wind turbine and its supporting circuitry and equipment from damage caused by lightning strikes?

   _____

5. Obtain information about the height of your location above sea level and determine the maximum expected efficiency level of operating the wind turbine at your location. Record these values on the following lines:

_____

_____

6. What is the approximate power output of this wind turbine if a smooth steady wind of 25 miles per hour is blowing?

_____

7. If the Annual Average Wind Speed at your geographic location is approximately 10 miles per hour, and the wind is typically smooth and steady, how much energy should the wind turbine contribute to the energy supply each month?

_____

8. Research the local residential power price for you location and determine the monetary value of the power you are generating (X kWh/mo x price/kWh—depends on local values).

_____

9. At what wind speed should this wind turbine startup?

_____

10. What is the range of expected voltages that the 12V wind turbine is specified to provide?

_____

11. What size fuse or circuit breaker is specified for this 12V wind turbine?

_____

12. At what wind speed should the turbine blades be removed from the wind turbine for protection purposes?

_____

Wind

Mounting the Wind Turbine

In an actual wind turbine installation, the turbine is typically mounted between 30 and 100 ft. above the ground (at least 25 ft. above any nearby obstructions). This requires that the turbine be mounted on a tower that can support the turbine even in high velocity wind situations. Mounting a residential wind turbine typically involves attaching the wind turbine to the tower on the ground, installing the blades and then elevating the complete assembly into position. Finally, the tower is secured in place by multiple guy wires.

In the case of commercial wind turbine installations, the turbine is installed atop the tower after the tower has been secured in place. Cranes with sufficient height and weight handling capabilities are used to carry out this operation.

In both cases, the tower must be designed to provide proper clearance of the wind turbine's blades both from the tower and the ground, as well as any other possible obstructions that may be present in the turbine's Sphere of Operation, as illustrated in Figure 2-12.

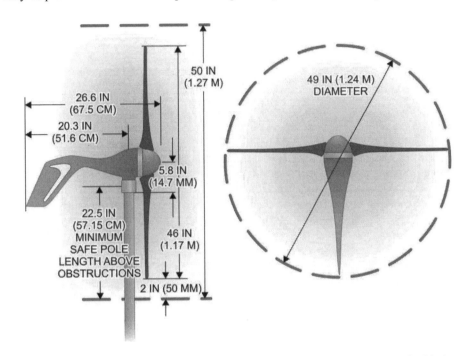

Figure 2-12: Mounting the Windmill

NOTE: To install the Marcraft wind turbine in a non-lab environment using the blades, a minimum of 2-inches (50 mm) of clearance must be provided between the blade tips and any obstructions if the blades are installed for operation.

Electrical wiring from the wind turbine travels down the tower to a control panel. The control panel provides key controls and indicators for safe and efficient operation of the wind turbine.

1. Obtain the wind turbine mounting mast and orient it behind the panel so that the wiring access opening is approximately even with the Wind Turbine STOP and DISCONNECT switches mounted on the front of the Clean Electron Generation Panel, as illustrated in Figure 2-13.

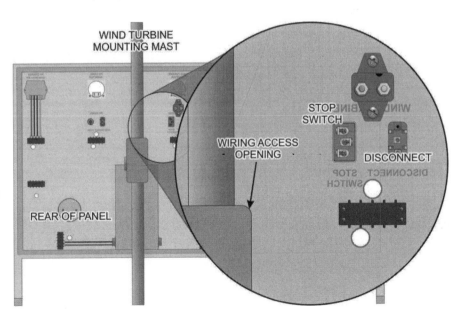

Figure 2-13: Aligning the Mounting Mast

CAUTION

Use only properly sized metal pipe for towers. The Marcraft wind turbine is designed to be mounted on tubing or pipe with a 1.875 inch (48mm) outside diameter. This is equivalent to 1-1/2 inch SCH 40 steel pipe, which can be used in some tower applications. The GT-1500 Clean Electron Generation panel includes a 3 ft. length of 1-1/2 inch schedule 80 PVC pipe to provide this function. This is suitable for desktop lab environments. However, for outdoor installations, plastic pipe should never be used as the wind turbine's mast.

2. If not already prepared, obtain one of the wind turbines and where the three wires (Red, Green and Black) that extend out of the base of the wind turbine, cut the three wires so that there is at least 3 inches of wire extending below the opening at the base of the wind turbine. Set the wind turbine aside. (Or use the wiring set that was previously prepared.)

3. Take the three wires that were cut from the wind turbine (or use the prepared wires that were previously prepared) and thread them from the wiring terminal block on the front of the panel through the mounting mast access opening and up inside of the the mast until they extend 3 inches above the top of the mast.

4. Attach crimp-on, female spade connectors to each of the wires extending from the top of the mast (if not already present). Use tape or cable ID tags to mark both ends of all the wires to identify the negative, positive and earth ground wires.

   Wiring color-codes:

   - RED = Positive
   - BLACK = Negative
   - GREEN = Ground

5. Make sure that the connections are properly insulated to insure they do not form a short circuit to the mast or to each other. Normally, this connection should not require any additional insulation because you are working with insulated crimp connectors and the PVC mast provided for classroom operation. However, when conducting an outdoor installation with a metal mast, additional insulation should be provided to the connection using either heat shrink tubing or a quality electrical tape.

6. Position the mast so that it rests securely on the tabletop with the top of the mast hanging off the edge of the table by about 4 inches.

WARNING

The blades and nose cone of the wind turbine are not used in an indoor laboratory environment. The moving blades present a real physical hazard if they are allowed to come into contact with personnel or equipment.

7. Loosen the Allen bolts in the Wind Turbine's yaw clamp, but do not completely remove them from the collar.

8. Verify that the soft rubber sleeve, yaw clamp pad, is fully and evenly installed in the wind turbine's yaw clamp.

NOTE: *The soft rubber sleeve, yaw clamp pad, in the wind turbine's yaw clamp serves several important purposes—it provides a secure fit between the wind turbine and its mast, it creates a weather seal for the electrical connections inside the mast and wind turbine, and it provides a vibration shock suppressor for the mechanical connection between the mast and wind turbine.*

9. On the three wires extending out of the base of the wind turbine, attach crimp-on male spade connectors, if not already present.

10. Position the wind turbine near the top of the mast so that the electrical connections can be made between the wind turbine and the cabling in the mast. Connect the wiring together and slide any excess wire into the mast. Be sure to leave enough slack in the wires so that the turbine can be removed if necessary.

11. Slide the wind turbine's yaw clamp fully onto the mast. Take care to avoid pinching the yaw wires while attaching the turbine to the mast.

12. After the mast has been inserted completely into the yaw clamp, slide the wind turbine back up the mast by about 1/8" (2 mm). This will prevent the bottom of the wind turbine from contacting the top of the mast. The only contact between the tower and yaw is through the yaw clamp pad, which acts to reduce the transmission of noise down the tower.

13. Firmly tighten the yaw clamp bolts with a 5/32" hex key (Apply 3 – 5 foot-pounds (4.1 – 6.8 Nm) to each bolt).

14. Check the wind turbine to be sure that it is securely attached to the mast. The wind turbine should yaw (swivel) freely around the mast without restrictions. Remember that in an outdoor installation, this attachment will have to hold in high winds.

15. Rest the mast and turbine securely on the table.

16. Position the mounting mast so that the bottom of the mast rests on the table top and insert the mast into the upper and lower mounting clamps on the back of the Clean Electron Generation Panel, as shown in Figure 2-14.

17. Place the arms of the clamps across the mast and secure both clamps closed using four 8 x 1-1/2" screws.

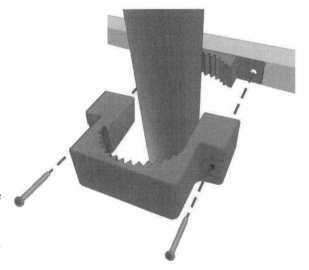

Figure 2-14: Securing the Mast

Wind

Hub and Rotor Assembly (Optional)

Do not mount the blades on the wind generator inside the classroom. The leading edges of the blades are sharp and pose a risk of significant injury. Only use the following procedure for outdoor installations where the wind turbine and its blades will be safely away from contact with personnel or equipment.

WARNING

Under no circumstances should you install the turbine where a person could come in contact with its moving rotor blades.

---

1. Remove the 5/8" nut from the wind turbine's shaft.

2. Carefully slide the blade assembly onto the shaft.

3. Place the nut on the shaft and thread the nut on by spinning the blade assembly.

4. Insert the 5/16" hex key torque wrench into the wind turbine shaft and tighten the nut by holding the hub in place and tightening the shaft with the torque wrench. The nut should be tightened to 50 – 65 foot-pounds (68 – 88 Nm) of torque.

5. After the blade set assembly has been tightened, spin it to insure that it turns freely.

CAUTION

While mounting the blade assembly to the turbine, be careful not to push the rotor shaft into the turbine.

---

6. Position the nose cone over the center of the hub and the blades.

7. Snap the nose cone into place. Be sure all three edges catch.

8. Verify that the nose cone is securely installed by gently but firmly pulling on it.

NOTE: The nose cone does not affect the performance of the turbine and may be omitted.

Examining the Control Panel

Figure 2-15 is a suggested schematic diagram (symbolic wiring diagram) for a single wind turbine installation designed to charge a set of batteries.

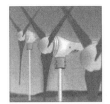

Wind

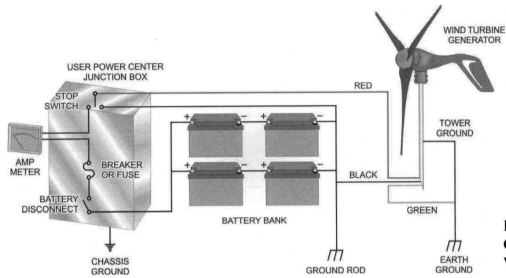

Figure 2-15: Control Panel Wiring

circuit breaker

sized

Stop switch

Battery Disconnect switch

Single Pole, Double Throw (SPDT)

The control panel typically contains a fuse or **circuit breaker** that protects the technician, the operator and the wind turbine circuitry from damage due to short circuits or excessive rotational speeds. A circuit breaker acts as a piece of wire, providing a path for current flow through itself until the current flow level reaches a designated level. If that level is exceeded, the circuit breaker becomes an open circuit to stop the current from flowing through it.

Circuit breakers and fuses must be properly **sized** to safely handle the maximum amount of current that the system is designed to supply, and then break the circuit (cause an open circuit) to interrupt the flow of electrons until the over current condition can be removed or repaired. In doing so the circuit breaker or fuse protects wiring, devices and personnel from damage and injury.

Other common control mechanisms include a **Stop switch** and a **Battery Disconnect switch**. The Stop switch is a **Single Pole, Double Throw (SPDT)** switch. It has one pole (the circle with the movable contact attached to it—and two *throws*—possible connection points represented by the other two small circles.

In operating position, the switch routes the current flow from the Positive (red) lead of the wind turbine to the ammeter the breaker and the Disconnect Switch. In the Stop setting, it creates a short circuit between the (red) lead of the wind turbine and its Negative (black) lead. This causes a braking action to occur inside the wind turbine circuitry, which can be used to protect the turbine in times of excess wind speeds.

The Disconnect switch disconnects the output of the wind turbine from the storage battery, grid or inverter circuitry so that these elements can be serviced safely, without power that is being generated by the wind turbine. The Disconnect Switch is a **Single Pole, Single Throw (SPST)** switch—there is one *pole* (the circle with the movable contact attached to it—and one *throw*—possible connection point. This representation of the SPST switch shows that it is a normally open switch—when the switch is in its "normal" position, there is no path for current to flow through the switch—when the switch is flipped to the active position (the movable contact swings into contact with the circle representing the throw position, creating a path for current flow through the switch.

Like fuses and breakers, switches, devices and wiring must be rated to handle the maximum designed current levels for their positions in the system. Switches are rated according to both voltage and maximum current handling capabilities. Therefore, a switch designed for operation in a 12 Vdc 15A automobile application would not be used in a 120 Vac 15A residential wiring environment. Doing so will potentially present both a damage and an injury situation.

From the control panel, the wiring may continue on to a set of storage batteries (as shown in the figure), to a DC-to-AC inverter, or to a connection into the commercial power grid. These options are explored in the next lab procedure.

1. Place the red lead in the multimeter's V/Ω /mA jack and the black lead in the Ground (COM) jack, as shown in Figure 2-16. Turn the multimeter to the **On** position.

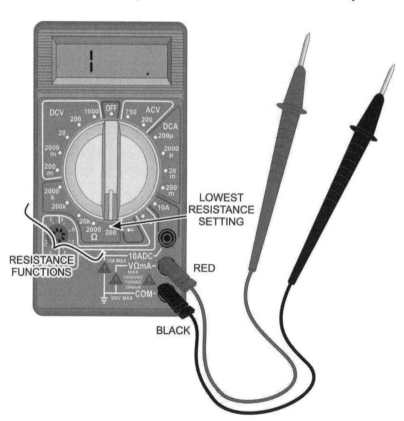

Figure 2-16: Meter Leads Set for Measuring Continuity

2. Set the multimeter to its lowest *resistance range* (used for checking Continuity of a device or circuit).

3. Referring to Figure 2-17, place the meter's leads on the opposite terminals of the Disconnect Switch. On the following lines, record the reading obtained from the multimeter with the switch in the up and down positions:

Switch Up: _____

Switch Down: _____

4. Referring to Figure 2-17, place the black lead of the multimeter on the center terminal of the Emergency Stop switch. Place the multimeter's red lead on the top terminal of the switch. On the following lines, record the reading from the multimeter with the switch in the up and down positions:

Switch Up: _____

Switch Down: _____

5. Move the multimeter's red lead to the bottom terminal of the switch. On the following lines, record the reading from the multimeter with the switch in the up and down positions:

Switch Up: _____

Switch Down: _____

6. Place the multimeter leads on opposite terminals of the breaker. Record the resistance measurement on the following lines. Move the leads to the opposite terminals and record the multimeter reading in this direction:

_____

_____

7. Connect the leads on opposite terminals of the turbine's ammeter. Record the resistance measurement on the following lines. Move the leads to the opposite terminals and record the multimeter reading in this direction:

_____

_____

Figure 2-17:
Emergency Stop Switch
Meter Leads

NOTE

You may want to use masking tape to create ON/OFF and STOP/RUN labels.

Wiring the Control Panel

When wiring all facets of the Clean Electron Generation Panel throughout all of the lab procedures, applying new wiring to the panel should only occur during the first application performance of the lab procedures. In all other cases, where available, use the existing wiring that as been prepared during the previous lab sessions.

1. Thread the free ends of the black and green wires through the access opening above the Wind Turbine Control Panel connection block.

Wind

2. Crimp a fork lug connector to the green and black wires and secure them to the two, center connection points on the top row of the Wind Turbine Control Panel connection block terminals, as illustrated in Figure 2-18.

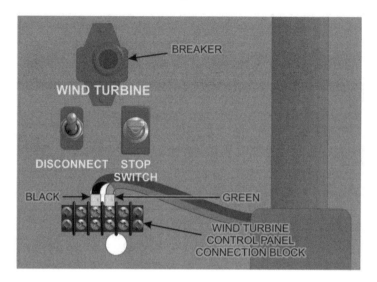

Figure 2-18: Wind Turbine Ground and Neutral Wiring

3. Attach a fork lug crimp connector to the red wire and connect the wire to the center terminal of the SPDT Stop switch.

4. Prepare and install a short red 10 AWG jumper wire to run between the top terminal of the Stop switch and the (+) terminal on the Wind Turbine Ammeter.

5. Prepare and install a short red 10 AWG jumper wire to run between the open terminal (-) of the Wind Turbine Ammeter and one of the terminals on the 50A wind turbine breaker as shown in Figure 2-19.

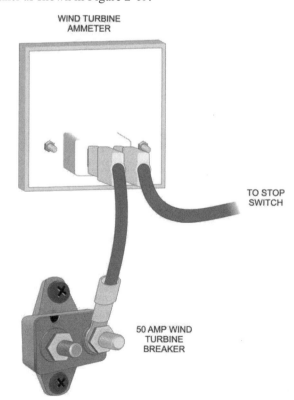

Figure 2-19: Connecting the Wind Turbine's Positive Side Wiring

6. Prepare and install a short red 10 AWG jumper wire to run between the open terminal on the 50A wind turbine breaker and the top terminal on the Wind Turbine Disconnect switch.

7. Thread the free end of a red 10 AWG wire through the opening in the Clean Electron Generation Panel above the Wind Turbine Control Panel connection block.

8. Crimp fork lug connectors to the ends of the red wire and secure it to the open left connection point on the top row of the Wind Turbine Control Panel connection block.

9. Attach the free end of the red jumper to the open terminal on the Wind Turbine Disconnect switch.

10. Run a short length of black 10 AWG wire through the opening below the right most terminal on the bottom of the Wind Turbine Control Panel connection block.

11. Attach fork lug crimp connectors to both ends of the jumper wire and attach one end to the bottom terminal of the Stop switch and the other end to the bottom right terminal of the Wind Turbine Control Panel connection block.

12. Install a small black 10 AWG jumper between the right-most and left-center terminals on the upper row of the Wind Turbine Control Panel connection block, as depicted in Figure 2-20.

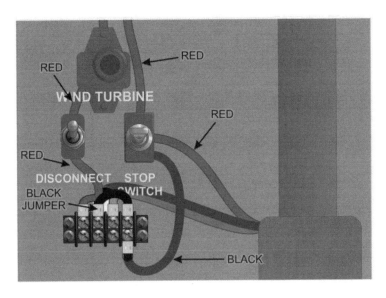

Figure 2-20: Wind Turbine Control Panel Connection Block Wiring

13. Verify your wiring against the schematic wiring diagram in Figure 2-21. Check off the leads on the drawing as you verify the connection pathway between each device.

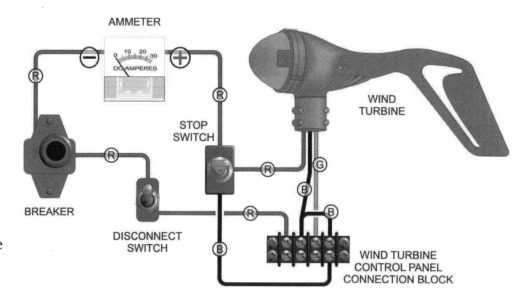

AMMETER

STOP
SWITCH

WIND
TURBINE

BREAKER

DISCONNECT
SWITCH

WIND TURBINE
CONTROL PANEL
CONNECTION BLOCK

**Figure 2-21:
Wind Turbine
Control Panel
Wiring**

Testing

There are a number of tests you can perform to verify that the wind generator is working properly. The following procedures can be used to perform simple manual tests on the wind turbine, as well as performance tests along the wind turbine's designed wind speed parameters.

Wind

Manual Test

1. With the blades and nose cone assembly removed from the turbine, place the Emergency Stop switch in the position to route the current through the ammeter and Disconnect Switch. (If necessary, refer to the "Examining the Control Panel" procedure from earlier in this lab to verify this position).

NOTE: Place the blade assembly in a safe location. (Do not stand the blade assembly against a wall.)

2. Place the Disconnect Switch in the closed (**ON**) position (so that the current can pass through it).

3. Spin the wind turbine's rotor shaft with your fingers (or with an Allen wrench—Be careful not to press the rotor shaft into the turbine body.)

4. While turning the rotor shaft, use a short length of 10 AWG wire to repeatedly short the wind turbine's Red and Black wires to each other at the connection strip.

5. With the wind turbine's wires jumpered, the rotor shaft should have a noticably different resistance when rotating and feel "lumpy". With the jumper removed from the wires, the turbine should spin freely.

Performance Test

Wind

In order to obtain visible results to complete this performance test, you will temporarily connect one of the batteries from the battery pack to the Wind Turbine Control Panel.

1. Be sure the jumper wire between the Red and Black wires at the Wind Turbine Control Panel connection block has been removed and attach the red and black multimeter leads to the terminal point so that they connect with the wire of the same color.

2. Prepare a red and black 15-inch length of wire with fork connectors on one end and female spade connectors on the other.

3. Attach the red wire fork connector to the left-most terminal on the bottom row of the Wind Turbine Control Panel connection block.

4. Attach the black wire fork connector to the left-center terminal on the bottom row of the Wind Turbine Control Panel connection block.

5. Attach the red wire female spade connector to a positive (red) terminal on one battery in the battery pack.

6. Attach the black female spade connector to the negative (black) terminal of the same battery.

7. Verify your wiring, as illustrated in Figure 2-22.

8. Set the multimeter to the 20-volt DCV setting, and measure the voltage with the battery connected.

    _____ (Volts)

9. With a 5/16" hex drive in an electric drill, make sure the bit is set up to turn in a clockwise direction when viewing the drill from the back.

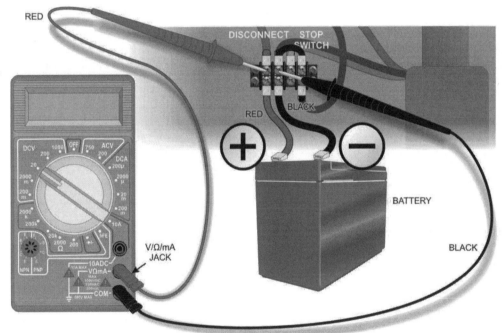

**Figure 2-22:
Connecting the Battery**

CAUTION! During the following section of this procedure, there are some safety concerns that you should be ware of. As you are performing this procedure you will be asked to operate both wind turbines in tandem (or at the same time. Because of the built-in safety features of these wind turbines, you must be aware of the kick back that can produced by the wind turbine under certain conditions. This kick back can be hazardous if you are not expecting it as the drill handle can rotate suddenly and forcefully.

10. Insert the hex drive in the slot in the wind turbine's rotor shaft and spin the shaft.

Pull the drill's trigger about 1/4 of the way back and observe the reading on the turbine's ammeter and the digital multimeter. Record the reading from each device on the following lines:

_____ (Amps)

_____ (Volts)

12. Pull the drill's trigger about 1/2 of the way back and observe the reading on the turbine's ammeter and the digital multimeter. Record the reading from each device on the following lines:

_____ (Amps)

_____ (Volts)

13. Pull the drill's trigger about 3/4 of the way back and observe the reading on the turbine's ammeter and the digital multimeter. Record the reading from each device on the following lines:

_____ (Amps)

_____ (Volts)

14. Pull the drill's trigger completely back and observe the reading on the turbine's ammeter and the digital multimeter. Record the reading from each device on the following lines:

_____ (Amps)

_____ (Volts)

15. From the power curve in Figure 2-23, using the smooth and steady wind curve, determine the approximate wind speed that correlates to each drill setting and record it on the following lines: (You will need to convert the multimeter readings to power using the formula P=V x I in each case).

_____ (1/4)

_____ (1/2)

_____ (3/4)

_____ (Full)

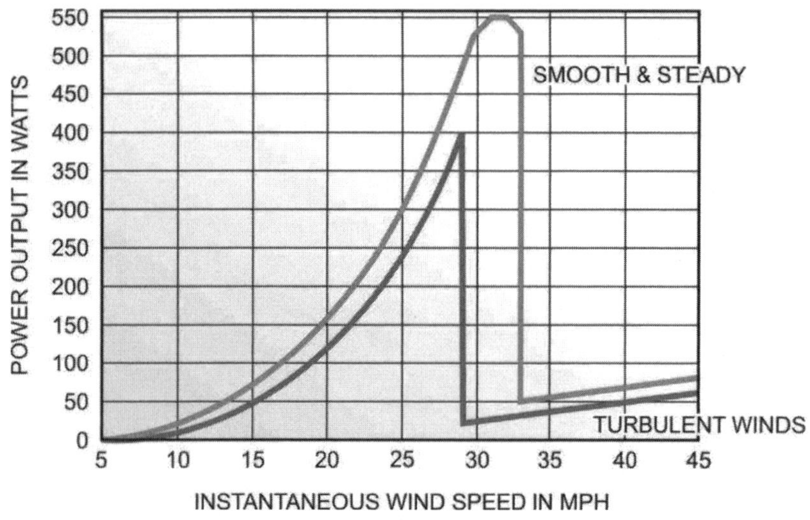

Figure 2-23: Wind Turbine Power Curve

16. Calculate the approximate speed of the drill in Steps 9 through 12 by multiplying its stated maximum speed by the percentage of trigger pull applied. Record the approximated RPM values on the following lines:

_____ (1/4)

_____ (1/2)

_____ (3/4)

_____ (Full)

17. Remove the multimeter leads from the Wind Turbine Control Panel connection block.

18. Remove the red and black wires that were connected to the bottom row of the Wind Turbine Control Panel connection block and the single battery in Step 5.

19. This concludes this hands-on lab procedure. Have your instructor review your results before moving on to the next procedure.

Procedure 5 Questions

1. What function does the Stop Switch serve in the single turbine—direct connect configuration used in this lab?

2. What is the maximum wind speed rating for the wind turbine used in this procedure? What should you do if you expect winds in excess of this rating?

3. What are the consequences of short-circuiting the wind turbine if it is not connected to a load?

4. What type of breaker is required for this wind turbine? Why?

5. How does the calculated wind speed correspond to the stated speed of the drill used to turn the wind turbine?

OFF-GRID WIND TURBINE SYSTEMS

The power output of a wind turbine is not steady. The voltage and current levels produced directly by the wind turbine varies with the speed of the wind driving it. Therefore, the wind turbine alone is not dependable as the primary source of power for most applications. In most residential applications, the output of the wind turbine is either used to charge a bank of **storage batteries**, or it is applied to the **commercial power grid** to supplement the incoming power supply to the residence.

storage batteries

commercial power grid

wind farms

megawatts (MW)

In large commercial **wind farms**, the outputs of several wind turbines are combined to provide hundreds of **megawatts** (million Watts or **MW**) of power that is applied directly to the commercial power grid. These turbines work with complex controllers that monitor the operation of the turbine and control parameters such as its operating temperature, optimum blade pitch, and generator torque control. These controllers are also designed to provide power to the grid in a format acceptable to the local electrical utility.

Batteries

Batteries are devices that produce DC electricity through a chemical reaction process. The chemicals in the battery react with its terminals when an external path for current flow is provided. The process causes free electrons to gather at the negative (-) terminal of the battery while a depletion of electrons occurs at the positive (+) terminal. This provides the push (-) and pull (+) to create current flow through an external circuit, as illustrated in Figure 2-24.

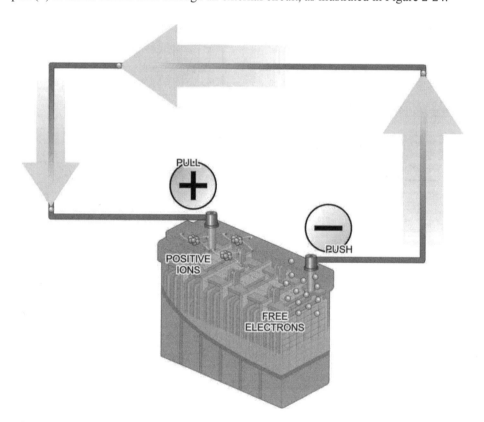

Figure 2-24: Operation of a Battery

When an external pathway is provided the electrons flow from the negative terminal through the external circuit (and the external load) and back into the positive terminal of the battery. If a very low resistance load is placed across the terminals, a large flow of electron current will occur. Larger resistive loads draw lower levels of current flow from the battery, as described by the basic Ohm's Law formula for current, voltage and resistance.

short circuit

In cases where a wire or other good conductor is placed across the terminals without a load (referred to as a **short circuit** condition), the flow through the circuit and the inside of the battery as quickly as the internal process can generate more free electrons. The acceleration of the process causes the battery to heat up, which in turn can cause it to overheat and possibly explode.

Some battery types (referred to as **secondary cells** or **storage** batteries) can be recharged by applying a reverse current to them, as illustrated in Figure 2-25. By applying an external voltage source to the battery at a voltage level *slightly higher* than its terminal voltage, a reverse current is forced to flow back into the battery and the internal chemical process is reversed. Under these circumstances, the battery becomes the load in the circuit instead of the source.

Over time, the reverse current flow restores the original chemical configuration inside the battery. The rate at which the battery **recharges** depends on the chemical configuration and the amount of reverse current flowing through the battery. The amount of reverse current is dependent on the voltage difference between the battery and the recharging source.

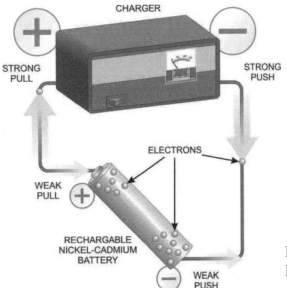

**Figure 2-25:
Recharging a Battery**

The recharging option is not available with all battery types (not all chemical current generating processes can be reversed). Applying a reverse voltage to these batteries (**primary cells**) can cause them to overheat and possibly explode.

> ## WARNING
>
> Applying a reverse voltage to non-rechargeable battery types can cause them to overheat and possibly explode.

Inverters

Inverters are electronic or electro-mechanical devices that converts DC into AC. DC sources such as wind turbines, photovoltaic solar panels and batteries are often connected to inverters to provide an AC output that has consistent voltage levels and frequencies. In a wind turbine system using a storage battery system, the inverter is used to convert the DC current coming from the storage batteries into AC power that can be used with typical household appliances.

Inverter Types

Off grid inverters

the grid

On grid inverters

On-grid/Off-grid
capable inverters

Most wind turbines installations require some type of battery-based storage system. Inverters designed to work specifically with this type of application are referred to as off-grid (or *no utility-needs batteries*) inverters. **Off grid inverters** are designed to work with batteries and are not designed for connection to the commercial AC power system (the electrical power delivered by the power company, also referred to as **the grid**).

On grid (also called *eno-battery-grid intertie*) **inverters** are designed for connection to the AC power system provided by the local electric utility company and do not require any batteries.

A third class of inverters referred to as **On-grid/Off-grid capable inverters**. These inverters are designed so that they can be connected directly to the utility grid and can also work with a battery storage system to provide backup power in the case of a power outage.

Inverter Sizing

Off grid and On-grid/Off-grid capable inverters must be sized so they are compatible with the *maximum* load they are, or will be, expected to supply. This is simply a matter of installing an inverter with a power rating high enough to supply the sum of all the wattage ratings of the devices that will be supplied at any one time. For example, if 200 watts of lighting, 1000 watt refrigerator and a 1500 watt oven need to be supplied at the same time, the inverter must be capable of delivering at least 2700 watts of power. The inverter's input voltage specification must match the system's storage battery configuration.

Load Diverter/Regulators

overcharge

load diverter

When the storage batteries of a wind turbine installation becomes fully charged, the wind turbine will continue to produce additional power as long as the wind continues unless some control circuitry is used to shut down the power generation process. If power continues to be applied to the storage batteries, it will **overcharge** them creating a potentially dangerous situation. Overcharged batteries can overheat and possibly explode. The additional power being generated is also being wasted.

A **load diverter** is a device that monitors the voltage of the load battery. While the voltage level of the battery is below its stated fully charged value, the diverter applies voltage to the battery. However, when the battery voltage reaches the fully charged level, the diverter shifts the current coming from the source to a different load. This load is most often some type of water heater that uses the excess power being generated by the source so that it is not wasted. Figure 2-26 shows the placement and configuration of the load diverter in the wind turbine/storage battery circuit.

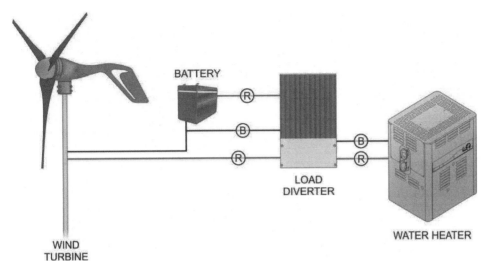

BATTERY

LOAD
DIVERTER

WATER HEATER

WIND
TURBINE

**Figure 2-26:
Implementing the
Load Diverter**

Safety Precautions

As indicated in the previous lab procedure, the wind turbine's rotating blades present a very serious mechanical hazard. ***THE WIND TURBINE'S BLADES SHOULD NOT BE INSTALLED WHILE CONDUCTING THESE LAB PROCEDURES.***

The inherent personal dangers from electrical current still exist in this procedure. Therefore you should always use caution when working with this and other electrical devices. The high current capabilities of the wind turbine create a potentially dangerous shock and burn hazard when the turbine is in operation. As before, using improper wire sizes (wires that are too small for the level of current they are required to carry) can result in excess heat that can damage the wiring, causing a fire, or cause a burn to humans.

> ### CAUTION
>
> It is important to follow the wire-sizing chart in Table 2-1 to insure a safe electrical system and to help avoid the risk of an electrical fire and personal injury.

Battery Hazards

Storage batteries are based on chemical reactions and can deliver dangerous amounts of current. If a short circuit situation occurs in the wiring from the batteries, a fire can result. In order to avoid this threat, a properly sized fuse or circuit breaker is required in the lines connecting the system to the storage batteries. Use the following fuse sizing information when working with the Marcraft wind turbine circuitry:

> ### CAUTION
>
> Follow the fuse sizing information to minimize the risk of fire and/or electrical failure.

- 12-volt model: 50 amps DC
- 24-volt model: 30 amps DC

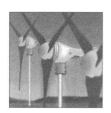

Wind

PROCEDURE 6 – OFF-GRID WIND TURBINE SYSTEMS

In this first procedure, you will connect a set of batteries in different standard configuration. Make sure you are confident your connections are correct before connecting them, as connecting batteries incorrectly can lead to damage and/or personal injury.

<u>Resources Needed</u>:

- Wind Turbine
- Electric Variable Speed Drill
- 5/16" Hex Key Bit
- Marcraft Green Electron Generation Experiment Panel
- Hand-Held Digital Multimeter
- Jumper Wires (8 AWG red, black, green)
- Jumper Wires (12 AWG red and black)
- 4-Battery Battery Pack (12V, 7 AH, Sealed Lead Acid)
- 120 Vac, 4 Watt Night Light

CAUTION

Be sure not to connect the wires to the battery until everything else has been completed and you are instructed to do so in this procedure.

Preparing the Battery Storage System

1. The Marcraft wind turbine and all of its support circuitry is designed to operate at a 12 Vdc level. With this in mind, which battery configuration from the previous procedure should be used as a storage system for this wind turbine?

2. Use four spade lug connectors to connect all four batteries in parallel with each other, as illustrated in Figure 2-27. This requires that you connect jumper wires between all the positive terminals, placing two wires in each spade lug connector except the first and last.

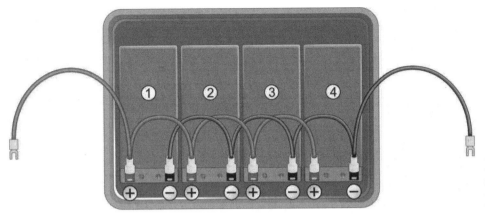

Figure 2-27: Connecting All the Batteries in Parallel

3. Attach an additional 12 AWG red wire to the last terminal so that it extends 2 feet outside the protective battery enclosure.

4. Crimp a fork connector to the external end of the wire.

5. Use the same process described in Step #2 to connect jumper wires between all four negative terminals on the batteries.

6. Attach an additional 12 AWG black wire to the last terminal so that it extends 2 feet outside the protective battery enclosure.

7. Crimp a fork connector to the external end of the wire.

8. Thread the external battery wires over the side of the case in positions that align with the exit openings in the side of the battery case's top cover. Fasten the top cover of the case in place with the external wires extending out of the case, as shown in Figure 2-28.

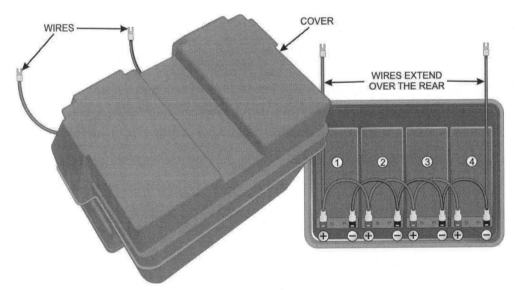

Figure 2-28: Securing the Protective Battery Case

9. Connect the black lead of the multimeter to the external negative battery lead and the red lead to the external positive battery lead. Record the total voltage level provided by this battery configuration on the following line:

_____

10. How does this value relate to the stated operating voltage level of the Marcraft wind turbine?

_____

11. Remove the multimeter from the battery configuration.

12. Place the battery pack on the back side of the Marcraft Green Electron Generation Experiment Panel.

Wind

Connecting the Wind Turbine Directly to the Storage System

1. Crimp a fork lug connector to a 12 AWG green ground wire and secure it to the right inside connection point on the bottom row terminal of the Wind Turbine Control Panel connection block as illustrated in Figure 2-29.

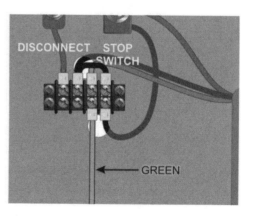

Figure 2-29: Preparing the Wind Turbine's Ground

2. Remove the cover from the Diversion Load Controller, if not already removed and store the cover and screws safely away.

3. Route the green ground wire into the Diversion Load Controller's connection bay and connect it to the ground lug. Refer to Figure 2-30.

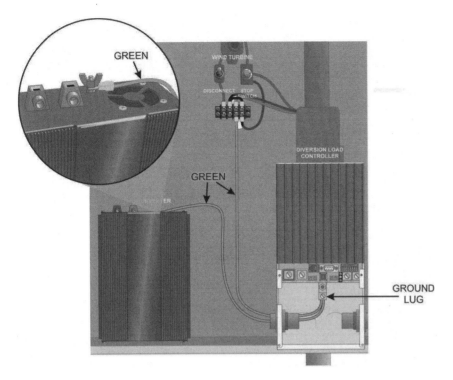

**Figure 2-30:
The Wind Turbine's
Complete Ground
Circuit**

4. Route another green 12 AWG ground wire from the Diversion Load Controller's ground lug to the ground terminal of the Inverter. Attach a crimp on ring connector for this connection.

5. This provides the complete ground circuit for the Marcraft Wind Turbine system, as shown in Figure 2-30. Check with your instructor to make sure that your system is properly grounded before proceeding.

IMPORTANT NOTICE

SEVERE UNIT DAMAGE MAY RESULT FROM IMPROPER GROUNDING.
FAILURE TO PROPERLY GROUND THE TURBINE WILL VOID YOUR WARRANTY.

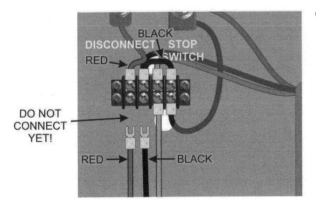

**Figure 2-31: Preparing the
Wind Turbine's Battery Cables**

6. Take the red and black 2 feet long wires from the battery's external connections and route them to the Wind Turbine Control Panel connection block. Refer to Figure 2-31.

CAUTION

Do not connect the wires to the battery or the terminal block at this point. If the wires are hooked-up backwards you will damage the wind turbine's electronics. (If you are uncertain of the polarity of the wires, simply spin the rotor shaft and measure the voltage direction with the multimeter).

Do not connect the wires to the battery or the terminal block at this point. If the wires are hooked-up backwards you will damage the wind turbine's electronics. (If you are uncertain of the polarity of the wires, simply spin the rotor shaft and measure the voltage direction with the multimeter).

7. Before attaching the wind turbine's wiring to the battery leads, make sure that:

    • All Disconnect Switches on the panel are in the **OFF** (disconnect) position

    • The Stop Switch is in the **STOP** or shorted position.

8. Secure the red and black wires to the two, left most connection points on the bottom row of the Wind Turbine terminal block as illustrated in Figure 2-32. The color of each wire should match the wiring on the opposite side of the terminal block (red on the far left and black on the inside left).

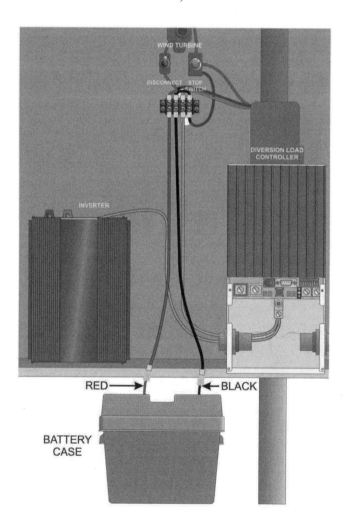

Figure 2-32: The Wind Turbine's Battery Connections

9. Move the Stop Switch to the **RUN** position.

10. Move the Wind Turbine's Disconnect Switch to the **ON** position.

11. Observe the wind turbine's LED indicator. When the wind turbine is first connected to the battery bank, its control circuitry will flash the LED twice to indicate that the control circuit is running correctly. The operation of the LED can be difficult to see in brightly lighted environments.

NOTE: After the initial application of power to the wind turbine, the LED will not come on again until the blades reach a speed of 500 RPM. At this point, the turbine will begin charging and the LED will turn on.

If you miss seeing the LED blink, move the Disconnect Switch to the OFF position for 5 seconds and then move the Disconnect Switch to the ON position. You may need to wait up to10 seconds between iterations of this test in order to let any internal voltage drain.

If the LED does not blink when the wind turbine is connected to a battery, check the following items:

- All switch positions
- All wiring between the wind turbine's output and the battery bank
- Check to make sure there are no electrical short circuits in the system

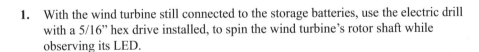

Testing

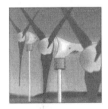

Wind

> ## CAUTION
>
> Be very careful not to push in on the rotor shaft while performing this test. Doing so could damage the control electronics.

1. With the wind turbine still connected to the storage batteries, use the electric drill with a 5/16" hex drive installed, to spin the wind turbine's rotor shaft while observing its LED.

2. Start slowly and steadily increase the speed of the drill. Below 500 RPM, the rotor should spin freely and the LED should remain **Off**.

3. At 500 RPM and above, the wind turbine should be charging the batteries. You should begin to feel some resistance on the rotor shaft and the LED should turn **On**. The shaft should provide a slight resistance to rotation, but it should still rotate fairly easily.

4. Record the approximate percentage of drill trigger pull being applied when the wind turbine's indicator LED comes on, using the following line.

NOTE: *Be sure your battery voltage is not high enough to activate the regulation mode during this test. Refer to the Wind Turbine's documentation to determine the factory set voltage level at which the turbine's internal circuitry shuts down its charging operation.*

WARNING

If the battery voltage is very low (more than 40-50% of its stated value), the turbine may bind up when you try to turn it with the drill. This is caused by the relatively high amount of current being pulled from the turbine by the heavily discharged batteries.

Wind

set point

regulation mode

Adjusting the Wind Turbine's Regulation Set Point

The Marcraft wind turbine contains an intelligent, internal regulator circuit that continually monitors the battery voltage and compares it to a preset internal regulation **set point**. When the battery voltage level rises above the set point, the turbine enters **regulation mode**. In this mode, the turbine automatically shuts off to prevent the batteries from being overcharged. It stops rotating and no power is generated. Before entering regulation mode, the wind turbine will momentarily stop charging in order to get a true reading of the battery voltage.

After entering regulation mode, the wind turbine will simply wait for the battery voltage to drop off. Normal charging will resume when the battery voltage drops slightly below the fully charged level. The Marcraft wind turbine should resume charging when the battery voltage drops off to about 12.75V. The wind turbine's internal controller will blink 10 times each second (fast blink) to indicate that it is in regulation mode.

NOTE: *In high winds there may still be a small trickle charge coming from the turbine's internal circuitry.*

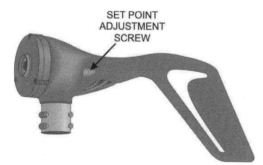

SET POINT
ADJUSTMENT
SCREW

The Marcraft wind turbine has an adjustable regulation set point (cut off level) that can be set to any value from 13.6 Vdc to 17.0 Vdc. The voltage adjustment is external as indicated in Figure 2-33. This adjustment enables you to set the charging voltage limit to meet the battery manufacturer's specifications for the particular battery type you are charging. The factory preset for this level is 14.1 Vdc. This setting is marked on the casting with a small indentation aligned with the screw slot.

NOTE: *In actual operations, you should refer to the battery manufacturers' specifications for exact regulation set points.*

Figure 2-33: The Wind Turbine's Set Point Adjustment

To change the voltage regulator setting, rotate the adjustment screw 1/8 of a turn for each 0.42 volt change desired. For example, if you want to set your voltage regulator to 14.52 volts, turn the adjusting screw clockwise by 1/8 turn, from the 14.1volt setting.

WARNING

Turning "up" the regulation set point adjustment will NOT increase the wind turbine's output voltage or amperage. It simply adjusts the "shut down" point for the generators' voltage regulator.

When the battery voltage reaches the regulation set point voltage, the turbine will slow down and stop charging the batteries.

Turning the screw completely clockwise will NOT increase the voltage or power output and will only increase the probability of overcharging the batteries.

NOTE: Bad connections, undersized wires, and inline diodes will cause the internal regulator to not work properly. It is very important that the wind turbine can "sense" the proper battery voltage.

When performing this test, it is important to note that when turning the turbine's shaft to obtain the blinking LED, you will have to turn the shaft for at least a minute. At somewhere less than a minute, the LED will start blinking and a strong resistance will be felt in the turning of the turbine's shaft. That resistance is the stopping or kickback action that occurs when the turbine's regulator stops the turbine from producing the charging voltage to the battery pack.

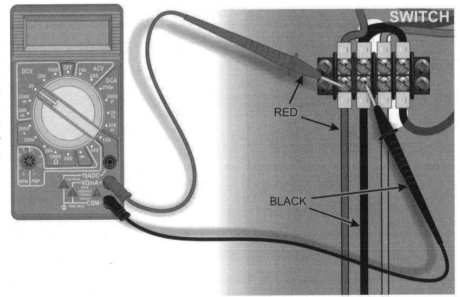

1. Set the multimeter to measure up to 20 Vdc.

2. Connect the multimeter's leads to the wind turbine's charging leads at the Wind Turbine Control Panel connection block, as illustrated in Figure 2-34.

3. Confirm that the Stop Switch is set to the **RUN** position and the Disconnect Switch is set to the **ON** position.

Figure 2-34: Monitoring the Wind Turbine Charging Voltage

4. Record the voltage level being measured with no input from the wind turbine on the following line. This reading represents the current battery voltage:

Battery Voltage: _____

Because of the time delay that is built into the turbine's internal regulator, the regulator does not kick in until the turbine's shaft has been turning up to 40 or 50 seconds. At this time the turbine will exhibit a braking action and is the point where the turbine stops charging the battery pack. To avoid the potential of burning up the drill motor, DO NOT run the drill motor more than a minute at a time during the following steps.

5. Use the electric drill with a 5/16" hex drive installed, to spin the wind turbine's rotor shaft while observing the multimeter.

6. Start slowly and steadily increase the speed of the drill until the wind turbine's indicator LED starts to blink slowly (2 times per second). At this time the turbine has gone into **regulation stall mode** and stops charging the batteries. Stop the drill and record the voltage level at which this occurs on the following line—you should also note a kickback, or the above noted braking actions being applied to the rotation of the drill.

regulation stall mode

Shut Down Voltage: _____

7. Move the Disconnect Switch to the **OFF** position.

8. Turn the wind turbine's regulator adjustment screw fully clockwise, turn it back to its default setting, then turn it 1/4 of a turn clockwise from its default setting.

NOTE: Remember not to run the drill motor much more than a minute in the next step.

9. Move the Disconnect Switch to the **ON** position, and start slowly and steadily increase the speed of the drill until the wind turbine's indicator LED shows that the turbine has entered regulation stall mode and the kickback action starts. Stop the drill and record the voltage level at which this occurs on the following line:

Adjusted Shut Down Voltage: _____

10. Stop the drill and move the Disconnect Switch to the **OFF** position.

11. Turn the wind turbine's regulator adjustment screw 1/2 of a turn clockwise from its present setting.

NOTE: Remember not to run the drill motor much more than a minute in the next step.

12. Move the Disconnect Switch to the **ON** position, and start slowly and steadily increase the speed of the drill until the wind turbine's indicator LED shows that the turbine has entered regulation stall mode and the kickback action starts. Stop the drill and record the voltage level at which this occurs on the following line:

New Adjusted Shut Down Voltage: _____

13. Move the Disconnect Switch to the **OFF** position and the Stop Switch to the **STOP** or **OFF** position.

14. Reset the wind turbine's regulator adjustment screw to its factory setting by aligning the slot with the marker on the wind turbine body.

15. Remove the red and black wires and the multimeter leads, if connected, from the Wind Turbine Control Panel connection block (left-most terminals) and set them aside.

External Voltage Regulator/Load Diverter Operation

There are some conditions in which the wind turbine's internal regulator is not appropriate as the primary regulator. These conditions include:

Wind

- Systems located where the ambient temperature around the batteries varies widely.

- In systems where the batteries are extremely sensitive to charge voltage

- When multiple turbines used with a bus system, where turbine to bus wire lengths or types vary

The Marcraft Green Electron Generation panel includes a *diversion style regulator* (also known as a Diversion Charge Controller or **Load Diverter**) that can be used to control the charging of the storage battery system. Using the Marcraft wind turbine's internal regulator to control the charging system causes the wind turbine to shut down when the battery voltage set point is reached.

Load Diverter

With the external load diverter controlling the charging system, the wind turbine will continue to produce useful output from the wind because the load diverter redirects the power to an external load such as a water heater. This allows the system to use the full output of the turbine even when the battery storage system is full. On the Marcraft training panel, a red 12 Vdc light represents this load. When the batteries are fully charged, the load diverter will redirect the generated power to this light.

*NOTE: If you elect to operate the Marcraft Wind Turbine in an outdoors environment, and elect to use an external regulator other than the one supplied with the trainer, do not use one that will open circuit the turbine as a means of regulation. The Marcraft wind turbine was not meant to operate in an **open-circuit** condition (no path for current flow) for extended periods of time. Most solar controllers will create an open circuit in the solar panel charging circuit when the batteries are full – which is perfectly acceptable for solar panels. However, this type of regulation can damage a wind turbine by causing it to "freewheel" when the batteries are full. If you choose to use an external regulator, be sure to use a diversion style regulator.*

open-circuit

1. Obtain the Load Diverter's Technical Specifications documentation. The Load Diverter can be configured to operate in three distinct modes—Solar Battery Charger, Load Controller, or Diversion Load Controller. You will be configuring the Load Diverter/Regulator as a "Diversion Charge Controller". Make certain to obtain the appropriate configuration information from the documentation (Sections 6.0 - 6.5). Locate and record the following information to set up the Diverter as a Diversion Charge Controller on the lines provided:

   a. DIP Switch Settings

   For Control Mode – SW 1 - Load: _____

   For System Voltage – SW 2, 3 - Auto Select: _____

   For Diversion Charge – SW 4,5,6 - Battery Type 3 */ 14.5V Equalization Voltage: _____

   For Select Diversion Mode – SW 7 - Diversion: _____

   For Battery Equalization – SW 8 - Auto: _____

> ┌─ **NOTE** ─────────────
> *The batteries supplied with the GT-1500 system are Sealed Lead Acid Batteries that cycle from 14.4 to 15.0 volts.

b. Battery State of Charge Indicator Lights

Red = On: _____

Yellow/Red = On: _____

Yellow = On: _____

Green/Yellow = On: _____

Green = On: _____

c. Fault and Alarm Lights

Red/Green – Yellow: _____

Red/Yellow – Green: _____

No LEDs lit: _____

2. If not already done, set the Load Diverter's DIP switches to match the settings specified in Step 1a.

3. Turn **Off** the wind turbine's internal regulator by gently turning the adjustment screw completely clockwise, as shown in Figure 2-35.

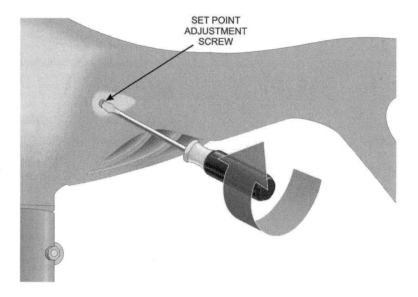

**Figure 2-35:
Disabling the Wind
Turbine's Internal
Regulator Setting**

4. Prepare a red and a black 12 AWG wire long enough to reach from the Wind Turbine Control Panel connection block to the positive and negative input terminals in the Diversion Load Controller's connection bay.

CAUTION

Do not connect the wires to the Diversion Load Controller or the terminal block at this point. If the wires are connected backwards you will damage the wind turbine's circuitry.

5. Crimp appropriate sized fork lug connectors to the red and black wires and secure them to the two, left most connection points on the bottom row of the Wind Turbine terminal block as illustrated in Figure 2-36. The color of each wire should match the wiring on the opposite side of the terminal block (red on the far left and black on the inside left).

6. Route the red and black wires into the Diversion Load Controller's connection bay (through the conduit opening in the left side of the housing).

7. Insert the red wire into the Diversion Load Controller's positive lug and tighten the screw down connector until the connection is secure.

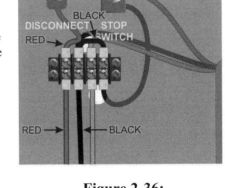

Figure 2-36: Preparing the Wind Turbine/Load Diverter Connection Cables

8. Insert the black wire into the negative lug and tighten the screw down connector until the connection is secure. Figure 2-37 shows the connections between the wind turbine's terminal block and the Diversion Load Controller.

9. Prepare a red and a black 12 AWG wire long enough to reach from the Battery connection block to the Diversion Load Controller's connection bay.

10. Crimp appropriate sized fork lug connectors to the red and black wires and secure them to the two bottom left terminals on the Battery connection block, as illustrated in Figure 2-38.

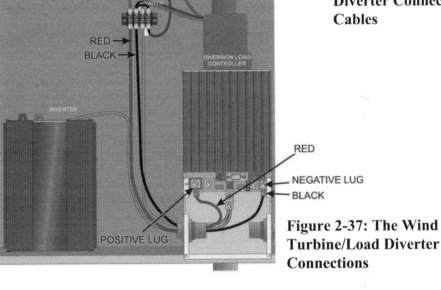

Figure 2-37: The Wind Turbine/Load Diverter Connections

11. Route the free ends of the red and black wires into the Diversion Load Controller's connection bay (through the opening in the right side of the housing).

12. Loosen the positive battery screw down terminal and insert the red wire into the Diversion Load Controller's positive lug. Then tighten the screw down connector until both wires are securely in the lug, as illustrated in Figure 2-38.

13. Loosen the negative screw down terminal and insert the black wire into the negative lug and tighten the screw down connector until both wires are securely clamped in the lug, as shown in Figure 2-38.

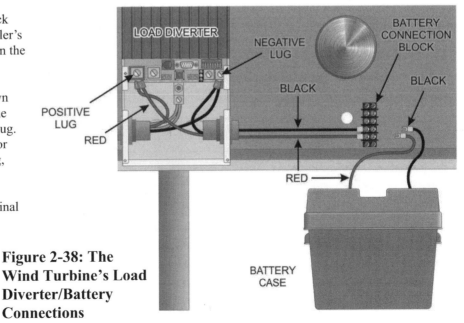

Figure 2-38: The Wind Turbine's Load Diverter/Battery Connections

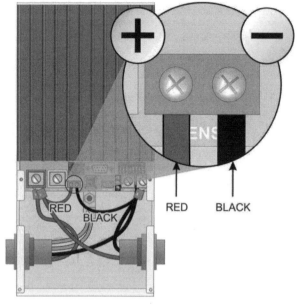

14. Attach a red and black 12 AWG wires from the Load Diverter's Sense lines to the positive and negative lugs, as illustrated in Figure 2-39.

15. Prepare a red and a black 12 AWG wire long enough to reach from the Load Diverter terminal connectors to the External Diverter Load light on the backside of the panel, if not already prepared.

16. Crimp appropriate sized ring connectors to both ends of the red and black wires, if not already applied.

17. Attach one end of the red wire to the plus (+) terminal of the External Load Diverter light and attach one end of the black wire to the negative (-) terminal of the External Diverter Load light connections on the back of the panel, as shown in Figure 2-40.

18. Route the red and black wires through the hole at the left of the Battery Terminal Connection Strip from the backside of the panel and into the Load Diverter, as shown in Figure 2-40.

Figure 2-39: The Load Diverter Sensing Connections

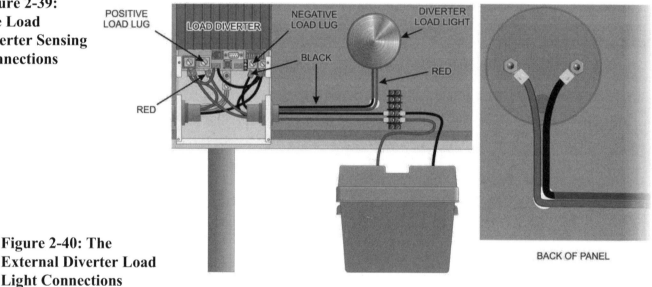

Figure 2-40: The External Diverter Load Light Connections

19. Before attaching the wiring to the Load Diverter's battery leads, make sure that:

   - All Disconnect Switches on the panel are in the **OFF** position

   - The Stop Switch is in the **STOP** or shorted position.

   - The fuses are removed from the Fuel Cell and Solar Panel fuse holders.

20. Attach the red and black wires from the battery pack to the Battery connection block, as shown in Figure 2-40.

21. Attach the red wire to the POSITIVE LOAD lug and the black wire to the NEGATIVE LOAD lug in the Load Diverter, as shown in Figure 2-40.

22. Set the multimeter to measure up to 20 Vdc.

23. Connect the multimeter's leads to the wind turbine's charging leads at the Wind Turbine Control Panel connection block.

24. Record the voltage level being measured with no input from the wind turbine, which represents the current battery voltage, on the following line:

    Initial Battery Voltage: _____

25. Move the Stop Switch to the **RUN** position.

26. Move the wind turbine's Disconnect Switch to the **ON** position.

27. Use the electric drill with a 5/16" hex drive installed, to spin the wind turbine's rotor shaft while observing the wind turbine's ammeter and the multimeter.

28. Start slowly and steadily increase the speed of the drill until the red LED on the Wind Turbine come on while observing the measurement on the wind turbine's ammeter and the multimeter display. Record both initial values when the red LED lights on the following lines:

    Initial Voltage (Multimeter reading): _____

    Initial Current (Ammeter reading): _____

> **CAUTION**
>
> Be very careful not to push in on the rotor shaft while performing this test. Doing so could damage the wind turbine's control electronics.

29. Continue charging the batteries until the red light on the panel above the Battery connection block, operating as the "external load" comes on. On the following lines, record the voltage and current levels from the meters when this first occurs:

    Diverted Voltage Point (Multimeter reading): _____

    Diverted Current Flow (Ammeter reading): _____

30. Stop turning the wind turbine and continue to monitor the voltage level on the multimeter display.

31. Record the level at which the diverter switches power away from the external load light on the following line:

    External Load Drop Out Voltage: _____

32. Move the Wind Turbine's Disconnect Switch to the **OFF** position.

33. Move the Stop Switch to the **STOP** position.

34. Remove the multimeter's leads from the Wind Turbine's charging leads at the Wind Turbine Control Panel connection block.

> **CAUTION**
>
> Do not apply a short circuit across the batteries as this will cause an unsafe overload condition that may damage the batteries, start a fire, or cause the batteries to explode.

Wind

Generating AC Output

The Marcraft Green Electron Generation panel includes an Off-Grid type inverter for generating power to run residential AC devices. This inverter accepts direct current input and produces a 120 Vac, 60 Hz (**Hertz** or *cycles per second*) output. The conversion occurs in two steps. First the incoming DC battery voltage is converted into a high DC voltage using high-frequency **pulse width modulation (PWM)** switching techniques. The high voltage signal is then applied to another PWM circuit to produce the 120 Vac, 60 Hz output voltage.

The inverter can continue to produce this output as long as the input voltage stays between 10.5 Vdc and 16.5 Vdc. The length of time different batteries can apply this level of power to the inverter depends on their **amp/hour (AH)** ratings and the current load placed upon them. The battery industry uses 20 hours and 80°F as the benchmarks for rating batteries. This rating also indicates that the output of the battery is only useful until it falls off to 87.5% of its stated value (10.5V for a 12 Vdc system such as this trainer).

When two or more batteries are connected in parallel, as they are in this procedure, their voltages remain the same but their current capacities add together. Therefore, the AH rating for the battery pack, is equal to the sum of all the batteries in the pack added together.

For example: A 40AH rated 12V battery can provide a constant current output of 2.0 amps for 20 hours before the output voltage drops to a level of 10.5V (87.5%).

$$\frac{AH}{20} = Constant\ Current$$

1. Obtain the Inverter's documentation – locate and record the following information on the lines provided:

    Model Number: _____

    Input Voltage Range: _____

    Output Voltage: _____

    Low Input Voltage Shut Down: _____

    High Input Voltage Shut Down: _____

2. Check the storage battery housings to obtain the AH rating for the batteries being used in your trainer. Calculate and record the AH rating being applied to the inverter (when the batteries are charged within their stated operational range) on the following line:

    Stated AH rating of a single battery: _____

    Total AH rating: _____

3. Prepare a red and a black 12 AWG wire long enough to reach from the wind turbine's inverter's positive and negative terminals to the positive and negative input terminals in the Diversion Load Controller's connection bay.

4. Plug in the red and black wires and secure them in the inverter's positive and negative connection terminals, as illustrated in Figure 2-41.

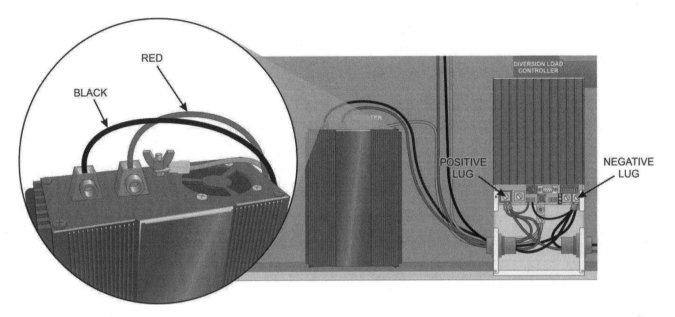

5. Route the red and black wires into the Diversion Load Controller's connection bay (through the conduit opening in the left side of the housing), as illustrated in Figure 2-41.

Figure 2-41:
Inverter Connections

6. Loosen the positive screw down terminal and insert the red wire into the Diversion Load Controller's positive lug. Then tighten the screw on the connector until all three wires are securely fastened in the lug.

7. Loosen the negative screw down terminal and insert the black wire into the negative lug and then tighten the terminal screw until all three wires are securely fastened in the lug.

8. Connect the multimeter's leads to the two left most terminals on the Wind Turbine's red and black wire connection points.

9. Record the voltage level being measured with no input from the Wind Turbine on the following line and represents the current battery voltage:

Initial Battery Voltage: _____

10. Insert the 120 Vac, 4 Watt night light in the inverter's AC output plug on the bottom of the inverter on the panel.

11. Turn the Inverter and light on by moving the rocker switch on the bottom of the inverter.

12. The voltage displayed on the multimeter should steadily decrease until it reaches the stated operating voltage of the battery. Measure the amount of time it takes between turning on the inverter and when the reading on the multimeter stops falling. Record this time on the following line:

_____ (Minutes)

13. Record the multimeter reading obtained when the inverter's output leveled out on the following line:

_____ (Volts)

14. Move the wind turbine's Stop Switch to the **RUN** position.

15. Move the wind turbine's Disconnect Switch to the **ON** position.

16. Use the electric drill with a 5/16" hex drive installed, to spin the wind turbine's rotor shaft while observing its ammeter and the multimeter.

CAUTION

Be very careful not to push in on the rotor shaft while performing this test. Doing so could damage the wind turbine's control electronics.

---

17. Start slowly and steadily increase the speed of the drill until the ammeter shows a current flow and the voltage reading on the multimeter increases by 0.4 volts above its steady output voltage obtained in Step 13.

18. While observing the measurement on the wind turbine's ammeter and the multimeter display, slow the drill's rotational speed to determine when the battery voltage has increased by 0.2 volts without input from the wind turbine.

19. Continue to use the wind turbine to charge the battery bank until it holds the 0.2 volt increase. On the following line, record the approximate amount of time required for the wind turbine to produce this additional charge in the battery:

_____ (Time to increase charge by 0.2 V)

20. On the following lines, record both the wind turbine current flow and voltage levels required to produce this increase:

Approximate Wind Turbine Voltage (Multimeter reading): _____

Approximate Wind Turbine Current (Ammeter reading): _____

21. Move the Wind Turbine's Disconnect Switch to the **OFF** position.

22. Move the Stop Switch to the **STOP** position.

23. Turn **off** the night light and inverter. Remove the red and black wires coming from the battery pack Battery connection block.

24. This concludes this portion of the hands-on lab procedure. Have your instructor review your results before completing this procedure.

Disassembly

Wind

After your instructor has reviewed your results of Procedures 5 and 6, the following steps will guide you through the removal of the wiring and wind turbine in preparation for the next group to perform the procedures. During the process of removing the wiring, label each set or group of wires to enable the next group to use the same wiring setups.

1. Remove the red and black 12 AWG wires from the Load Diverter's Sense lines to the battery terminals attached in Step 16 of "External Voltage Regulator/Load Diverter Operation" in Procedure 6.

2. Remove the red and black 12 AWG wires from the Load Diverter's Load plus (+) and Load negative (-) lugs to the External Diverted Load light attached in Steps 17 through 21 of "External Voltage Regulator/Load Diverter Operation" in Procedure 6.

3. Remove the red and black 12 AWG wires from the Battery connection block to the positive (+) and negative (-) Battery lugs in the Load Diverter attached in Steps 9, 11, and 13 of "External Voltage Regulator/Load Diverter Operation" in Procedure 6.

4. Remove the two green 12 AWG wires from the Load Diverter's grounding lug, the Wind Turbine's Terminal Block, and the ground terminal of the Inverter attached in Steps 1 through 4 of "Connecting the Wind Turbine Directly to the Storage System" in Procedure 6.

5. Remove the red and black 12 AWG wires from the Load Diverter's Battery (+) and Battery (-) lugs to the Inverter's positive (+) and negative (-) connection terminals attached in Steps 3 through 6 of "Generating AC Output" in Procedure 6.

6. Remove the 120 Vac, 4 Watt Night Light from the bottom of the Inverter, inserted in Step 10 of "Generating AC Output" in Procedure 6, and store it away in the supplies container.

7. Remove the red and black 12 AWG wires from the bottom row of the Wind Turbine's Terminal Block and the Load Diverter's Battery (+) and Battery (-) lugs attached in Steps 4 through 8 of "External Voltage Regulator/Load Diverter Operation" in Procedure 6.

8. Remove the small black 10 AWG jumper wire from the Wind Turbine Control Panel connection block attached in Step 12 of "Wiring the Control Panel" in Procedure 5.

9. Remove the short black 10 AWG wire from the bottom row of the Wind Turbine Control Panel connection block and the bottom terminal of the Stop Switch attached in Step 11 of "Wiring the Control Panel" in Procedure 5.

10. Remove the short red 10 AWG jumper wire from the top terminal of the Stop Switch to the (+) terminal on the Wind Turbine Ammeter attached in Step 4 of "Wiring the Control Panel" in Procedure 5.

11. Remove the short red 10 AWG jumper wire from the (-) terminal of the Wind Turbine Ammeter to the terminal on the 50A Wind Turbine Breaker attached in Step 5 of "Wiring the Control Panel" in Procedure 5.

12. Remove the short red 10 AWG jumper wire from the 50A Wind Turbine Breaker to the Wind Turbine Disconnect Switch attached in Step 6 of "Wiring the Control Panel" in Procedure 5.

13. Remove the red 10 AWG wire from the Wind Turbine Disconnect Switch to the left connection point on the top row of the Wind Turbine Control Panel connection block attached in Steps 7, 8, and 9 of "Wiring the Control Panel" in Procedure 5.

14. Remove the black and green Wind Turbine wires from the two center terminals on the top row of the Wind Turbine Control Panel connection block attached in Steps 1 and 2 of "Wiring the Control Panel" in Procedure 5.

15. Remove the above black and green wires from the Panel by threading them back through the holes.

16. Remove the red Wind Turbine wire from the center terminal of the Stop Switch attached in Step 3 of "Wiring the Control Panel" in Procedure 5.

17. Remove the clamp arms from the two mast clamps on the back of the Panel and carefully lay the Wind Turbine and Mast securely on the table. The Wind Turbine and Mast was attached in Steps 16 and 17 of "Mounting the Wind Turbine" in Procedure 5.

18. Loosen the yaw clamp bolts and separate the Wind Turbine from the Mast and disconnect the red, black, and green wires at the separation of the Wind Turbine and Mast.

19. Store the Wind Turbine away in the supplies container.

20. Remove the three Wind Turbine red, black, and green wires from the Mast and label them Wind Turbine/Mast wires and store them away for use by the next group of students. Also store the Mast away with the Wind Turbine.

Procedure 6 Questions

1. Why does this wind turbine feature an adjustable set point option?

2. Why should the voltage produced by the wind generator be higher than the voltage displayed by the battery?

3. What are the consequences of connecting the wind turbine's power leads incorrectly to the battery bank?

4. Using the information about the batteries that make up your 4 battery bank, what current output level should it take to reduce the battery voltage to 10.5 Vdc in 20 hours?

5. What condition must occur after the wind turbine enters regulation mode to get it to start generating power again?

PROCEDURE 7 – WIND POWER RESEARCH

Wind

In order to participate in successful scholarship, the student must be capable of conducting research, or at the very least developing the necessary skills to do so. In spite of the fact that a greater number of information sources are available to the modern student than ever before, the ability to research a given subject is often underrated. Traditional avenues of research involving cardfile searching, book reading, newspaper clipping, and magazine microfilming have often given way to Internet browsing, where library terminals or home computers are used to conduct fruitful information searches.

Basic Internet research skills are currently required to avoid the unwanted exposure to overwhelming amounts of information that can quickly drown the unsuspecting and inquisitive mind. The ability most useful to the modern scholar is the capability of locating relevant information quickly, while avoiding those time-wasting searches through mountains of available data. In order to effectively utilize the time spent researching wind power, making effective use of an Internet search engine is critical regardless of which service is being utilized. Certain advanced methods of searching will zero-in on the desired information quickly, regardless of which search engine is being used.

To locate documents containing an exact phrase, type the phrase, surrounded by quotation marks, into the search field. For example, by typing "*wind turbines*" (with the quotation marks) will return documents that contain the phrase *wind turbines*, but not Web pages that contain only *wind* or *turbines*. To locate documents containing these words, but not necessarily together, type the words separated by the Boolean operator *AND* in all caps. For example, typing *wind AND turbines* (without the quotation marks) will return Web pages that contain *wind*, *turbines*, and *wind turbines*.

To locate documents containing either one word or the other, type the words separated by the Boolean operator *OR* in all caps. For example, typing *wind OR turbines* (without the quotation marks) will return documents that contain *wind*, or *turbine*s, or both.

Keep in mind that certain words can be deliberately excluded from a search, as well. For example, to exclude a word from the search, type the word to be excluded into the search field, preceded by the Boolean operator *NOT* in all caps. Using this approach, typing *wind NOT turbines* (without the quotation marks) will return only documents that do contain the word *wind*, and do not contain the word *turbines*. To zero in on documents that contain two terms separated by between 10 to 25 words, type the two terms separated by the Boolean operator *NEAR*, in all caps, into the search field. If the search expression is lengthy or complicated, use parentheses to separate the different parts. For example, typing *wind OR turbines NOT (nacelle OR torque)* will get you entries that have the words *wind*, or *turbines*, or both, but do not have the words *nacelle* or *torque*.

Billions of individual files residing on the Internet can never be completely identified, cataloged, or retrieved, considering the fact that thousands more have probably been added to the stack during the time you've taken to read this far. Additional data delivery services are available, including electronic mail, file transfers, Internet group memberships, interactive collaborations, and multimedia displays.

These various data services use a number of Internet protocols in an effort to reduce the complexity. However, the student is ultimately responsible for dealing with the fact that Internet addresses are frequently changed, or even removed. Due to the volatility of Internet websites, any useful research information that the student uncovers, including both text and graphics, should be immediately copied and stored. This ensures the availability of relevant information, regardless of the future status of the source Internet site.

Be aware that the information provided on certain Internet sites may be protected, or formatted in such a way as to prevent it from being copied. This is often the situation encountered on product vendor websites containing proprietary information. In these situations, it often becomes necessary for the researcher to type and save the relevant text using a word processor. When pictures and illustrations cannot be copied directly, third-party graphics tools can be used to capture, and convert them into usable picture formats.

Due to the fact that Internet information can be posted by anyone, for a variety of reasons, the information you choose to use must be verified for correctness and integrity. This is in contrast to any data you gather using the traditional researching formats previously mentioned, because in those cases a certain amount of verification has been conducted by the publishers. However, you should never assume that the information you gather from an Internet site, a newspaper, or a magazine/book article is completely accurate or true. The veracity of any information becomes more likely when it can be supported from a variety of sources!

Wind power strategies and components are vital to the creation of alternative energy resources, so your beginning research should be concerned with identifying those strategies and components, while learning how they augment the production of alternative energies.

Resources Needed:

- Books
- Newspapers
- Magazines
- Computer with Internet access and graphic capture software

1. Examine the following list of wind power strategies. The Alternative Energy technician will need to be familiar with the categories mentioned here.

   - Wind turbine types-horizontal axis wind turbine (HAWT) / vertical axis wind turbine (VAWT)
   - Wind turbine siting strategies
   - Wind turbine site and data analysis
   - Wind turbine hazards
   - Over-speed protection designs
   - Excess energy management

2. Use Tables 2-2 through 2-7 to organize the specified details about the wind power strategies listed. For each item, try to locate at least two information sources.

Table 2-2: Wind Turbine Types

TYPE	DESCRIPTION	MANUFACTURERS	DRAWBACKS	ADVANTAGES	COST

Table 2-3: Wind Turbine Siting Strategies

STRATEGY	DESCRIPTION	IMPORTANCE	DRAWBACKS

Table 2-4: Wind Turbine Site and Data Analysis

PARAMETER	DESCRIPTION

Table 2-5: Wind Turbine Hazards

HAZARD	DESCRIPTION	SYMPTOMS	SOLUTION

Table 2-6: Wind Turbine Over-speed Protection Designs

DESIGN	DESCRIPTION	ANALYSIS	CONCLUSION

Table 2-7: Wind Turbine Excess Energy Management

TYPE	DESCRIPTION	POLICY	ANALYSIS

The Alternative Energy technician should also be familiar with the components that make up a wind turbine system. This is because energy costs and production constraints make the construction of wind turbine systems more and more imperative.

To make your remaining research time more productive, concentrate on information about wind turbine components in the product areas listed below. This type of research will be of benefit for checking out ideas for a wind turbine installation, including its size, layout, and the particular requirements of the local and national governing agencies. Information gathered here will help when considering and comparing specific wind turbine components and equipment, their system capabilities, available vendors, and estimated costs.

3. Examine the following list. It identifies wind turbine components and schemes with which an Alternative Energy technician will most likely be working.

- Propeller design

- Gear ratios and torque

- Electric motors, generators, alternators, and inverters

4. Use Tables 2-8 through 2-10 to organize the specified details about the wind turbine components and schemes listed. For each item, try to locate at least two information sources.

Table 2-8: Wind Turbine Propeller Design

TURBINE TYPE AND CONSTRUCTION	DESCRIPTION	ANALYSIS	CONCLUSION

Table 2-9: Wind Turbine Gear Ratios and Torque

COMPONENT	SPEED	GEAR RATIO	TORQUE

Table 2-10: Wind Turbine Electricity Generation

STRATEGY	DESCRIPTION	ANALYSIS	CONCLUSION

Residential or rural farm clients seeking to install their own wind turbine generating systems usually require some practical information and advice on addressing the existing barriers to home and farm wind projects. For example, they need to understand when and how to approach their local boards and state agencies in order to secure the necessary permits. It may be necessary for them to build support for their proposed installations. They need to understand how to work successfully with their installer and with their local utilities in order to interconnect their wind systems.

Applicable Regulations

Various local, state, or federal regulating bodies have jurisdiction over residential alternative energy sources. A completed wind turbine installation must satisfy specific requirements; otherwise, it testifies to the ignorance of the Residential Alternative Energy technicians who installed it.

Local

Local coding authorities are often very sensitive about being ignored. This is because Residential Alternative Energy technicians usually make a great effort to strictly adhere to the federal and state regulations with which they are most familiar. This adherence is often good enough to result in the installation of a locally compliant wind turbine system, but not always. Although local codes usually involve local commercial generating structures rather than residential installations, they must also be taken into account before the installation begins! In addition, when local governments opt to run their own power generation systems, they often end up offering spare capacity to the local community. City or county restrictions have increased with the advent of residential power generating equipment, especially in communities where local governments directly control their own power production facilities. These arrangements have often resulted in the subsequent prosecution for chronic violators of local power generating regulations.

Local power generating code information can be obtained from local planning commissions or coding departments. These bodies are usually responsible for controlling the governmental utility development in the local community, including the power planning commission. Specific information about residential alternative energy installations and/or equipment requirements not addressed by state or federal codes can be gathered by contacting your local planning commission, or the city/county agencies responsible for code enforcement. For example, environmental conditions could place unique restrictions on the local use of certain wind-driven power generating equipment.

5. Examine the following list. It identifies specific areas of concern regarding wind turbine installations and/or equipment that may be strictly controlled by your local codes.

    - Local wind turbine legislation

    - Local wind data

6. Use Table 2-11 to organize the specified details about any local legislation regarding the use of wind turbine installations and/or equipment. Use Table 2-12 to organize the specified details of local wind data. Try to locate more than one source of information for each area of concern.

Table 2-11: Local Wind Turbine Legislation

CITY/COUNTY	LEGISLATION/CODE	DATE	TITLE	DETAILS

Table 2-12: Local Wind Data at 50 Meters

LOCATION	DESCRIPTION	ANALYSIS	CONCLUSION

State

State-sponsored regulations are aimed at appropriate use of state resources in the development of alternative energy sources. These guidelines normally restrict the use of state resources to legitimate government or college business, support for various departmental mandates, or carrying out institutional missions. Energy generating sources that are used to power state governmental or university offices must comply with use requirements applying to any equipment to which they connect.

State governmental jurisdictions limit the legitimate uses of their energy resources to official legislative and administrative functions. Legal interagency agreements dictate that such resources must not be used for personal, commercial, or for-profit purposes without some form of official written approval.

It's important to understand what the legitimate usage of state resources in the production of alternative energy in your state is. This information can be located by browsing your state government's web pages.

7. Examine the following list. It identifies specific areas of concern regarding wind turbine installations and/or equipment that may be strictly controlled by your state codes.

- State wind turbine legislation

- State wind data

8. Use Table 2-13 to organize the specified details about any state legislation regarding the use of wind turbine installations and/or equipment. Use Table 2-14 to organize the specified details of state wind data. Try to locate more than one source of information for each area of concern.

Table 2-13: State Wind Turbine Legislation

STATE	LEGISLATION/CODE	DATE	TITLE	DETAILS

Table 2-14: State Wind Data at 50 Meters

LOCATION	DESCRIPTION	ANALYSIS	CONCLUSION

Federal

Alternative energy manufacturers and consumers around the world recognize certain research facilities and/or governmental agencies that have been mandated to determine the suitability of wind power as a viable energy resource. As various products have recently emerged, the recognition of suitable guidelines has helped to achieve some control over the technical development explosion in this field.

The federal organizations listed here can be consulted regarding the viability of various products relating to the use of wind power as an alternative energy resource. The Residential Alternative Energy technician can depend on the information published by these organizations to provide guidance in the selection of appropriate equipment for a particular installation.

Energy and Environmental Research Center (EERC)

The Energy and Environmental Research Center (EERC) is a research facility located in the southeast corner of the University of North Dakota (UND) in Grand Forks. It is recognized as one of the world's leading developers of cleaner, more efficient energy and environmental technologies to protect and clean our air, water, and soil. Originally founded in 1951 as the "U.S. Bureau of Mines—Robertson Lignite Research Laboratory," it became a federal energy technology center under the United States Department of Energy in 1977, and became known as the Energy and Environmental Research Center in 1989.

The EERC is a high-tech, nonprofit branch of UND. Yet, it operates like a business; conducts research, development, demonstration, and commercialization activities dedicated to moving promising technologies out of the laboratory and into the commercial marketplace. The EERC provides practical, cost-effective solutions to today's most critical energy and environmental issues and challenges. Its research portfolio consists of a wide array of strategic energy and environmental solutions, including clean coal technologies, CO_2 sequestration, energy and water sustainability, hydrogen technologies, air toxics and fine particulate, mercury measurement and control, alternative fuels, wind energy, biomass, water management, flood prevention, global climate change, waste utilization, energy-efficient technologies, and contaminant cleanup.

The EERC's business partners range in size from large multinational corporations to regional utilities to small local businesses. Its government partners include not only federal agencies such as the U.S. Department of Energy, the U.S. Environmental Protection Agency, the U.S. Department of Defense, and the U.S. Department of Agriculture, but also state and local government entities.

U.S. Department of Energy (DOE)

The Department of Energy's overarching mission is to advance the national, economic, and energy security of the United States. In order to do this, it promotes scientific and technological innovation, while working to ensure the environmental cleanup of the national nuclear weapons complex. Strategic goals to achieve the mission are designed to deliver results along five strategic themes, including:

- Energy security. The DOE's philosophy is that America's energy security should be achieved through the production of reliable, clean, and affordable energy.

- Nuclear security. Ensuring America's nuclear security is also a critical component of DOE's working agenda.

- Scientific discovery and innovation. The DOE works to strengthen scientific discovery, economic competitiveness, and to improve the quality of life in the United States through innovations in science and technology.

- Environmental responsibility. The DOE helps to protect the environment by providing a responsible resolution to the environmental legacy of nuclear weapons production.

- Management excellence. The DOE believes in enabling its mission through sound management.

U.S. Department of Transportation (DOT)

The Department of Transportation serves the United States by ensuring a fast, safe, efficient, accessible and convenient transportation system that meets our vital national interests and enhances the quality of life of the American people, today and into the future. As an administrative office of the DOT, the Federal Aviation Administration (FAA) has become involved with the safety aspects of aircraft navigation near wind turbine farms.

Although the need for renewable energy sources in America is undeniable, wind energy requires years of planning and preparation to find suitable locations to develop. By the time a location is identified and the financing is secured, one of the last hurdles before actual construction is passing an FAA Aeronautical Study (AS). All too often, development plans are jeopardized by difficult issues resulting from the AS that have few mitigation solutions. This makes it critical that wind energy and the aviation community find creative ways to share the nation's airspace.

National Renewable Energy Laboratory (NREL)

The National Renewable Energy Laboratory (NREL) is the nation's primary laboratory for renewable energy, and energy efficiency research and development. NREL's mission and strategy are focused on advancing the U.S. Department of Energy's and our nation's energy goals. It began operating in 1977 as the Solar Energy Research Institute. In September of 1991, it was designated a national laboratory of the U.S. Department of Energy (DOE), and its name changed to NREL.

The laboratory's scientists and researchers support critical market objectives to accelerate research from scientific innovations to market-viable alternative energy solutions. The laboratory thereby directly contributes to our nation's goal for finding new renewable ways to power our homes, businesses, and cars. At the core of this strategic direction are NREL's research and technology development areas, including an understanding of renewable resources for energy, the conversion of these resources to renewable electricity and fuels, and ultimately to the use of renewable electricity and fuels in homes, commercial buildings, and vehicles.

9. Search the information pages of several federal governmental agencies and locate the applicable policies regarding the operation of wind turbine systems.

   - Federal wind turbine legislation

   - National wind data

10. Use Table 2-15 to organize the specified details about any federal legislation regarding the use of wind turbine installations and/or equipment. Use Table 2-16 to organize the specified details of federal wind data. Try to locate more than one source of information for each area of concern.

Table 2-15: Federal Wind Turbine Legislation

AGENCY	LEGISLATION/CODE	DATE	TITLE	DETAILS

Table 2-16: Federal Wind Data at 50 Meters

LOCATION	DESCRIPTION	ANALYSIS	CONCLUSION

11. This concludes the hands-on lab procedure. Have your instructor review your results before moving on to the next procedure.

Procedure 7 Questions

1. What are the two basic types of wind turbines recognized by the industry?

2. Which type of turbine blade composition is not recommended for corrosive climates?

3. What makes the repair of wind turbines extremely hazardous?

4. Which type of wind legislation carries more weight, local, state, or federal?

5. What is the significance of the Emergency Economic Stabilization Act of 2008?

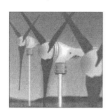

Wind

PROCEDURE 8 – WIND ENERGY DESIGN

Objectives:

- Given the scope of a proposed wind farm project, determine the project's feasability.
- Provide a cost estimate of the entire project.

Resources Needed:

- The American Wind Energy Association (www.awea.org)
- Danish Wind Energy Association (www.windpower.org)
- Windustry (www.windustry.org)
- Computer with Internet access and graphic capture software

ABOUT THE AUTHOR

George Lister is a professional Control Systems Technician skilled in and knowledgeable of pneumatic, mechanical, and electronic instrumentation. Currently, he is an instructor at Texas State Technical College teaching Wind Energy Technology, SCADA & Industrial Networking. As a Wind Turbine Technician, he maintained wind turbine systems to ensure availability for Mitsubishi Power Systems. A Senior Member of the International Society for Automation (ISA), he is a lifetime member of the Electronics Technicians Association – International (ETA-I) and a member of the Certification Committee. He has many certifications, including:

- **International Society for Automation (ISA)**
  Certified control Systems Technician Level 3 (CCST3)

- **Electronics Technicians Association – International (ETA-I)**
  Master Certified Electronics Technician

- **Computing Technology Industry Association (CompTIA)**
  A+, Network+, Linux+, Server+, HTI+, DHTI+, e-Biz+, i-Net+, Security+, RFID+

- **Fiber Optic Association**
  Certified Fiber Optic Specialist/Testing

- **Telecommunications Industry Association (TIA)**
  Certified in Convergent Networking Technology (CCNT)

Discussion

A wind turbine is a device that converts the kinetic energy in wind to the rotating mechanical energy needed to turn the generator to produce electricity. Unlike the Dutch windmill designs of old, which relied mostly on the force of the wind to push the blades into motion, modern wind turbines use more aerodynamic principles to capture the energy in the wind more effectively.

In order to properly design, site, and build wind farms to be as cost effective and efficient as possible, engineers must calculate the amount of energy to be found in the wind and how best to harness it. German physicist Albert Betz developed a theory to define the maximum possible energy to be derived from a wind turbine.

Read the following scenario:

Wind Partners Inc., a wind energy developer, is creating a proposal to present to a group of potential investors. The proposed wind farm will generate an estimated 150 MW of power utilizing 75 wind turbines capable of producing 2MW of electricity each. The group of investors is new to the wind industry and an overview of the requirements necessary to properly site a wind farm would be very beneficial in attempts to secure financing for this multi-million dollar project.

Total costs for installing a commercial-scale wind turbine will vary significantly depending on the cost of financing, when the turbine purchase agreement is executed, construction contracts, the type of machine, the location of the project, and other factors. Cost components for wind projects can include wind resource assessment and site analysis; the price and freight of the turbine and tower; construction expenses; permitting and interconnection studies; utility system upgrades, transformers, protection, and metering equipment; insurance; operations, warranty, maintenance, and repair; legal and consultation fees.

Procedure

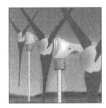

Wind

You have been given the assignment to prepare a Presentation using the software of your choice (i.e. Microsoft PowerPoint, OpenOffice Impress, etc) to show this group of potential investors. In your presentation explain:

1. What factors affect the power of the wind? The amount of energy which the wind transfers to the rotor of the turbine generator depends on three major variables. Identify and report how each can determine the amount of available power.

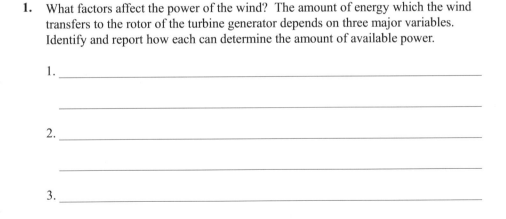

1. _____

   _____

2. _____

   _____

3. _____

   _____

2. How the wind is harnessed? Aerodynamics plays a big part in the design and construction of wind turbine blades. Explore the concept of lift as it applies to wind turbine blades. Give an explanation of these principles in your presentation.

_____

_____

_____

3. How efficient are wind turbines? Discover the fundamental physical law for the aerodynamics of wind turbines. Explain to your audience why we can only harness less than 59% of the wind's energy.

_____

_____

_____

4. What factors can influence the site selection for a wind farm? The American Wind Energy Association (www.awea.org) outlines 10 steps in building a wind farm. Identify and elaborate on these 10 steps and provide an in-depth overview of the factors to consider.

1. _____

_____

2. _____

_____

3. _____

_____

4. _____

_____

5. _____

_____

6. _____

_____

7. _____

_____

8. _____

_____

9. _____

_____

10. _____

_____

5. Explore a variety of large-scale turbine manufacturers and provide an estimate for the purchase of wind turbine with the specified generating capacity.

_____

_____

_____

REVIEW QUESTIONS

The following questions test your knowledge of the material presented in this chapter.

1. What do we call a low-pressure area moving from west to east?

2. What type of wind turbine features blades that are mounted horizontally?

3. How many current waveforms are generated by the Marcraft wind turbine?

4. How many feet above ground would a wind turbine be mounted?

5. What control mechanism causes a breaking action to occur inside the wind turbine circuitry, to protect the turbine in times of excess wind speeds?

6. What research facility develops clean energy and environmentally friendly technologies?

7. In a 12.5 Vdc system, at what voltage will the battery output become useless?

8. What type of circuitry can be used to control a wind turbine's battery charging system?

9. How does the Marcraft wind turbine's internal controller indicate that it is in regulation mode?

10. What type of inverter works solely with a battery-based storage system, and is not designed for connection to a commercial AC power system?

11. What is the range of the Marcraft wind turbine's adjustable regulation set point?

12. Why is a wind turbine not a dependable single source of power for most applications?

CHAPTER

3

Photovoltaic Panels

Upon completion of this chapter, you will be able to perform the following tasks:

1. Identify the major components of a photovoltaic electrical generation system.

2. Install, combine and test PV panels.

3. Connect the PV panel to common protective/control devices.

4. Test the direct output of the PV panel.

5. Configure PV panel to achieve necessary voltage/current/power requirements.

6. Mount multiple solar panels to create a solar array.

7. Document PV panel output at various light intensities.

8. Correlate light intensity-to-power generation.

9. Test various battery configuration options.

10. Connect the Marcraft PV Array Generation circuitry to storage batteries.

11. Supply a DC load with the Marcraft PV Array Generation system.

12. Document battery charge/discharge rates.

13. Implement excess capacity management by driving auxiliary loads.

14. Connect the PV array circuitry to an AC inverter.

15. Drive an AC load with the Marcraft PV Array Generation system.

16. Document battery charge/discharge rates vs. inverter output (system efficiency).

17. Search for solar power services.

18. Research various solar power components and strategies.

19. Locate applicable solar power regulations and legislation.

20. Given a scenario for an alternative energy power supply project, determine the correct technology to employ to meet the specifications of the project.

21. Determine the PV panel specifications required to meet the power requirements of the project.

22. Determine the PV panel configurations need to meet the project requirements.

23. Determine other equipment components required to complete the project as described.

24. Establish the projected cost of producing the project.

25. Select components that will meet the specifications for each section of the project scenario.

CHAPTER 3

Photovoltaic Panels

INTRODUCTION

Solar energy is radiated energy received from the sun in the form of light and heat. This energy can be captured and used in both passive and active solar power applications. Typical **passive solar** applications include designing homes and buildings to use the heat and light received directly from the sun for space heating, water heating, ventilation, distillation, and solar lighting purposes.

Active solar applications involve the use of technologies to capture and convert solar energy into other energy forms—particularly a source of *clean electrons*. The primary active solar technologies in use today include **Stirling engines** and **photovoltaic devices**.

> Solar energy
>
> passive solar
>
> Active solar
>
> Stirling engines
>
> photovoltaic devices

INTRODUCTION TO PHOTOVOLTAIC PANELS

Solar Stirling engines use mirrors to collect and focus sunlight on one end of the engine, as illustrated in Figure 3-1. This causes a difference of temperature on the opposite ends of the engine, which in turn causes a piston inside the engine to move. This mechanical movement is then converted into electric energy through generator action.

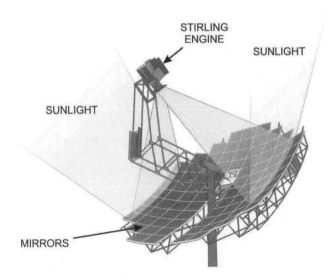

Figure 3-1: Solar Stirling Engine

Photovoltaic devices have long been the most common active solar devices used to generate electricity from solar energy. This is accomplished through a process known as the *photovoltaic effect*. The solar cell consists of a **semiconductor** material, such as *silicon*, or *thin film cells*, that absorbs light. The absorbed light energy causes the atoms in semiconductor material to give up electrons that can be channeled into an electrical **current flow**, as illustrated in Figure 3-2. The flow of free electrons provides a source of energy (free electrons give off energy) that can be used to perform **work**.

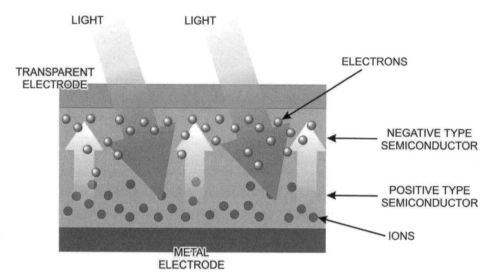

Figure 3-2: Photovoltaic Action

What makes solar energy so interesting as an alternative energy source is that the amount of solar energy being absorbed by the Earth (atmosphere, lands and oceans) in one hour is more energy than the world uses in a year. The measurement of radiation energy received on a given surface (such as the photovoltaic cell) is referred to as **insolation** and is specified in terms of average **irradiance** in watts per square meter, or kilowatts (thousands of watts or kW), per-day, divided by the area of the surface—kW/m^2.

The average amount of solar radiation at the outer edge of Earth's atmosphere is about 1.3 kW per square meter. As the solar energy moves downward through the atmosphere its power is diminished due to reflection, so that only about 1 kW/m^2 on a clear day. Insolation is also commonly expressed in terms of **Suns**. A Sun is equal to 1000 watts per square meter (1000 W/m^2). This variable is affected by the following factors:

- The angle the light hits the surface (time-of-day)

- The angle the light hits the surface (time-of-year)

- The cloudiness/haziness of the atmosphere

- The height above sea level where the surface is located

Solar Cells

Solar cells, more correctly referred to as **photovoltaic (PV) cells**, are devices that convert solar energy (sun light) into electricity (the term photovoltaic is a more generic term used when the light source may be something other than sun light).

The internal construction of the PV cell creates an electrical energy field that gives the cell an electrical **polarity**—one side of the cell has a positive charge while the other side has a negative charge), as illustrated in Figure 3-3. The size of the charge difference between the two sides is referred to as **voltage (V)**. Voltage is an **electromotive force (EMF)** that places an electrical push and pull on the different sides of the cell.

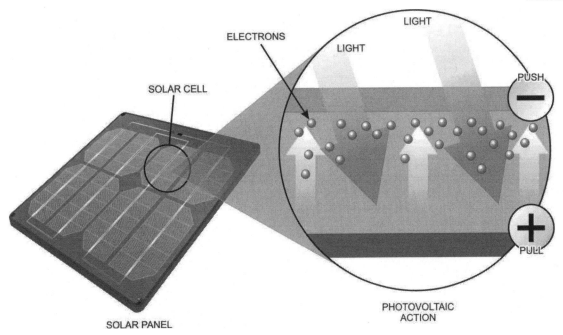

**Figure 3-3:
Solar Cell
Basics**

The amount of voltage (electrical push) developed across the cell is determined by the type of material used to build the cell, the physical surface area of the cell and the amount of light energy applied to the cell. Because the type of charge on each side of the cell is always the same, the electrons are always being pushed in the same direction. Therefore, the PV cell is a **direct current (DC)** supply device.

If an acceptable external pathway is provided for the movement of the electrons from the pushing end of the cell to the pulling end, an electrical **circuit** is created. This concept is depicted in Figure 3-4. You can envision this as electrons hopping from one atom to the next to move around the circuit from the pushing end of the device (PV cell) to the pulling end. The electromotive force is applied to all of the atoms between the two ends of the conductor, which causes a flow (or **current**) of electrons to move through the circuit.

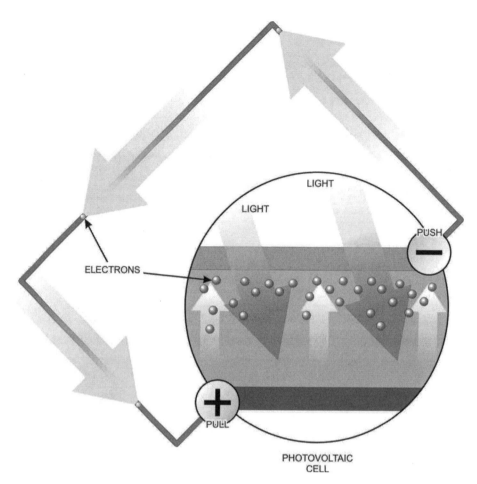

Figure 3-4: Electron Current Flow

power

Watts

The voltage level created by the electrical fields generated within the cell's internal structure and the flowing free electrons current created by the light hitting the semiconductor material establishes the PV cell's **power** output abilities in **Watts** (Ohms Law for power is $P = V \times I$). A single PV cell may be capable of supplying enough power to operate a small, low power device such as a calculator or low power LCD displays. For higher power applications, multiple individual cells are connected together to form PV modules or PV panels.

The semiconductor material is covered with a non-reflective coating so that the maximum amount of light energy is absorbed (instead of being reflected away from the material). Electrical contacts are placed on the front and back of the semiconductor materials to provide a connection point and current path between the cell and the external load. Finally, a glass cover is placed over the cell to protect it from the environment. Figure 3-5 depicts the construction of a simple PV cell.

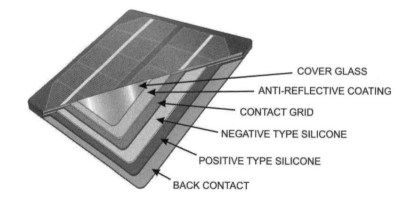

Figure 3-5: PV Cell Structure

PV Panels

Solar cells are routinely connected together and mounted in a common frame to form modules referred to as **photovoltaic (PV) panels** or **solar panels**. Solar modules are made up of solar cells that are typically wired in a series connection scheme that provides a more usable voltage output. The individual voltages of PV cells connected in series add together to give the module a total voltage equal to the sum of all the individual cell voltages. With this connection scheme, the same current flows through each PV cell and the external load. This relationship is described in Figure 3-6.

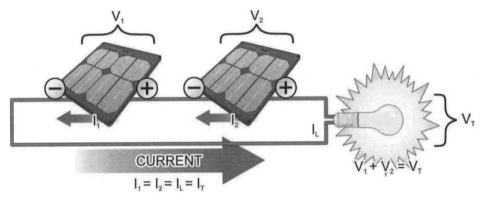

Figure 3-6: Series Connected PV

In actual field installations, multiple PV panels are often mounted together to form a **photovoltaic array** (or **solar array**). The individual PV panels may be wired together in a series circuit to provide additional voltage capabilities, in parallel to provide greater current flow capabilities, or in a series-parallel combination to match the voltage and current requirements of a given load device. Figure 3-7 shows multiple PV panels mounted in an array.

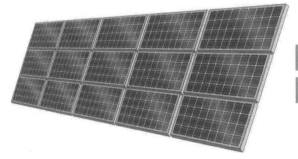

Figure 3-7: An Array of PV Panels

Electrical Loads

The reason to generate an electric current is to accomplish something—such as creating heat or light, or performing electrical work. We attach different types of devices to the electrical energy source to perform these activities. Collectively, these devices can be referred to as **loads**.

Loads such as light bulbs and fluorescent tubes convert electrical energy into light, while resistive heating elements convert the same electrical flow into heat. Electric motors are designed to convert electrical energy back into mechanical energy. In each case, the load (or loads) placed between the terminals of the voltage source provides some level of **resistance** to the flow of electrons through the circuit. In an AC circuit the load may also pose a **reactance** to the changing push being applied. In a DC circuit the load is strictly resistive. This resistance acts against the current flow being pushed by the voltage and the electrical energy is converted into one of the other energy forms mentioned earlier, as illustrated in Figure 3-8.

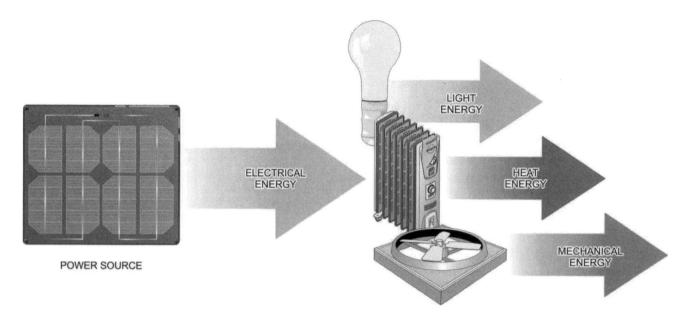

Figure 3-8: Converting Electrical Energy

open circuit

conductors

short circuit

Amperes

Volts

Ohms

ampere

When no external circuit is present, the voltage source pushes against the atoms in the internal wiring, but without a path no current can flow—you still have voltage (push) but no current (flow). This is referred to as an **open circuit**. If a complete path is provided through a material whose atoms offer very little resistance to giving up electrons (called **conductors**), then the electrical push will provide a very heavy flow of electrons through the material between the terminals. If the amount of resistance provided is too low, this is referred to as a **short circuit**.

Electrical load devices typically provide some level of resistance between these extremes. The relationship between voltage, resistance and current flow in a circuit is expressed in a law called Ohm's Law. This relationship simply states that the amount of current that flows in a circuit is directly related to the voltage applied and inversely related to the resistance of the load. This is expressed as:

$$I = \frac{V}{R}$$

where I is current in **Amperes***, V is voltage in **Volts** and R is resistance in **Ohms**.

*An **ampere** is a measure of how many electrons are moving past a point in one second. One ampere equals 6.24 x 10 to the 18th electrons passing a single point in one second. That's a lot of electrons hopping down the wire at one time—nobody wants to count that many electrons or keep track of them, so we just refer to them in terms of amperes.

In plain terms, the amount of current flowing in a circuit *increases* directly with the amount of push being applied (double the voltage and the current will double as well). The amount of current flowing also *decreases* directly with an increase in resistance (if the push remains constant but the amount of resistance is doubled, the current flow will be cut in half).

Power

The **power** (the ability to perform work) supplied by a PV cell, panel or array is governed by the power formula for Ohms Law:

$$P = V \times I \text{ or } I = \frac{P}{V}$$

where P is power in **Watts**, I is current in *Amperes*, and V is voltage in *Volts*.

The power output of the PV device varies with the load applied. Figure 3-9 shows a typical set of power output curves for a PV panel manufacturer's line of devices. Notice how the level for the given irradiance and cell temperature changes with respect to the current being pulled from the device over a range of output voltages present at its output terminals.

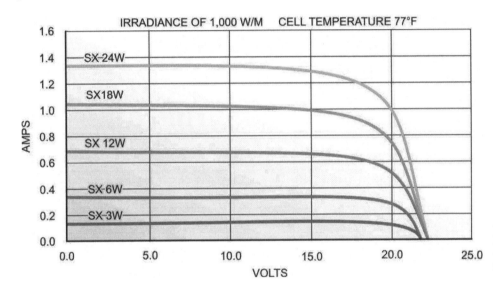

Figure 3-9: PV Panel Power Curves

PV Device Ratings

PV device manufacturers specify operating voltage, current and power capabilities for their devices. These specifications typically include:

- *Rated Power (Watts)* – The manufacturer's stated electrical power production (in Watts) for the device under a specified range of current and voltages under specified standard temperature and irradiance conditions.

- *Rated Voltage (Vmp)* – The manufacturer's stated output voltage level under specified load, temperature and irradiance test conditions.

- *Rated Current (Imp)* – The manufacturer's stated output current level under specified load, temperature and irradiance test conditions.

- *Open Circuit Voltage (Voc)* – The voltage produced from the device when no load is applied to the output terminals (other than the test equipment).

- *Short Circuit Current (Isc)* – The current expected from the device if its external contacts are connected directly together.

- *Physical Dimensions (Inches or cm^2)* – The physical dimensions of the cell or panel—used for matching panels to mounting systems.

- *Measured Temperature (Centigrade - C)* – The temperature of the ambient air under which testing for the previous values is conducted—these values can change with variations in temperature.

- *Irradiance (W/m^2)* – The standard amount of light applied to the device for testing—typically 1 Sun.

PV Array Mounting Systems

After the PV panels have been gathered into an array they must be mounted so they can catch the sunlight. One common mounting method is to place the PV array on the top of a building or home, as illustrated in Figure 3-10. The mounting brackets must be secure enough to hold the array in place during high **wind loading** conditions (thunder and wind storms). In homes that have truss roofs, this type of mount is normally used on the south facing side of the roof.

wind loading

**Figure 3-10:
Roof Mounted
PV Panels**

Roof mounting often produces panel orientations and angles that do not provide optimum conditions for the panel to receive the available solar energy. Also, because the mounting hardware must penetrate the seal of the roof, leaks may be introduced. At least 3 inches of clearance should be provided between the roof and the array to provide for adequate cooling and maximized operation of the array.

Similar hardware maybe used for ground-mounted arrays. These installations place the array on adjustable standoffs anchored to the ground. The adjustable standoffs enable the installer to optimize the vertical orientation to the solar exposure. As with roof mounted panels, ground mounted panels must be securely anchored to resist the highest winds expected in the geographical area.

It is also common to install pole mounted PV arrays. These arrays can be attached to the pole using mounting hardware that either attaches to the top of the pole (**Top of Pole Mounts**) or to the side of the pole (**Side of Pole Mounts**). Figure 3-11 depicts common examples of both pole-mount hardware types.

These mount types allow the PV panel to be mounted in areas where there are no obstructions. They also routinely furnish horizontal and vertical adjustments that enable the installer to optimize the panels' exposure to the sunlight.

Installing pole mounts involves:

- Assembling the PV panels into arrays by fastening them to pairs or sets of rails

- Firmly anchoring the pole in the ground

- Securing the bracket base to the pole (either on the side of the pole or as a cap on top of the pole)

- Attaching the rails with the panel array to the bracket base

- Adjusting the horizontal and vertical alignment of the PV panels for maximum exposure to the sun

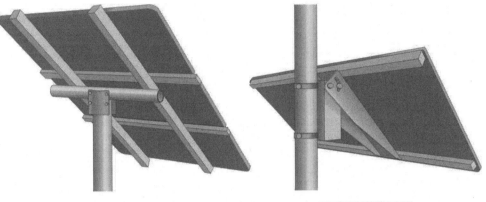

TOP POLE MOUNTED

SIDE POLE MOUNT

**Figure 3-11:
Pole Mounted PV
Panel Hardware**

Tracking Systems

To obtain maximum use of a PV array throughout the year, a tracking mount is required. There are two types of tracking mounts used with PV panels—**passive trackers** and **active trackers**. Passive Trackers use the sun's heat to move liquid from side to side inside the tracker, allowing gravity to turn it and follow the sun, using no motors, no gears and no controls to fail. Optical sensors that drive horizontal and vertical **positioning motors** are used to guide active trackers. Active tracking systems typically use power from the storage battery bank the PV panels are charging or directly from the PV panels themselves. Commercial solar farms employ computer-controlled systems to accurately track the position of the sun and focus the PV system on it throughout the day and throughout the year.

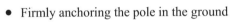

Safety Precautions

All PV systems pose electrical hazards. You must be aware of how these hazards are presented by the PV system and take steps necessary to prevent injury or damage from these causes. The Marcraft PV array consists of two 12-volt PV panels capable of producing up to 12 Watts of power each. The relationship between electrical power, current and voltage is an extended part of Ohm's Law and is expressed as:

$$P = V \times I \text{ or } I = \frac{P}{V}$$

where P is power in *Watts*, V is voltage in *Volts*, and I is current in *Amperes* (amps)

Therefore, a 12-volt PV panel system operating at the 12-Watt level would be delivering 1.0 amp of current to the load under full output conditions. With the two panels wired in parallel, the array is capable of delivering up to 2.0 amps of current. In parallel circuits the source voltage is the same as the individual sources, but the current flow capabilities double. Current levels as low as 0.1 - 0.2 amps can be fatal to humans under certain circumstances. Therefore caution should always be used when working with this or any other electrical devices.

Another danger associated with electrical current flow is the possibility of **burns** or **fire** related to **conductors** (wiring and devices that give up electrons easily) heating up. Even though the conductor materials give up electrons more easily than other substances, their electrons do not just fall off the atom—even conductors have some level of resistance in them. Therefore, some energy is given off as heat when current passes through the conductor.

Heat in wiring systems is often a result of too much current flowing through an undersized wire or through a bad connection. One of the keys to minimizing the amount of heat generated in wiring is to use the proper size wiring and the correct external insulation coating. A wire with a larger cross sectional area carries a given amount of current more easily than a smaller wire of the same material. There are simply more atoms across the face of the larger wire to give up the necessary number of electrons. Therefore, less heat is produced for that level of current.

| burns |
| fire |
| conductors |
| American Wire Gauge (AWG) |
| ampacity |
| fuse |
| circuit breaker |

Table 3-1: Wire Gauge vs. Maximum Current Capacity

AWG	120 Vac	240 Vdc	12 Vdc
22	5A	2.5A	5A
20	7.5A	3.75A	8A
18	10A	5A	10A
16	13A	6.5A	20A
14	17A	8.5A	40A
12	23A	11.5A	60A
10	33A	16.5A	100A
8	46A	23A	150A
6	60A	30A	N/A
4	80A	40A	N/A
2	100A	50A	N/A
1	125A	62.5A	N/A
0	150A	75A	N/A
00	190A	95A	N/A
000	240A	120A	N/A
0000	300A	150A	N/A

In the United States, wiring is specified by a measurement standard called the **American Wire Gauge (AWG)**. This standard specifies wire diameter in a descending relationship—larger AWG gauge numbers represent smaller wire diameters. The reason this is important for an installer is because the cross sectional area (diameter) of the wire is directly related to its ability to carry electrical current (referred to as the wire's **ampacity**). It is important to use proper wire sizes and insulation types when working with the Marcraft PV array to insure a safe electrical system and to help avoid the risk of electrical fire. To calculate the proper wire size for a given installation, add up all the current sources and select a cable size that can handle the maximum level of sustained current that the circuit can produce. You can use Table 3-1 as a general wire-sizing guide for PV system installations.

PV arrays can deliver a dangerous amount of current. If a short circuit occurs in the wiring system, a fire can result or components can be damaged. Likewise, if you are the source of the short circuit you can be injured, burned or killed. In order to avoid these threats, a properly sized **fuse** or **circuit breaker** is required in the lines coming from the PV array (or any other electrical source). These devices sense the level of current flowing through them and are designed to interrupt the path of current flow (open circuit) if the current level gets to a certain point (the fuse rating).

CAUTION

Always perform installations using proper wire sizing to help avoid the risk of an electrical fire.

To calculate the proper fuse size, calculate the maximum amount of current that the PV panel (or array) is designed to provide and select a fuse with the closest current rating to this value. The fuse is a protective device so you should select a lower fuse rating rather than a higher value if an exact fuse size is not available. The fuse must also have a proper voltage rating for the voltages present in the circuit where it is used.

PROCEDURE 9 – INTRODUCTION TO PHOTOVOLTAIC PANELS

Solar

photovoltaic (PV)

In this lab procedure you will identify the key components of a **photovoltaic (PV)** electrical generation system, mount and correctly wire photovoltaic panels for use, and test the basic operation of the photovoltaic system.

You will also test the operation of the PV system for performance related to optimized positioning of the system with respect to the location of the light source.

Resources Needed:

- 12V, 12W Photovoltaic Solar Panels (2)
- Variable Intensity Lamp with variable height adjustment
- Marcraft Green Electron Generation Experiment Panel
- Hand-held Digital Multimeter
- PV Panel Data Sheets

As with any electrical system, one of the keys to installing a photovoltaic generation system is to read and understand its documentation. Locate and record the following information from the Owners Manual:

1. Obtain the PV Panel's Data Sheets from your instructor and verify that all of the PV panel parts are present in your work area.

2. According to the data sheets for the SC12-12V panels, what is the rated power of these panels?

    _____

3. According to the data sheets for the panels, what is the rated output voltage of these panels?

    _____

4. According to the data sheets for the panels, what is the rated current production of these panels?

    _____

5. What voltage level should you expect to measure at the output of these panels if they are not attached to any type of load?

    _____

6. Under what temperature conditions are the measurements in the data sheets accurate?

_____

7. How is Irradiance specified in the data sheets?

_____

8. What wire size is used for the individual 12V version of the PV Panel?

_____

9. Refer to the Internet and access the site at http://howto.altenergystore.com. Click on the Library link and select the "Solar Insolation Map …" option for your location. This will produce a *PV Solar Radiation* map similar to the one depicted in Figure 3-12.

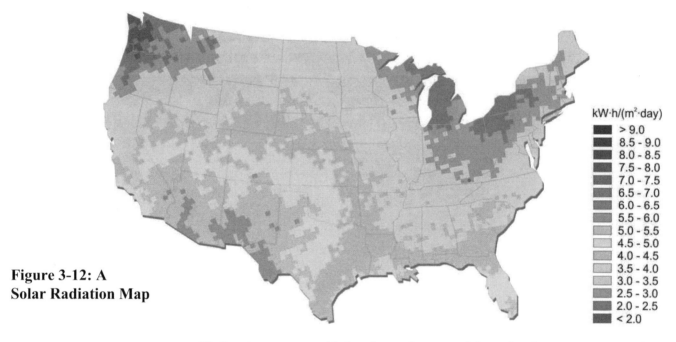

Figure 3-12: A Solar Radiation Map

kW·h/(m²·day)
> 9.0
8.5 - 9.0
8.0 - 8.5
7.5 - 8.0
7.0 - 7.5
6.5 - 7.0
6.0 - 6.5
5.5 - 6.0
5.0 - 5.5
4.5 - 5.0
4.0 - 4.5
3.5 - 4.0
3.0 - 3.5
2.5 - 3.0
2.0 - 2.5
< 2.0

10. Locate your geographic location on the map and determine the average amount of **PV Solar Radiation** your area receives per day. Record this value on the following line:

_____

11. From the data sheets, what is the area of your panels in square centimeters (cm^2)? The conversion from square inches to square centimeters (cm^2) is 6.45 cm^2 for each square inch.

_____

12. What is the area of the panel in m^2? The conversion from cm^2 to m^2 is 10,000 to 1.

_____

13. What is the total surface area of the two panels combined in an array?

_____

14. Using the total area of the PV array and the PV solar radiation value for your area, calculate the kWh of energy the panel receives per day.

_____

15. If the PV array is 100% efficient, what is the power production each day?

_____

16. Research the local price for residential power price at your location and calculate the monetary value of the power you are generating. Record this value on the following line:

_____

17. Calculate the monthly savings from using energy from the PV array (use 30 days per month).

_____

18. Actually, crystalline solar cells/panels are between 14% and 16% efficient at converting sunlight into electricity. With this information, calculate the maximum power and savings likely to be generated at your location.

Maximum Power: _____

Maximum Savings: _____

Mounting the PV Panels

Solar

1. Obtain the following mounting hardware for the PV panels:

- PV panel mounting pipe (1-1/2" schedule 80 PVC pipe)
- Three 1-1/2" pipe mounting clamps
- Two steel cross arm rails
- Two steel panel support mounting rails
- Two 12V 12W PV panels.
- Twelve #8 x 3/4" bolts with lock nuts (panels to rails and cross arms to support rails)
- Two #8 x 1-1/2" sheet metal screws (clamps to panel frame)
- Four #8 x 1-1/2" bolts and lock nuts (clamps to cross arms)

2. Attach the PV Panel mounting pipe to the experiment panel by sliding one end of the pipe into the horizontal T-connector in the Wind Turbine Mounting mast. Orient the pipe so that the wiring access hole closest to the mounting mast is approximately 11 inches away from the mast. Align this access hole so that it is pointing just slightly forward from vertical and with the other access hole facing horizontally downward, as illustrated in Figure 3-13.

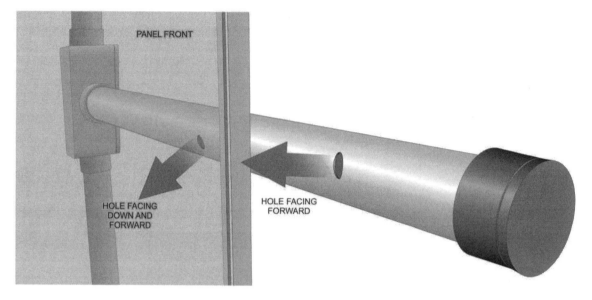

Figure 3-13: Orienting the PV Panel Mounting Pipe

3. Position one of the mounting clamps along the vertical edge of the Clean Electron Generation panel and align the screw holes in the clamp with those in the back of the experiment panel's frame.

4. Place the arms of the clamp across the pipe and secure it to the base of the clamp and the rear of the experiment panel frame using two #8 x 1-1/2" screws, as depicted in Figure 3-14.

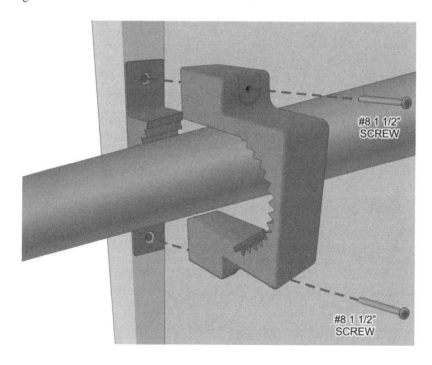

Figure 3-14: Securing the PV Panel Mounting Pipe

5. Next, create the PV Panel support frame by attaching the two steel cross arms to the two steel panel support rails using four #8 x 3/4" bolts and lock nuts. Align the intermediate holes of the support rails and the end holes of the cross arms, as shown in Figure 3-15.

6. Use four #8 x 1-1/2" bolts and lock nuts to attach the PV Panel support frame to the mounting pipe using two mounting clamps as illustrated in Figure 3-16.

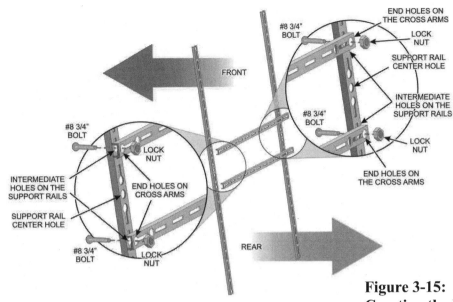

Figure 3-15: Creating the PV Panel Support Frame

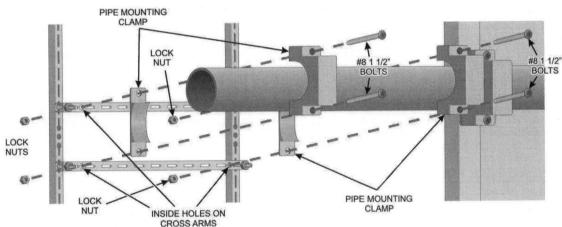

Figure 3-16: Securing the PV Panel Frame to the Mounting Pipe

7. Insert four 8-32 x 5/8 bolts through the inner holes in the frame on the back of the PV panel marked PV Panel #1, as illustrated in Figure 3-17.

8. Place #8 nuts on all four bolts and tighten them securely to the PV panel frame.

9. Attach PV Panel #1 to the top of the panel support rails by inserting the bolts through the corresponding holes in the rail and securing them all with #8 lock nuts, as shown in the figure.

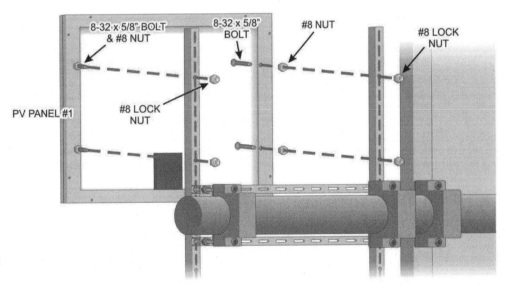

Figure 3-17: Securing PV Panel #1

10. Repeat Steps 7 through 9 to attach the panel marked PV Panel #2 to the lower half of the support rail, as illustrated in Figure 3-18.

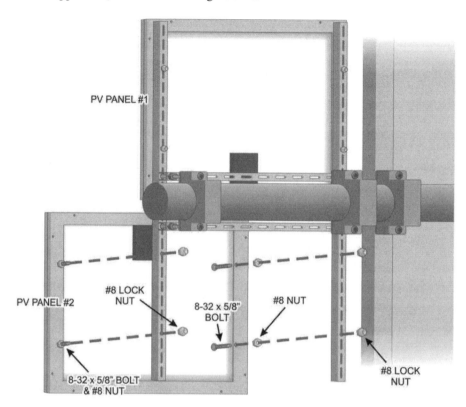

**Figure 3-18:
Securing PV Panel #2**

11. Thread the connecting cables from both PV panels through the wiring access opening in the experiment panel and channel them into the wiring access opening in the mounting pipe.

12. Pull the PV connection cables through the wiring access hole behind the experiment panel.

Figure 3-19: Basic PV Panel Wiring

13. Route the connection cable from PV Panel #1 and #2 through the hole beneath the PV Panel connection block.

14. Crimp a fork lug connector to each of the wires and secure them to the bottom row of the PV Panel connection block, as illustrated in Figure 3-19. The PV Panel #1 wires should be on the left side while the PV Panel #2 wires are on the right side. Place the red wires on the left of the corresponding black wires from each cable (as viewed form the front of the panel).

Configuring the Solar Panel

PV panels are DC power sources and can be considered light controlled batteries. Like batteries, solar cells and panels can be connected together to provide different voltage and current capabilities to fit different load/installation requirements. When PV panels are connected in **series** (positive terminals are connected to negative terminals in a *daisy-chain* connection) as illustrated in Figure 3-20, the voltage level provided to an external load is equal to the sum of all the individual PV panel voltages.

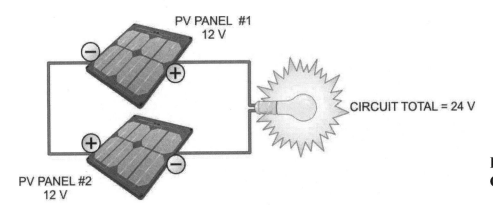

Figure 3-20: Series Connected Solar Panels

In this configuration, the same current flows through all the PV panels and the load. This arrangement enables multiple PV panels to be combined to provide power to a piece of equipment that requires a higher voltage source—such as using two 12-volt PV panels to provide a 24 Vdc source for a portable device with this input requirement.

When PV panels are connected in **parallel** (positive terminals are connected to positive terminals) as illustrated in Figure 3-21, the voltage level is the same as the lowest individual PV panel's output (all of the PV panels in such an array should have the same stated voltage ratings). However the current delivery capabilities of parallel PV panels is equal to the sum of the currents produced by each of the panels. This is helpful in situations where devices that require heavy DC current loads need an acceptable source of power.

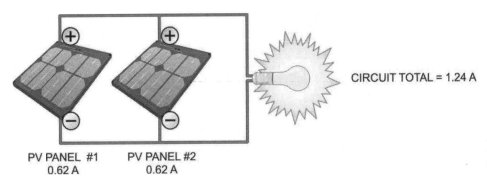

Figure 3-21: Parallel Connected PV Panels

Solar

Testing the PV Panels

1. Turn on the hand-held digital multimeter and set it to its 200 DCV setting, and replace the solar panel fuse.

2. With only the ambient light from the room shining on the PV panels, measure the voltage level present at the terminals of each PV panel supply by placing the black lead of the multimeter on the terminal where the black wire from the PV panel supply is connected and touching the red lead from the multimeter to the red wire connection from the same PV panel. Record these values on the following lines:

   PV Panel #1 (ambient output): _____

   PV Panel #2 (ambient output): _____

3. Form a series PV panel supply connection by attaching a jumper wire between the positive (+ or red wire) terminal of PV panel #1 to the negative (- or black) terminal of PV panel #2, as illustrated in Figure 3-22.

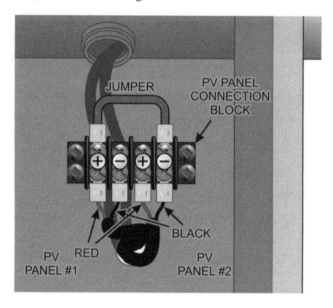

**Figure 3-22:
Connecting PV
Panels in Series**

4. Connect the black lead of the multimeter to the negative terminal of PV panel #1 and the red lead to the positive terminal of PV panel #2. Record the total voltage level provided by the series PV panels on the following line:

   Series PV Panels: _____

5. How does this value relate to the individual voltages of PV panels #1 and #2 measured in Step 2?

   _____

6. Reconfigure the PV panel supply connections to form a parallel PV panel connection by moving the first jumper wire so that it is connected between the positive (+) terminal of PV panel #1 to the positive (+) terminal of PV panel #2.

7. Attach another jumper wire between the negative (-) terminal of PV panel #1 to the negative (-) terminal of PV panel #2, as illustrated in Figure 5-23.

8. Connect the black lead of the multimeter to the negative terminal of PV panel #1 and the red lead to the positive terminal of PV panel #1. Record the total voltage level provided by the parallel PV panels on the following line:

_____

9. How does this value relate to the individual voltages of PV panels #1 and #2 measured in Step 2?

_____

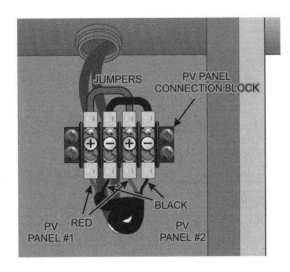

Figure 3-23: Connecting Batteries in Parallel

Solar Panel Controls

PV cells, panels and arrays generate an output whenever they are exposed to light. Therefore, every PV installation must have a set of control devices that can be used to separate the PV device from the rest of the PV system. The most fundamental PV Control panel should contain at least an ammeter, a fuse or circuit breaker, and a Disconnect switch. These components are typically wired in series in the positive lead of the PV system. Figure 3-24 is a suggested **schematic diagram** (symbolic wiring diagram) for a solar panel installation designed to charge a set of storage batteries.

Solar

schematic diagram

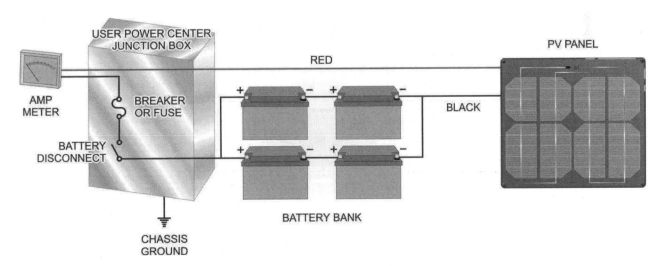

The control panel for a PV panel installation typically contains a fuse or circuit breaker that protects the technician, the operator and the PV array circuitry from damage due to short circuits. A circuit breaker acts as a piece of wire, providing a path for current flow through itself until the current flow level reaches a designated level. If that level is exceeded, the circuit breaker becomes an open circuit to stop the current from flowing through it.

Figure 3-24: PV System Control Panel Wiring

sized

Circuit breakers and fuses must be properly **sized** to safely handle the maximum amount of current that the system is designed to supply, and then break the circuit (cause an open circuit) to interrupt the flow of electrons until the over current condition can be removed or repaired. In doing so the circuit breaker or fuse protects wiring, devices and personnel from damage and injury.

Battery Disconnect switch

Other common control mechanisms include a **Battery Disconnect switch**. The Disconnect switch disconnects the output of the PV panels from the storage battery, grid or inverter circuitry so that these elements can be serviced safely, without power that is being generated by the PV array.

Single-Pole, Single-Throw (SPST)

The Disconnect Switch is a **Single-Pole, Single-Throw (SPST)** switch—there is one *pole* (the circle with the movable contact attached to it—and one *throw*—possible connection point. This representation of the SPST switch shows that it is a normally open switch— when the switch is in its "normal" position, there is no path for current to flow through the switch—when the switch is flipped to the active position (the movable contact swings into contact with the circle representing the throw position, creating a path for current flow through the switch.

Like fuses and breakers, switches, devices and wiring must be rated to handle the maximum designed current levels for their positions in the system. Switches are rated according to both voltage and maximum current handling capabilities. Therefore, a switch designed for operation in a 12 Vdc 15A automobile application would not be used in a 120 Vac 15A residential wiring environment. Doing so will potentially present both a damage and an injury situation.

From the control panel, the wiring may continue on to a set of storage batteries (as shown in Figure 3-24), to a DC-to-AC inverter, or to a connection into the commercial power grid. These options are explored in the next lab procedure.

1. Place the red lead in the multimeter's V/Ω /mA jack and the black lead in the Ground (COM) jack, as shown in Figure 3-25. Turn the multimeter to the **On** position.

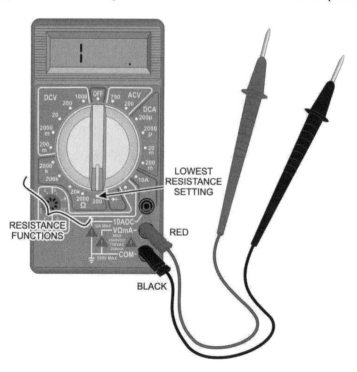

Figure 3-25: Meter Leads Set for Measuring Continuity

2. Set the multimeter to its lowest *resistance range* (used for checking Continuity of a device or circuit).

3. Place the meter's leads on the opposite terminals of the Disconnect Switch. On the following lines, record the reading obtained from the multimeter with the switch in the up and down positions:

   Switch Up: _____

   Switch Down: _____

4. With the fuse removed from the fuse holder, place the multimeter leads on opposite terminals of the fuse holder. Record the resistance measurement on the following line. Move the leads to the opposite terminals and record the multimeter reading in this direction:

   _____

   _____

5. Install the fuse in the fuse holder and repeat the activities in Step 4. Record the resistance measurements on the following lines:

   _____

   _____

6. Connect the leads on opposite terminals of the PV Panel's ammeter. Record the resistance measurement on the following line. Move the leads to the opposite terminals and record the multimeter reading in this direction.

   _____

   _____

7. Remove the multimeter leads from the terminals.

Wiring the Control Panel

1. Prepare a red and a black 12 AWG jumper wire to run between the top-left terminals on the PV Control Panel connection block and the two lower-right terminals of the PV Panel connection block. See Figure 3-26.

2. Crimp fork lug connectors on the red and black wires and secure them under the two, left-most connection points on the top row of the PV Panel connection block (red on the left and black on the right—these jumpers may be combined with the red and black parallel PV panel supply jumpers from the previous procedure).

NOTE: The PV Charge Controller is NOT used in this procedure—therefore, no wiring should be connected to the bottom row of the connection block at this time.

Solar

3. Crimp fork lug connectors to the free ends of the red and black wires and secure them to the two, right-most connection points on the bottom row of the PV Panel connection block, as illustrated in Figure 3-26 (red on the left and black on the right).

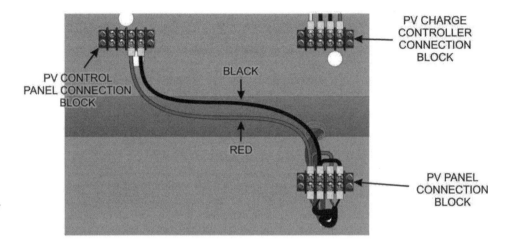

Figure 3-26: Intermediate PV Panel Wiring

4. Prepare and install a short red 12 AWG jumper wire to run between the right-center connection point on the top row of the PV Panel connection block and the (+) terminal on the PV Panel Ammeter. Refer to Figure 3-27.

5. Prepare and install a short red 12 AWG jumper wire to run between the open terminal (-) of the PV Panel Ammeter and the spade terminal on the fuse holder closest to the panel mounting. Refer to Figure 3-27.

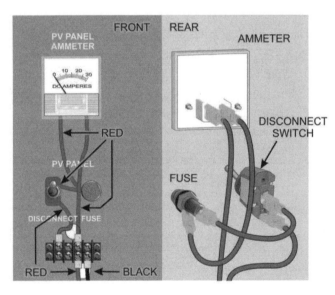

Figure 3-27: Connecting the PV Panel's Positive Side Wiring

6. Prepare and install a short red 12 AWG jumper wire to run between the open terminal at the end of the fuse holder and the top terminal on the PV Panel's Disconnect switch. Refer to Figure 3-27.

7. Thread the free end of a red 12 AWG wire through the left most opening (looking from the front of the panel) in the Clean Electron Generation Panel above the PV Panel connection block. Refer to Figure 3-27.

8. Crimp fork lug connectors to the ends of the red wire and secure it to the open left-most connection point on the top row of the PV Panel connection block.

9. Attach the free end of the red jumper to the bottom terminal on the PV panel's Disconnect switch. This completes the positive side wiring for the PV Panel, as shown in Figure 3-27.

10. Install a small black 12 AWG jumper between the right-most and left-center terminals on the upper row of the PV Control Panel connection block, as depicted in Figure 3-28.

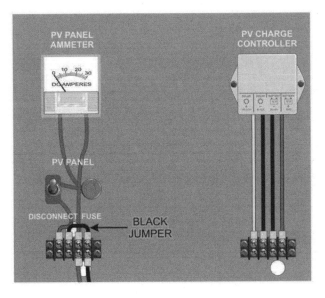

Figure 3-28: PV Control Panel Connection Block Wiring

11. Verify your wiring against the schematic wiring diagram in Figure 3-29. Check off the leads on the drawing as you verify the connection pathway between each device.

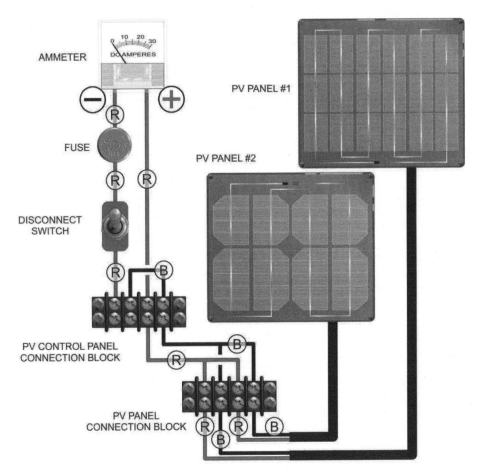

Figure 3-29: PV Panel Wiring Diagram

Solar

Testing

The operation of a PV array is normally straightforward and quite simple. These systems are typically easy to test—they include checking the output of individual panels to verify their operation, checking connections between panels and testing the performance of the panels/array under different lighting intensities and circumstances. The following procedures can be used to perform simple function and more advanced operational tests on the PV panel.

1. Attach the red and black multimeter leads to the left-most connection points on the bottom row of the PV Control Panel connection block so that they connect with the wires of the same color, as illustrated in Figure 3-30.

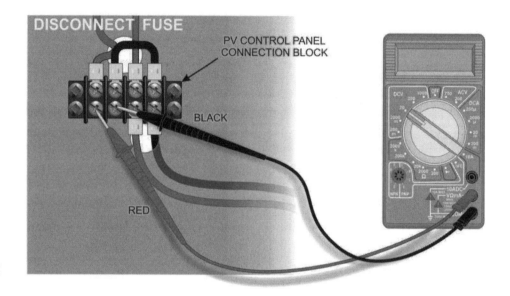

Figure 3-30: Attaching the Meter for Testing

2. Set the multimeter to the 20-volt DCV setting.

3. Place the Disconnect Switch in the closed (**ON**) position (so that the current can pass through it—If necessary, refer to the "Examining the Control Panel" procedure from earlier in this lab to verify this position).

4. Make sure the PV Panels are rotated to be vertically centered with the vertical end rail of the Clean Electron Generation Panel.

5. Plug in the adjustable dual light source, position the tripod so the handle is centered on the PV panels at approximately 1 foot away from the panels, and adjust the height of the tripod so the lamps are centered on the upper panel.

6. Press and release the left switch button on the back of the left lamp head to turn on one lamp bulb. Observe the reading on the PV Panel's ammeter and the digital multimeter. Record the reading from each device on the following lines:

_____ (Amps)   _____ (Volts)

7. Press and release the right switch button on the back of the left lamp head to turn on a second lamp bulb. Observe the reading on the digital multimeter. Record the reading from each device on the following lines:

_____ (Volts)

8. Press and release the left switch button on the back of the right lamp head to turn on a third lamp bulb. Observe the reading on the digital multimeter. Record the reading from each device on the following lines:

_____ (Volts)

9. Press and release the right switch button on the back of the right lamp head to turn on a fourth lamp bulb. Observe the reading on the digital multimeter. Record the reading from each device on the following lines:

_____ (Volts)

10. Lower the tripod so that the two lamps are focused directly on the center of the lower PV panel and repeat Steps 6 though 9 in reverse, turning each lamp bulb off, recording the results on the following lines:

1 Lamp Bulb On: _____ (Amps)   _____ (Volts)

2 Lamp Bulbs On: _____ (Amps)   _____ (Volts)

3 Lamp Bulbs On: _____ (Amps)   _____ (Volts)

4 Lamp Bulbs On: _____ (Amps)   _____ (Volts)

11. Remove the multimeter leads from the PV Control Panel connection block and turn off all lamps.

Testing Under Load

In this section, you will connect the PV panels to the Load Light on the Clean Electron Generation Panel to test the panels under load.

Solar

1. Prepare a red and black 12 AWG jumper wire with fork lugs on each end of the wires to go from the Clean Electron Generation Panel backside of the red load light under the panel to the front-side of the panel up to the bottom row of the PV Control Panel connection block terminals.

2. From the backside of the Clean Electron Generation Panel attach the black jumper wire to the right terminal on the red load light and the red jumper wire to the left terminal.

3. Route the red and black jumper wires under the Clean Electron Generation Panel and attach the red wire to the left-most terminal on the bottom row of the PV Control Panel connection block and the black wire to the left-center terminal.

4. Attach the red and black meter leads to the left-most connection points on the bottom row of the PV Control Panel connection block so they connect with the wires of the same color.

5. Place the Disconnect Switch in the closed (**ON**) position.

6. Adjust the lamp stand so that the two lamps are centered on both the upper and lower panels. On the back of the left lamp head, press and release the left switch button to turn on one lamp bulb.

7. Observe the reading on the PV Panel's ammeter and the digital multimeter, and record the reading from each meter on the following lines:

   1 Lamp Bulb On: _____ (Amps) _____ (Volts)

8. On the back of the left lamp, press and release the right switch button to turn on a second lamp bulb. Observe the reading on the PV Panel's ammeter and the digital multimeter, and record the reading from each meter on the following lines:

   2 Lamp Bulbs On: _____ (Amps) _____ (Volts)

9. On the back of the right lamp, press and release the left switch button to turn on a third lamp bulb. Observe the reading on the PV Panel's ammeter and the digital multimeter, and record the reading from each meter on the following lines:

   3 Lamp Bulbs On: _____ (Amps) _____ (Volts)

10. On the back of the right lamp, press and release the right switch button to turn on a fourth lamp bulb. Observe the reading on the PV Panel's ammeter and the digital multimeter, and record the reading from each meter on the following lines:

   4 Lamp Bulbs On: _____ (Amps) _____ (Volts)

11. Turn off all four lamp bulbs and convert the meter readings to power using the formula P=V x I in each case on the following lines:

   1 Lamp Bulb On: _____   3 Lamp Bulbs On: _____

   2 Lamp Bulb On: _____   4 Lamp Bulbs On: _____

12. On the following lines explain why there were no current readings while in Step 11 four different current power ratings were obtained:

   _____

   _____

Effects of Lighting Angle

1. Move the lamp stand so that it shines on the PV Panel at an angle of approximately 30 (degrees) from the panel, still maintaining the 1-foot distance, as illustrated in Figure 3-31.

Solar

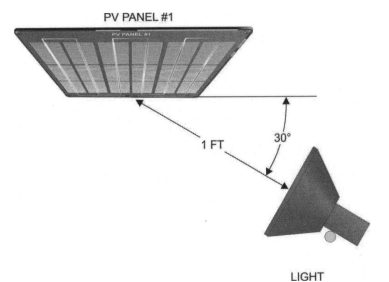

Figure 3-31: Light from a 30 Degree Angle

2. Turn all four lamp bulbs **On** and record the voltage and current produced on the following lines:

   Full On (30 degrees) _____ (Amps) _____ (Volts)

3. Simulate morning sunlight by positioning the light source so that it shines on the PV Panel at an angle of approximately 45 (degrees), as illustrated in Figure 3-32. The distance should still be approximately 3 feet from the panel.

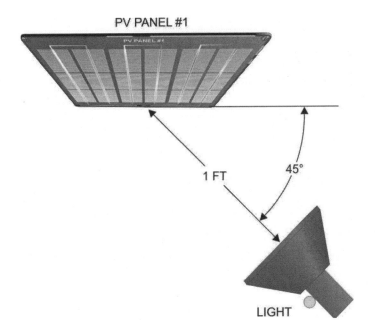

Figure 3-32: Light from a 45 Degree Angle

4. With the lamp still set to the Full-On setting, turn the lamp **On** and record the voltage and current produced on the following lines:

Full On (45 degrees): _____ (Amps) _____ (Volts)

5. Repeat Steps 1 through 4 using the angle from the opposite end of the panel, as illustrated in Figure 3-33. This represents afternoon and late afternoon sunlight. Record the voltages and currents produced on the following lines:

Full On (45 degrees reversed): _____ (Amps) _____ (Volts)

Full On (30 degrees reversed): _____ (Amps) _____ (Volts)

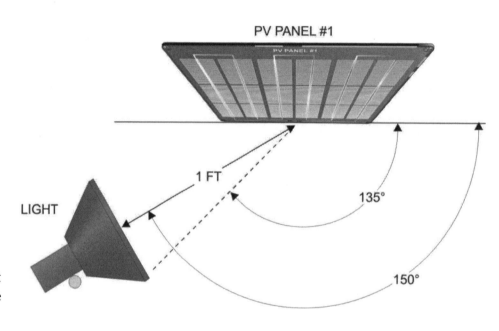

Figure 3-33: Light from a 150 Degree Angle

6. Turn all 4 lamp bulbs **Off** and convert the multimeter readings for each angle to power output using the formula P=V x I in each case.

_____ (30 degrees − Early Morning)

_____ (45 degrees − Mid Morning)

_____ (30 degrees reversed − Early Afternoon)

_____ (45 degrees reversed − Mid Afternoon)

7. Remove the meter leads from the PV Control Panel connection block terminal and remove the red and black jumper wires from the two left-most terminals on the bottom of the connection block terminal and the red load light.

8. This concludes the Introduction to Photovoltaic Panels.

Procedure 9 Questions

1. How many 12V, 12W PV panels would be required to supply a load that requires a 48-volt supply that can push at least 2.5 amps of current, if you assume that the minimum light level is at 50% of the panel's stated value?

2. How are the panels in question #1 configured to supply the power requirements of the load? How does the voltage and current output of the panel change as the angle of light striking the panel moves from straight on to a steeper angle?

3. With a stationary mounted PV array, what affect does the movement of the sun across the horizon have on the performance of the array?

4. What is the purpose of the Disconnect Switch in the PV array circuitry?

5. What size fuse should be installed in this PV system if you had four 12V, 12W PV panels wired in parallel to supply the load?

6. What is the approximate power output of your 2-panel PV array per day, if the irradiance level remains at a level where the PV panels can generate their maximum output for 6 hours per day?

7. How many of your panels would be required to provide 1 square meter of surface area?

8. How much power could be delivered from your PV array if it was made up of 10 panels?

9. How may of your panels would be required to create a 1kW panel?

10. How much space (in square meters) would a 1kW PV array made up of your panels take up?

11. In this procedure you moved the light source so that it struck the panels at different angles to simulate morning, noon, and afternoon sunlight. How would you simulate the affects of spring, summer, fall, and winter sunlight on the PV array?

OFF-GRID PHOTOVOLTAIC POWER SYSTEMS

The power output of a PV panel or array is not steady. The voltage and current levels produced from the panels varies with the time of day, time of year and atmospheric conditions. Therefore, the PV array alone is not dependable as the primary source of power for most applications. In most residential applications, the output of the PV array is either used to charge a bank of **storage batteries**, or it is applied to the **commercial power grid** to supplement the incoming power supply to the residence.

In large commercial **solar farms**, the outputs of several PV panels are combined to provide hundreds of **megawatts** (million Watts or **MW**) of power that is applied directly to the commercial power grid. These arrays work with complex controllers that monitor the operation of the array and control parameters such as its optimum horizontal and vertical positioning. These controllers are also designed to provide power to the grid in a format acceptable to the local electrical utility.

Batteries

Batteries are devices that produce DC electricity through a chemical reaction process. The chemicals in the battery react with its terminals when an external path for current flow is provided. The process causes free electrons to gather at the negative (-) terminal of the battery while a depletion of electrons occurs at the positive (+) terminal. This provides the push (-) and pull (+) to create current flow through an external circuit, as illustrated in Figure 3-34.

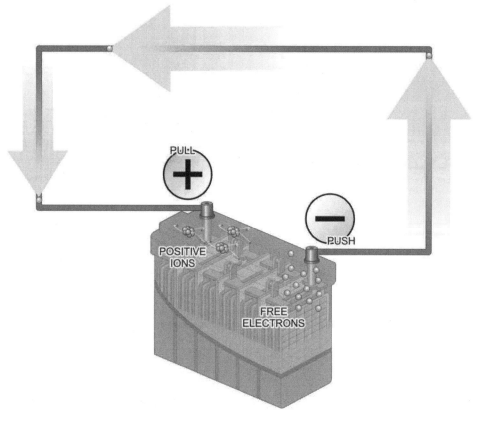

Figure 3-34: Operation of a Battery

When an external pathway is provided the electrons flow from the negative terminal through the external circuit (and the external load) and back into the positive terminal of the battery. If a very low resistance load is placed across the terminals, a large flow of electron current will occur. Larger resistive loads draw lower levels of current flow from the battery, as described by the basic Ohm's Law formula for current, voltage and resistance.

In cases where a wire or other good conductor is placed across the terminals without a load (referred to as a **short circuit** condition), the flow through the circuit and the inside of the battery as quickly as the internal process can generate more free electrons. The acceleration of the process causes the battery to heat up, which in turn can cause it to overheat and possibly explode.

short circuit

Some battery types (referred to as **secondary cells** or **storage** batteries) can be recharged by applying a reverse current to them, as illustrated in Figure 3-35. By applying an external voltage source to the battery at a voltage level *slightly higher* than its terminal voltage, a reverse current is forced to flow back into the battery and the internal chemical process is reversed. Under these circumstances, the battery becomes the load in the circuit instead of the source.

secondary cells

storage

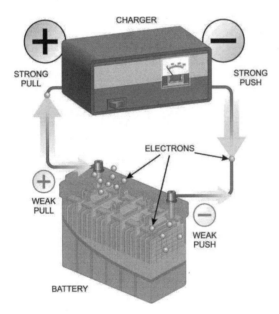

**Figure 3-35:
Recharging a
Battery**

Over time, the reverse current flow restores the original chemical configuration inside the battery. The rate at which the battery **recharges** depends on the chemical configuration and the amount of reverse current flowing through the battery. The amount of reverse current is dependent on the voltage difference between the battery and the recharging source.

recharges

The recharging option is not available with all battery types (not all chemical current generating processes can be reversed). Applying a reverse voltage to these batteries (**primary cells**) can cause them to overheat and possibly explode.

primary cells

WARNING

Applying a reverse voltage to non-rechargeable battery types can cause them to overheat and possibly explode.

Battery Configurations

Batteries can be connected together to provide different voltage and current capabilities to fit different load/installation requirements. When batteries are connected in **series** (positive terminals are connected to negative terminals in a *daisy-chain* connection) as illustrated in Figure 3-36, the voltage level provided to an external load is equal to the sum of all the individual battery voltages. The current flow is the same through all the batteries and the load. This arrangement enables batteries to be combined to provide power to a piece of equipment that requires a higher voltage source—such as using two 6 volt batteries to provide a 12 Vdc source for a portable lantern.

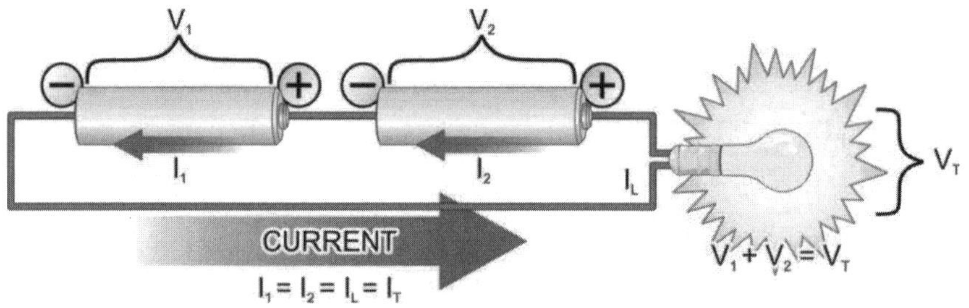

Figure 3-36: Series Connected Batteries

When batteries are connected in **parallel** (positive terminals are connected to positive terminals) as illustrated in Figure 3-37, the voltage level is the same as the individual batteries (all of the batteries should have the same voltage ratings). However the current delivery capabilities of parallel batteries is equal to the sum of the currents produced by each of the batteries. This is helpful in situations where devices that require heavy DC current loads need an acceptable source of power.

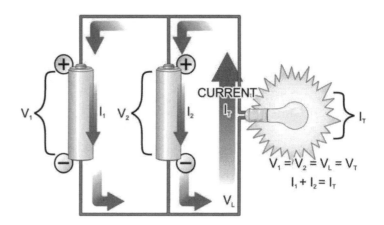

Figure 3-37: Parallel Connected Batteries

Inverters

Inverters are electronic or electro-mechanical devices that converts DC into AC. DC sources such as wind turbines, photovoltaic solar panels and batteries are often connected to inverters to provide an AC output that has consistent voltage levels and frequencies. In a PV solar panel system using a storage battery system, the inverter is used to convert the DC current coming from the storage batteries into AC power that can be used with typical household appliances.

Inverter Types

Most PV array installations require some type of battery-based storage system. Inverters designed to work specifically with this type of application are referred to as off-grid (or *no utility-needs batteries*) inverters. **Off grid inverters** are designed to work with batteries and are not designed for connection to the commercial AC power system (the electrical power delivered by the power company, also referred to as **the grid**).

On grid (also called *no-battery-grid intertie*) **inverters** are designed for connection to the AC power system provided by the local electric utility company and do not require any batteries.

A third class of inverters referred to as **On-grid/Off-grid capable inverters**. These inverters are designed so that they can be connected directly to the utility grid and can also work with a battery storage system to provide backup power in the case of a power outage.

Inverter Sizing

Off grid and On-grid/Off-grid capable inverters must be sized so they are compatible with the *maximum* load they are, or will be, expected to supply. This is simply a matter of installing an inverter with a power rating high enough to supply the sum of all the wattage ratings of the devices that will be supplied at any one time. For example, if 200 watts of lighting, 1000-watt refrigerator and a 1500-watt oven need to be supplied at the same time, the inverter must be capable of delivering at least 2700 watts of power. The inverter's input voltage specification must match the system's storage battery configuration.

Output Regulators and Load Diverters

When the storage batteries of a PV solar panel array installation becomes fully charged, the array will continue to produce additional power as long as the sun is present, unless some control circuitry is used to shut down the power generation process. If power continues to be applied to the storage batteries, it will **overcharge** them creating a potentially dangerous situation. Overcharged batteries can overheat and possibly explode. The additional power being generated is also being wasted.

The Marcraft Green Electron Generation panel includes two types of charging regulators commonly used in alternative energy installations—an **open circuit regulator** and a **diversion style regulator** (also known as a *load diverter*) that can be used to control the charging of the storage battery system.

An open circuit regulator monitors the balance of voltage in the charging system and creates an open circuit condition to separate the PV array from the charging system. When the battery voltage falls off to a predetermined level, the regulator closes the circuit so the PV array can start charging the storage batteries again. The drawback to this type of regulator is that the PV array will continue to produce energy as long as light is present—the energy generated while the regulator is in the open circuit condition is simply wasted.

load diverter

A **load diverter** is a device that monitors the voltage of the load battery. While the voltage level of the battery is below its stated fully charged value, the diverter applies voltage to the battery. However, when the battery voltage reaches the fully charged level, the diverter shift the current coming from the source to a different load. This load is most often some type of water heater that uses the excess power being generated by the source so that it is not wasted. Figure 3-38 shows the placement and configuration of the load diverter in the PV array/storage battery circuit.

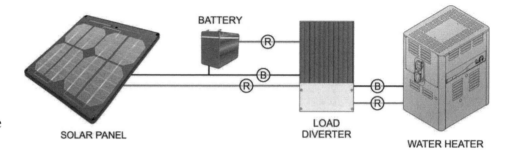

Figure 3-38: Implementing the Load Diverter

Safety Considerations

Don't forget that the inherent personal dangers from electrical current still exist in these procedures. Therefore you should always use caution when working with this and other electrical devices. The high current capabilities of PV arrays can create a potentially dangerous shock and burn hazard when the PV solar panel system is in operation. As mentioned before, using improper wire sizes (wires that are too small for the level of current they are required to carry) can result in excess heat that can damage the wiring, causing a fire, or cause a burn to humans.

> ### CAUTION
>
> It is important to follow the wire-sizing chart in Table 3-1 to insure a safe electrical system and to help avoid the risk of an electrical fire and personal injury.

Battery Hazards

Storage batteries are based on chemical reactions and can deliver dangerous amounts of current. If a short circuit situation occurs in the wiring from the batteries, a fire can result. In order to avoid this threat, a properly sized fuse or circuit breaker is required in the lines connecting the system to the storage batteries.

PROCEDURE 10 – ADVANCED PV SYSTEMS

Solar

Before the photovoltaic system can generate usable AC power for residential use, several component systems must first be prepared, wired, and connected. In this lab, you will first prepare an adequate battery storage system, by connecting all four batteries in such a way as to provide power for a 12 Vdc system. The control panel will require a certain amount of rewiring at this point, so that the charge controller from the PV array is connected the charging circuitry. Once the batteries are protected from overcharging, the PV array can then be connected directly to the storage batteries.

Once a battery storage system is fully charged, the problem arises as to what to do with the PV array's additional output when it is operating at full potential. In these situations, a load diverter can be utilized in order to divert the additional output to some external load. Finally, in order to generate usable AC power for residential devices using 120 Vac 60 Hz, it becomes necessary to utilize an inverter.

Resources Needed:

- 12V, 12W Photovoltaic Solar Panels (2)
- Variable Intensity Lamp with variable height adjustment
- Marcraft Green Electron Generation Experiment Panel
- Hand-held Digital Multimeter
- Jumper Wires (12 AWG red, black, green)
- Battery Pack (consisting of 4 - 12V batteries)

CAUTION

Be sure NOT to connect the wires to the battery until everything else has been completed and you are instructed to do so in this procedure.

Preparing the Battery Storage System

1. The Marcraft PV array's support circuitry is designed to operate at a 12 Vdc level. With this in mind, which battery configuration from the previous procedure should be used as a storage system for this PV array?

2. Use four spade lug connectors to connect all four batteries in parallel with each other, as illustrated in Figure 3-39. This requires that you connect jumper wires between all the positive terminals, placing two wires in each spade lug connector except the first and last.

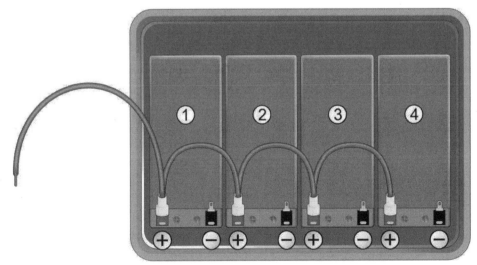

Figure 3-39: Connecting All the Batteries in Parallel

3. Attach an additional 24 AWG red wire to the last terminal so that it extends 24 inches outside the protective battery enclosure.

4. Crimp a fork lug connector to the external end of the wire.

5. Use the same process described in Step #2 to connect jumper wires between all four negative terminals on the batteries.

6. Attach an additional 24 AWG black wire to the last terminal so that it extends 24 inches outside the protective battery enclosure.

7. Crimp a fork lug connector to the external end of the wire.

8. Thread the external battery wires over the side of the case in positions that align with the exit openings in the side of the battery case's top cover. Fasten the top cover of the case in place with the external wires extending out of the case, as shown in Figure 3-40.

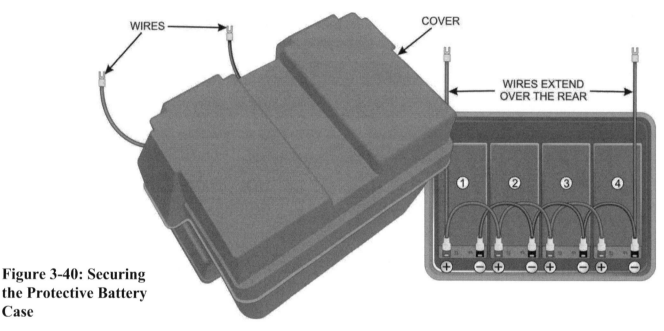

Figure 3-40: Securing the Protective Battery Case

9. Connect the black lead of the multimeter to the external negative battery lead and the red lead to the external positive battery lead. Record the total voltage level provided by this battery configuration on the following line:

_____

10. How does this value relate to the stated operating voltage level of the Marcraft PV array?

_____

┌─ **NOTE** ─────────┐
│ Do not connect the battery │
│ leads to the panel at this │
│ time. │
└──────────────────────┘

11. Remove the multimeter from the battery configuration.

12. Place the PV array's Disconnect Switch in the **OFF** position.

Rewiring the Control Panel for External Connections

Solar

The Marcraft Green Electron Generation experiment panel contains an open-circuit charging regulator that monitors the voltage level of the external circuitry and isolates it from the PV array when the external voltage reaches a predetermined level. This prevents the PV array from overcharging the external batteries. You will use the following steps to connect the PV array charge controller into the PV array charging circuitry.

1. Disconnect and remove the red and a black 12 AWG jumper wires from the two, left-most connection points on the top row of the PV Panel connection block, and the two right-most connection points on the bottom row of the PV Control Panel connection block.

2. Prepare a short red and black 12 AWG jumper wire to run between the top row left two terminals on the PV Panel connection block and the bottom row left-most two terminals of the PV Charge Controller connection block. Attach fork lug connectors to both ends of the two jumper wires.

3. Attach the red jumper wire to the top row left-most terminal on the PV Panel connection block and the bottom row left-most terminal of the PV Charge Controller connection block. (Be sure to leave the red jumper from the top row left-most and right-center points installed.) See Figure 3-41.

NOTE: This should produce a red-to-yellow connection with the PV Charge Controller wiring.

4. Attach the black jumper wire to the top row left-center terminal on the PV Panel connection block and the bottom row left-center terminal of the PV Charge Controller connection block. (Be sure to leave the black jumper from the top row left-center and right-most points installed.) See Figure 3-41.

5. Prepare a red and black 12 AWG wire to run between the bottom row right two connection points of the PV Charge Controller connection block and the bottom row right two connection points of the PV Control Panel connection block. Attach fork lug connectors to both ends of the two wires.

6. Attach the red wire between the bottom row right-most connection point of the PV Charge Controller connection block and the bottom row right-center connection point of the PV Control Panel connection block, as shown in Figure 3-41. (The color should match the PV Charge Controller wiring.)

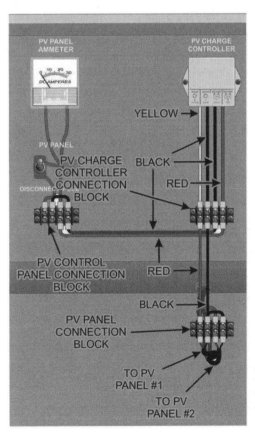

Figure 3-41: PV Charge Controller Wiring

7. Attach the black wire between the bottom row right-center connection point of the PV Charge Controller connection block and the bottom row right-most connection point of the PV Control Panel connection block, as shown in Figure 3-41. (The color should match the PV Charge Controller wiring.)

8. Turn on the multimeter and set it to the 20-volt DCV setting.

9. Attach the red and black meter leads to the left-most connection points (Solar-In Connections) on the upper row of the PV Charge Controller connection block so that they connect with a red to yellow and black to black color scheme.

10. Plug in the adjustable light source and position it approximately 1 foot away from the Solar panel, focused directly on the center of both PV panels.

11. Turn **On** all four lamp bulbs and observe the reading on the digital multimeter. Record the reading from the meter on the following line:

_____(Volts)

NOTE: *This is the maximum output of the PV array with the available light without a load being applied.*

12. Move the red and black meter leads to the right-most connection points on the lower row of the PV Charge Controller connection block so that they connect with the wires of the same color. Verify this connection against the one depicted in Figure 3-42.

Figure 3-42: Attaching the Meter for Testing

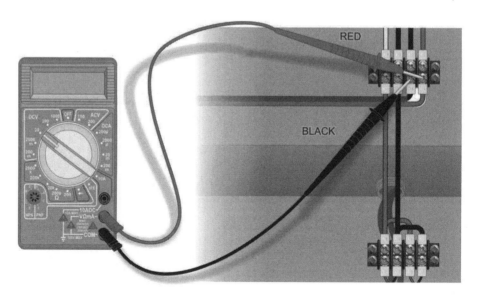

13. Observe the reading on the digital multimeter. Record the reading from the meter on the following line:

_____(Volts)

14. Remove the multimeter leads and turn **off** the four lamp bulbs.

Connecting the PV Array Directly to the Storage System

With the Solar Charge controller in place it is safe to connect the PV array to the storage batteries. This circuitry will prevent the PV array from overcharging the external batteries.

Grounding is another important part of any electrical installation. In this procedure you will be making **equipment ground** connections for the different pieces of support equipment. This type of ground is created to provide a common reference point for all of the electrical components and provide protection to personnel that might come into contact with the components in the event of a short circuit.

If the PV array installation were being made in the field, you would also need to create an **Earth Ground** connection to protect the system from environmental electrical discharges (lightning). This is done by creating a ground path between all the devices and a copper rod placed in the ground.

1. Prepare a 12 AWG green wire to go from the Diversion Load Controller's ground lug to the ground terminal of the Inverter, as shown in Figure 3-43.

Solar

Grounding

equipment ground

Earth Ground

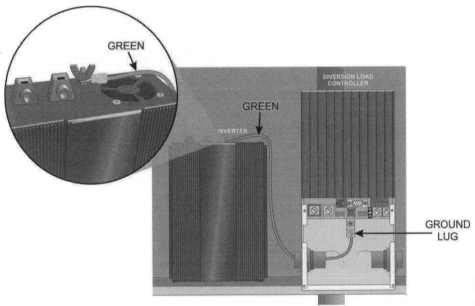

Figure 3-43: The PV Array's Complete Ground Circuit

2. Strip a 1/2" of insulation from one end of the wire and insert it into the ground lug of the Diversion Load Controller and tighten the screw on the lug to secure the green wire.

3. Thread the remaining end through the left conduit opening to the top of the Inverter and crimp a circle connector to it. Then, connect the connector to the ground terminal of the Inverter, as shown in Figure 3-43.

4. This provides the complete ground circuit for the Marcraft PV array charging system, as shown in Figure 3-43. Check with your instructor to make sure that your system is properly grounded before proceeding.

5. Obtain the battery storage system and position it so the external red and black leads can be attached to the PV Control Panel connection block.

> ## CAUTION
>
> Do NOT connect the wires to the battery or the terminal block at this point. IF THE WIRES ARE HOOKED-UP BACKWARDS YOU WILL DAMAGE THE PV ARRAY'S PANELS. (If you are uncertain of the polarity of the wires, simply measure the voltage direction with the multimeter).

6. The prepared external battery red and black wires will connect to the two left-most connection points on the bottom row of the PV Control Panel connection block, as illustrated in Figure 3-44. The color of each wire should match the wiring on the opposite side of the terminal block (red on the far left and black on the inside left). Do not connect the wires to the battery wires at this point.

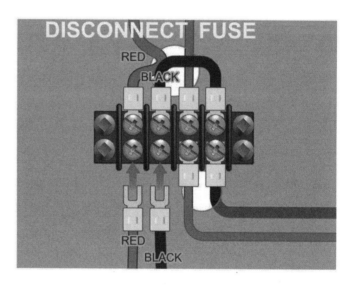

Figure 3-44: Preparing the PV Array's Battery Cables

7. Before attaching the PV array's wiring to the battery leads, make sure that:

- All Disconnect Switches on the panel are in the **OFF** position
- The fuse is removed from the Fuel Cell fuse holder.
- The Wind Turbine's Stop Switch is in the **STOP** position.

8. Attach the wires to the battery leads — Red wire to positive — Black wire to negative, as shown in Figure 3-45.

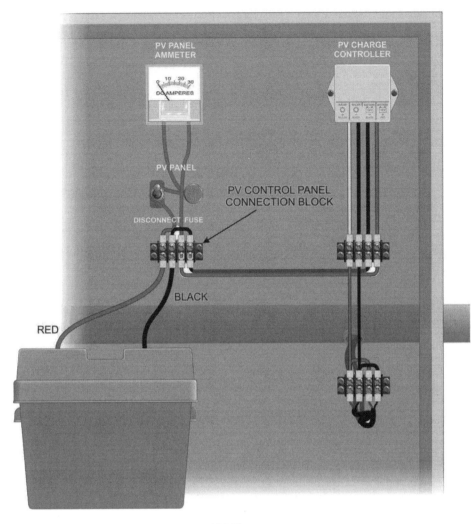

Figure 3-45: The PV Array's Battery Connections

9. Set the multimeter to measure up to 20 Vdc.

10. Connect the multimeter's leads to the PV array's charging leads at the lower left terminal of the PV Control Panel connection block, as illustrated in Figure 3-46.

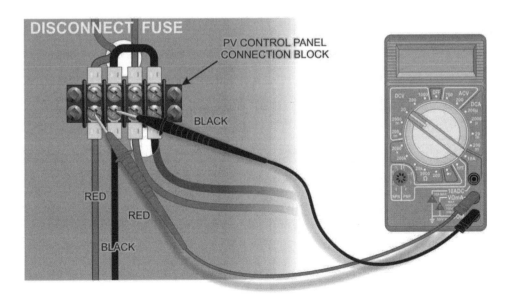

Figure 3-46: Monitoring the PV Array's Charging Voltage

11. On the following line, record the voltage level being measured with no input from the PV array:

(The PV Panel Disconnect Switch prevents current from the PV array from flowing into the charging system so this reading represents the current battery voltage)

Battery Voltage:

_____

12. Move the PV Array's Disconnect Switch to the **ON** position.

13. Turn **ON** the four lamp bulbs while observing the PV array's ammeter and the hand-held multimeter. Record both values on the following lines:

Voltage (Multimeter reading): _____

Current (Ammeter reading): _____

NOTE: If the multimeter does not produce a reading when the PV array is connected to a battery and the switch is closed, check the following items:

- *Verify all switch settings.*

- *Check all wiring between the PV array's output and the battery bank.*

- *Check to make sure there are no electrical short circuits in the system.*

- *Check the output of the PV Charge Controller to make sure it is passing the output from the PV array to the charging circuitry—this will not occur if the battery voltage is at (or above) the rated cut out voltage of the controller.*

14. Turn the four lamp bulbs **OFF**.

15. Move the PV array's Disconnect Switch to the **OFF** position.

16. Turn off the multimeter and remove the multimeter leads from the two left-most terminals on the bottom row of the PV Control Panel connection block.

17. Disconnect the battery by removing the red and black wires from the left-most terminals on the bottom row of the PV Control Panel connection block and set them aside.

External Voltage Regulator/Load Diverter Operation

diversion style regulator

Load Diverter

The Marcraft Green Electron Generation panel also includes a **diversion style regulator** (also known as a **Load Diverter**) that can be used to control the charging of the storage battery system. With the external load diverter controlling the charging system, the PV array will continue to produce output from light because the load diverter redirects the power to an external load such as a water heater. This allows the system to use the full output of the PV array even when the battery storage system is full. On the Marcraft training panel, a red 12 Vdc light represents this load. When the batteries are fully charged, the load diverter will redirect the generated power to the light.

Connecting the Load Diverter/Regulator

Solar

1. Obtain the Load Diverter's Technical Specifications documentation. The Load Diverter can be configured to operate in three distinct modes—Solar Battery Charger, Load Controller, or Diversion Load Controller. You will be configuring the Load Diverter/Regulator as a "Diversion Charge Controller". Make certain to obtain the appropriate configuration information from the documentation (Sections 6.0 - 6.5). Locate and record the following information to set up the Diverter as a Diversion Charge Controller on the lines provided:

   a. DIP Switch Settings

   For Control Mode – SW 1 - Load: _____

   For System Voltage – SW 2, 3 - Auto Select: _____

   For Diversion Charge – SW 4,5,6 - Battery Type 3 */ 14.5V Equalization Voltage: _____

   For Select Diversion Mode – SW 7 - Diversion: _____

   For Battery Equalization – SW 8 - Auto: _____

   b. Battery State of Charge Indicator Lights

   Red = On: _____

   Yellow/Red = On: _____

   Yellow = On: _____

   Green/Yellow = On: _____

   Green = On: _____

   c. Fault and Alarm Lights

   Red/Green – Yellow: _____

   Red/Yellow – Green: _____

   No LEDs lit: _____

> **NOTE**
>
> *The batteries supplied with the GT-1500 system are Sealed Lead Acid Batteries that cycle from 14.4 to 15.0 volts.

2. If not already done, set the Load Diverter's DIP switches to match the settings specified in Step 1a.

3. Prepare a red and a black 12 AWG wire long enough to reach from the PV Control Panel connection block terminal to the positive and negative input terminals in the Diversion Load Controller's connection bay.

> **CAUTION**
>
> Do NOT connect the wires to the Diversion Load Controller or the terminal block at this point. IF THE WIRES ARE CONNECTED BACKWARDS YOU WILL DAMAGE THE PV PANELS OR ITS SUPPORT CIRCUITRY.

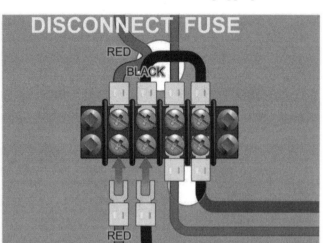

**Figure 3-47:
Preparing the PV
Array/Load Diverter
Connection Cables**

4. Crimp appropriate sized fork lug connectors to the red and black wires and secure them to the two, left most connection points on the bottom row of the PV Control Panel connection block as illustrated in Figure 3-47. The color of each wire should match the wiring on the opposite side of the terminal block (red on the far left and black on the inside left).

5. Route the red and black wires into the Diversion Load Controller's connection bay (through the conduit opening in the right side of the housing).

6. Insert the red wire into the Diversion Load Controller's positive lug and tighten the screw down connector until the connection is secure.

7. Insert the black wire into the negative lug and tighten the screw down connector until the connection is secure. Figure 3-48 shows the connections between the PV Control Panel connection block and the Diversion Load Controller.

8. Prepare a red and black 12 AWG wire long enough to reach from the Diversion Load Controller's positive and negative lugs to the Battery connection block.

9. Crimp appropriate sized fork lug connectors to the ends of the red and black wires. Secure one end of each to the two lower left Battery connection block terminals. (Red on the bottom, black immediately above that.)

10. Route the red and black wires into the Diversion Load Controller's connection bay (through the conduit opening in the right side of the housing).

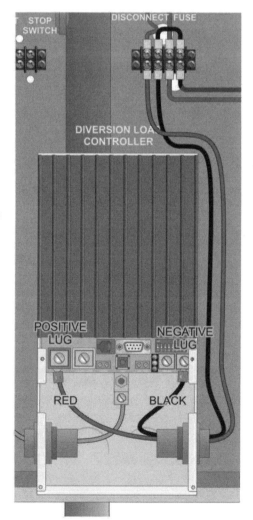

**Figure 3-48: The PV
Array/Load Diverter
Connections**

11. Loosen the positive screw down terminal and insert the red wire into the Diversion Load Controller's positive lug. Then tighten the screw down connector until both wires are securely in the lug, as shown in Figure 3-49.

12. Attach the red and black wires coming from the battery case to the lower right terminals of the Battery connection block (red wire to red wire and black wire to black wire).

13. Attach two 12 AWG wires from the Load Diverter's Sense lugs to the positive and negative lugs combined with the external battery wires and the PV Panel wires, as illustrated in Figure 3-50.

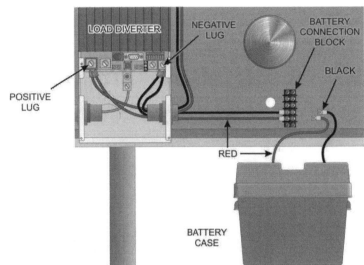

Figure 3-49: The PV Panel's Load Diverter Battery Connections

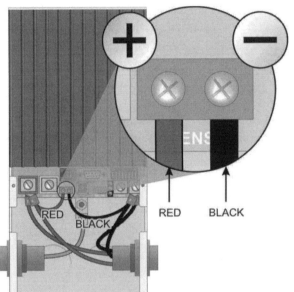

Figure 3-50: The Load Diverter Sensing Connections

14. Prepare a red and black 12 AWG wire long enough to reach from the Diversion Load Controller terminal connectors to the Diverter Load light on the back side of the panel.

15. Crimp appropriate sized ring connectors to one end of the red and black wires.

16. Attach the red wire ring connector to the plus (+) terminal of the Diverter Load Light and attach the black wire ring connector to the negative (-) terminal of the Diverter Load Light, as shown in Figure 3-51.

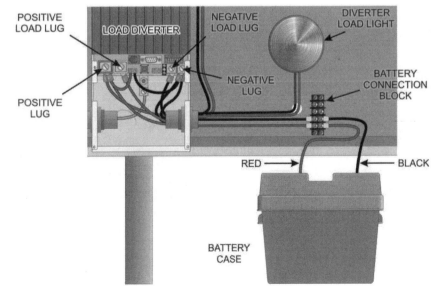

Figure 3-51: Battery Connections

17. Route the red and black wires through the hole at the Battery Connection Strip from the backside of the Panel and into the Diversion Load Controller, as shown in Figure 3-51.

18. Strip 1/2" of insulation from the ends of the red and black wires and insert the red wire into the POSITIVE LOAD lug and the black wire into the NEGATIVE LOAD lug, as shown in Figure 3-51.

19. Loosen the negative screw down terminal and insert the black wire into the neutral lug and tighten the screw down connector until both wires are securely clamped in the lug, as shown in Figure 3-49.

20. Before attaching the Load Diverter's wiring to the battery leads, make sure that:

    • All Disconnect Switches on the panel are in the **OFF** position

    • The Stop Switch is in the **STOP** or shorted position

    • The fuse has been removed from the Fuel Cell fuse holder

21. Turn on the multimeter and set it to 20 Vdc.

22. Connect the multimeter leads to the PV array's charging leads at the PV Control Panel connection block.

23. Record the voltage level being measured with no input from the PV array on the following line. This reading represents the current battery voltage:

    Initial Battery Voltage: _____

24. Move the PV array's Disconnect Switch to the **ON** position.

25. Turn all four lamps **ON** and observe the measurement on the PV array's ammeter and the multimeter display. Record both values on the following lines:

    Voltage (Multimeter reading) _____

    Current (Ammeter reading) _____

26. Continue charging the batteries for 5 minutes. On the following lines, record the voltage and current levels from the meters:

    Voltage Point (Multimeter reading) _____

    Current Flow (Ammeter reading) _____

CAUTION

Do NOT apply a short circuit across the batteries as THIS WILL CAUSE AN UNSAFE OVERLOAD CONDITION THAT MAY DAMAGE THE BATTERIES, START A FIRE, OR CAUSE THE BATTERIES TO EXPLODE.

27. Turn the 4 lamp bulbs **OFF** and calculate the amount of time it would take for the solar panels to charge the battery pack to the point where charging stops and the load light turns on:

    Time: _____

28. Move the PV array's Disconnect Switch to the **OFF** position.

Generating AC Output

Solar

The Marcraft Green Electron Generation panel includes an Off-Grid type inverter for generating power to run residential AC devices. This inverter accepts direct current input and produces a 120 Vac, 60 Hz (**Hertz** or *cycles per second*) output. The conversion occurs in two steps. First the incoming DC battery voltage is converted into a high DC voltage using high-frequency **pulse width modulation** (**PWM**) switching techniques. The high voltage signal is then applied to another PWM circuit to produce the 120 Vac, 60 Hz output voltage.

Hertz

pulse width modulation (PWM)

amp/hour (AH)

The inverter can continue to produce this output as long as the input voltage stays between 10.5 Vdc and 16.5 Vdc. The length of time different batteries can apply this level of power to the inverter depends on it **amp/hour** (**AH**) rating and the current load placed upon it. The battery industry uses 20 hours and 80°F as the benchmarks for rating batteries. This rating also indicates that the output of the battery is only useful until it falls off to 87.5% of its stated value (10.5V for a 12 Vdc system such as this trainer).

When two or more batteries are connected in parallel, as they are in this procedure, their voltages remain the same but their current capacities add together. Therefore, the AH rating for the battery pack, is equal to the sum of all the batteries in the pack added together.

1. Obtain the Inverter's documentation—locate and record the following information on the lines provided:

    Model Number: _____

    Input Voltage Range: _____

    Output Voltage: _____

    Low Input Voltage Shut Down: _____

    High Input Voltage Shut Down: _____

2. Using the AH rating for the batteries being used in your trainer, calculate and record the AH rating being applied to the inverter (when the batteries are charged within their stated operational range) on the following lines:

    Stated AH rating of a single battery: _____

    Total AH rating: _____

3. Prepare a red and a black 12 AWG wire long enough to reach from the inverter's positive and negative terminals to the positive and negative input terminals in the Diversion Load Controller's connection bay.

4. Plug in the red and black wires and secure them in the inverter's positive and negative connection terminals, as illustrated in Figure 3-52.

5. Route the red and black wires into the Diversion Load Controller's connection bay (through the connector in the side of the housing).

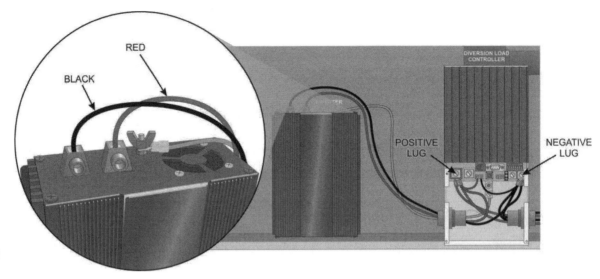

Figure 3-52: Inverter Connections

6. Loosen the positive screw down terminal and insert the red wire into the Diversion Load Controller's positive lug. Then tighten the screw down connector until all three wires are securely fastened in the lug.

7. Loosen the negative screw down terminal and insert the black wire into the neutral lug and then tighten the terminal screw until all three wires are securely fastened in the lug.

8. Record the voltage level being measured with no input from the Solar Panels and represents the current battery voltage on the following line:

   Battery Voltage: _____

9. Plug a 120 Vac, 4 Watt night light in the inverter's AC output connector and turn the lamp **On**.

10. Turn the Inverter **On** by pressing the rocker switch on its front panel.

11. The voltage displayed on the multimeter should steadily decrease as time increases. Continue to monitor the voltage for 10 minutes and record the meter reading on the following line:

    After 10 Minutes: _____

12. Calculate the amount of voltage that was lost during the time the inverter was on and record it on the following line:

    Amount of Voltage Lost: _____

13. Move the PV array's Disconnect Switch to the **ON** position.

14. Slowly turn **On** the 4 lamp bulbs and monitor the ammeter and multimeter for 10 minutes. Record the multimeter reading on the following line:

    After 10 Minutes of Charging: _____

15. Calculate the amount of voltage gain obtained during the time the Solar Panels were charging and record it on the following line:

    Amount of Gain/Charging: _____

16. Using the above information, what is the Gain/Hour?

Gain/Hour: _____

17. If our current voltage after charging the Solar Panels is 12.23V, how much voltage is needed to reach the rated diversion voltage?

Needed Voltage for Diversion Voltage: _____

18. Based on the above information, how long will it take for the Solar Panels to charge the battery pack to full charge while at the same time the Inverter is operating?

Time to Fully Charge the Battery Pack: _____

19. Turn **Off** the 120 Vac, 4 Watt night light plugged into the Inverter and turn **Off** the Inverter.

20. Turn **Off** the 4 lamp light bulbs and move the PV Panel Disconnect Switch to the **OFF** position.

Solar

Disassembly

After your instructor has reviewed your results of Procedures 9 and 10, the following steps will guide you through the removal of the wiring and wind turbine in preparation for the next group to perform the procedures. During the process of removing the wiring, label each set or group of wires to enable the next group to use the same wiring setups.

1. Remove the multimeter leads and turn the multimeter **Off**.

2. Remove the External Battery wires from the positive (+) and negative (-) lugs in the Diversion Load Controller.

3. Remove the wires from the 4 batteries in the battery pack.

4. Remove the red, black, and green wires from the Inverter to the Diversion Load Controller.

5. Remove the red, black, and green wires from the External Diverted Load Light and the Diversion Load Controller.

6. Remove the red and black wires from the bottom row left two connection points on the PV Control Panel connection block and the Diversion Load Controller.

7. Remove the red and black 12 AWG Sense wires from the Diversion Load Controller.

8. Remove the red and black wires from the bottom row right two connection points on the PV Control Panel connection block and the bottom row right two connection points of the PV Charge Controller connection block.

9. Remove the red and black wires from the bottom row left two connection points on the PV Charge Controller connection block and the top row left two connection points of the PV Panel connection block.

10. Remove the red and black jumper wires from the top row of the PV Panel connection block.

11. Remove the black jumper wire from the left-inside and right-most connection points on the PV Control Panel connection block.

12. Remove the red jumper wire from the left-most connection point on the top row of the PV Control Panel connection block and the bottom terminal of the PV Panel Disconnect Switch.

13. Remove the red jumper wire from the top row right-inside connection point on the PV Control Panel connection block to the plus (+) terminal of the PV Panel ammeter.

14. Remove the red jumper wire from the top terminal of the PV Panel Disconnect Switch to the bottom terminal of the PV Panel fuse.

15. Remove the red jumper wire from the minus (-) terminal of the PV Panel ammeter to the top terminal of the PV Panel fuse.

16. Remove the red jumper wire from the minus (-) terminal of the PV Panel ammeter to the top terminal of the PV Panel fuse.

17. Remove the 4 wires from the 2 Solar Panels to the bottom row 4 connection points on the PV Panel connection block.

18. Remove the 2 Solar Panels from the Panel Support Rails and store away.

19. Remove and disassemble the PV Panel Support Frame and store the frame members away.

20. Remove the PV Panel mounting pipe and clamps from the Experiment Panel frame and store them away.

21. Double check to see that all Fuses have been replaced, all Disconnect Switches are in the **OFF** position, and the Stop Switch is in the **OFF** position.

22. Replace the Diversion Load Controller cover.

23. This concludes the hands-on lab procedure for "Off-Grid Photovoltaic Power Systems". Have your instructor review your results before moving on to the next procedure.

Procedure 10 Questions

1. What conditions can cause a PV Charge Controller to produce a 0-volt output? (Provide two answers.)

2. Why should the voltage produced by the PV array be higher than the voltage displayed by the battery?

3. What are the consequences of connecting the PV array's power leads incorrectly to the battery bank?

4. Using the information about the batteries that make up your battery bank, what current output level should it take to reduce the battery voltage to 10.5 Vdc in 20 hours?

5. In an actual PV array installation would both types of charge controller be needed for safe operation of the system?

PROCEDURE 11 – SOLAR POWER RESEARCH

Solar

The scholarly mind must be prepared to conduct research on any subject of interest. To do so effectively requires a specific set of skills, which can be developed if or when necessary. The ability to research a given subject in today's scholastic environment has been aided by the availability of many information sources. Traditional avenues of research are still with us, such as library card files, books, newspapers, and magazine microfilms. However, the inclusion of library terminals and home computers has placed the Internet browser at the forefront of current researching tools. In addition, data delivery services such as electronic mail, file transfers, Internet group memberships, interactive collaborations, and multimedia displays can help the student to navigate the Internet, without getting bogged down. Although helping to reduce the complexity, data services employ a number of Internet protocols with which the student is ultimately responsible for using.

The sheer quantity of information available on the Internet makes it necessary to avoid the unwanted exposure to information that does not fit the student's search criteria. The modern scholar is best served by avoiding time-wasting searches through mountains of available data, and locating any relevant information quickly. In order to effectively utilize the time spent researching solar power, making effective use of an Internet search engine is critical regardless of which service is being utilized. Certain advanced methods of searching will zero-in on the desired information quickly, regardless of which search engine is being used.

To locate documents containing an exact phrase, type the phrase, surrounded by quotation marks, into the search field. For example, by typing *"solar panels"* (with the quotation marks) will return documents that contain the phrase *solar panels*, but not Web pages that contain only *solar* or *panels*. To locate documents containing these words, but not necessarily together, type the words separated by the Boolean operator *AND* in all caps. For example, typing *solar AND panels* (without the quotation marks) will return Web pages that contain *solar*, *panels*, and *solar panels*.

To locate documents containing either one word or the other, type the words separated by the Boolean operator *OR* in all caps. For example, typing *solar OR panels* (without the quotation marks) will return documents that contain *solar* or *panels*, or both.

Keep in mind that certain words can be deliberately excluded from a search, as well. For example, to exclude a word from the search, type the word to be excluded into the search field, preceded by the Boolean operator *NOT* in all caps. Using this approach, typing *solar NOT panels* (without the quotation marks) will return only documents that do contain the word *solar*, and do not contain the word *panels*. To zero in on documents that contain two terms separated by between 10 to 25 words, type the two terms separated by the Boolean operator *NEAR*, in all caps, into the search field. If the search expression is lengthy or complicated, use parentheses to separate the different parts. For example, typing *solar OR panels NOT (selenium OR crystal)* will get you entries that have the words *solar*, or *panels*, or both, but do not have the words *selenium* or *crystal*.

The extraordinary volatility of Internet websites makes it important for students to quickly gather any useful research information that they uncover, including the copying and storing of any related text and graphics data. The current availability of relevant information does not guarantee its future status at the source Internet site. In addition, certain Internet sites protect or format their information in such a way as to prevent it from being copied. This is often the situation encountered on product vendor websites containing proprietary information. In these situations, it often becomes necessary for the researcher to type and save the relevant text using a word processor. When pictures and illustrations cannot be copied directly, third-party graphics tools can be used to capture, and convert them into usable picture formats.

The use of traditional researching formats is more likely to provide information that has already gone through a certain amount of verification by its publishers. This is not necessarily true with Internet information, which can be posted by anyone, for a variety of reasons. Therefore, Internet-based information you choose to use must be verified for correctness and integrity. This does not mean, however, that information you gather from an Internet site, a newspaper, or a magazine/book article is completely accurate or true either. When supported from a variety of sources, the veracity of any information becomes more likely!

Resources Needed:

- Books
- Newspapers
- Magazines
- Computer with Internet access and graphic capture software

Solar power strategies and components are vital to the creation of alternative energy resources, so your beginning research should be concerned with identifying those strategies and components, while learning how they augment the production of alternative energies.

1. Examine the following list of solar power strategies. The Alternative Energy technician will need to be familiar with the categories mentioned here.

- Solar cell types
- Solar cell connections
- Solar cell power generation capabilities
- Excess energy management

2. Use Tables 3-2 through 3-5 to organize the specified details about the solar power strategies listed. For each item, try to locate at least two information sources.

Table 3-2: Solar Cell Types

TYPE	DESCRIPTION	USE	DRAWBACKS	ADVANTAGES	COST

Table 3-3: Solar Cell Connections

STRATEGY	DESCRIPTION	IMPORTANCE

Table 3-4: Solar Cell Power Generation Capabilities

PRODUCT MODEL	CELL TYPE	CELL USE	CELL MATRIX	MODULE DIMENSION	WT	MAX PWR STC	SYS	FIRM

Table 3-5: Solar Cell Excess Energy Management

TYPE	DESCRIPTION	POLICY	ANALYSIS

The Alternative Energy technician should also be familiar with the components that make up a solar powered system. This is because energy costs and production constraints make the construction of solar cells systems increasingly imperative.

To make your remaining research time more productive, gather information about light concentration strategies in the product areas listed below. This type of research will be of benefit for checking out ideas for a solar power installation, including its size, layout, and the particular requirements of the local and national governing agencies. Information gathered here will help when considering and comparing specific solar cell power components and equipment, their system capabilities, available vendors, and estimated costs.

3. Examine the following list. It identifies light concentration components and strategies with which an Alternative Energy technician will most likely be working.

- Mirrors
- Fresnel (Magnifying) Lenses

4. Use Tables 3-6 and 3-7 to organize the specified details about the solar power concentrating components and schemes listed. For each item, try to locate at least two information sources.

Table 3-6: Mirror Components Used for Concentrating Solar Power

COMPONENT	DESCRIPTION	ANALYSIS	CONCLUSION

Table 3-7: Fresnel (Magnifying) Lenses Used for Light Concentration

PRODUCT	FOCAL LENGTH	PITCH	APPERATURE	MATERIAL	SIZE	THICKNESS	MANUFACTURER

PMMA = Polymethylmethacrylate

5. Examine the following list. It identifies raw materials used for light concentration components and the disposal strategies with which an Alternative Energy technician will most likely be working.

- Selenium
- Silicon
- Boron
- Phosphorous
- Palladium
- Silver
- Nickel

- Copper
- Titanium
- Ethylene vinyl acetate
- Mylar
- Tedlar
- Glass
- Plastic

6. Use Table 3-8 to organize the specified details about the raw materials listed below used for light concentration components. Use Table 3-9 to organize details about related disposal strategies. For each item, try to locate at least two information sources.

Table 3-8: Raw Materials Used For Light Concentration Components

MATERIAL	DESCRIPTION	PROCESS	USE

Table 3-9: Raw Material Disposal Strategies For Solar Power Components

MATERIAL	DESCRIPTION	TREATMENT	DISPOSAL

Residential or rural farm clients seeking to install their solar cell power generating systems usually require some practical information and advice on addressing the existing barriers to home and farm solar power projects. For example, they need to understand when and how to approach their local boards and state agencies in order to secure the necessary permits. It may be necessary for them to build support for their proposed installations. They need to understand how to work successfully with their installer and with their local utilities in order to interconnect their solar cell power systems.

Applicable Regulations

Various local, state, or federal regulating bodies have jurisdiction over residential alternative energy sources. A completed solar cell power generation installation must satisfy specific requirements; otherwise, it testifies to the ignorance of the Residential Alternative Energy technicians who installed it.

Local

Local coding authorities are often very sensitive about being ignored. This is because Residential Alternative Energy technicians usually make a great effort to strictly adhere to the federal and state regulations with which they are most familiar. This adherence is often good enough to result in the installation of a locally compliant solar cell power generating system, but not always. Although local codes usually involve local commercial generating structures rather than residential installations, they must also be taken into account before the installation begins! City or county regulations have increased with the advent of residential power generating equipment, especially in communities where local governments directly control their own power production facilities. These arrangements may result in the subsequent prosecution for chronic violators of local power generating regulations.

Local power generating code information can be obtained from local planning commissions or coding departments. These bodies are usually responsible for controlling the governmental utility development in the local community, including the power planning commission. Specific information about residential alternative energy installations and/or equipment requirements not addressed by state or federal codes can be gathered by contacting your local planning commission, or the city/county agencies responsible for code enforcement. For example, environmental conditions could place unique restrictions on the local use of certain solar power generating equipment.

7. Examine the following list. It identifies specific areas of concern regarding solar cell power generating installations and/or equipment that may be strictly controlled by your local codes.

    - Local solar panel legislation
    - Local solar data

8. Use Table 3-10 to organize the specified details about any local activity regarding the use of solar cell power generation installations and/or strategies. Helpful information may be obtained at *http://www.solaramericacities.gov/*. Use Table 3-11 to organize the specified details of local solar data, and how much potential this is for generating solar power. For solar data calculations, visit: *http://welsh.wunderground.com/calculators/solar.html*.

Table 3-10: Local Solar Cell Power Generation Activity

CITY/COUNTY	MAYOR	DATE	TITLE	GOAL

Table 3-11: Local Solar Data for 1,000 Square Feet of Panel Coverage

INSTALLED LOCATION	LATITUDE	LONGITUDE	PANEL TYPE	PANEL SIZE	PANEL EFFICIENCY	NUMBER OF PANELS	SUN ENERGY KWATTS

State

State-sponsored regulations are aimed at appropriate use of state resources in the development of alternative energy sources. These guidelines normally restrict the use of state resources to legitimate government or college business, support for various departmental mandates, or carrying out institutional missions. Energy generating sources that are used to power state governmental or university offices must comply with use requirements applying to any equipment to which they connect.

State governmental jurisdictions limit the legitimate uses of their energy resources to official legislative and administrative functions. Legal interagency agreements dictate that such resources must not be used for personal, commercial, or for-profit purposes without some form of official written approval.

It's important to understand what the legitimate usage of state resources in the production of alternative energy in your state is. This information can be located by browsing your state government's web pages.

9. Examine the following list. It identifies specific areas of concern regarding solar power installations and/or equipment that may be strictly controlled by your state codes.

    *   State solar power legislation

    *   State solar data

10. Use Table 3-12 to organize the specified details about any state legislation regarding the development and use of solar cell installations and/or equipment. Use Table 3-13 to organize the specified details of state-based solar radiation data. A helpful source of information might be located at:
    http://www.genproenergy.com/peak_sun_data.html.

Table 3-12: State Solar Cell Installation Legislation

STATE	LEGISLATION/CODE	DATE	TITLE	DETAILS

Table 3-13: State Solar Radiation Collector Data in kWh/m^2/Day (1961 to 1990 Averages)

CITY/ STATE	COLLECTOR TYPE	DATA	JAN	FEB	MAR	APR	MAY	JUN	JUL	AUG	SEP	OCT	NOV	DEC

Federal

Alternative energy manufacturers and consumers around the world recognize certain research facilities and/or governmental agencies that have been mandated to determine the suitability of solar power as a viable energy resource. As various products have recently emerged, the recognition of suitable guidelines has helped to achieve some control over the technical development explosion in this field.

The federal organizations listed here can be consulted regarding the viability of various products relating to the use of solar power as an alternative energy resource. The Residential Alternative Energy technician can depend on the information published by these organizations to provide guidance in the selection of appropriate equipment for a particular installation.

Energy and Environmental Research Center (EERC)

The Energy and Environmental Research Center (EERC) is a research facility located in the southeast corner of the University of North Dakota (UND) in Grand Forks. It is recognized as one of the world's leading developers of cleaner, more efficient energy and environmental technologies to protect and clean our air, water, and soil. Originally founded in 1951 as the "U.S. Bureau of Mines - Robertson Lignite Research Laboratory," it became a federal energy technology center under the United States Department of Energy in 1977, and became known as the Energy and Environmental Research Center in 1989.

The EERC is a high-tech, nonprofit branch of UND. Yet, it operates like a business; conducts research, development, demonstration, and commercialization activities dedicated to moving promising technologies out of the laboratory and into the commercial marketplace. The EERC provides practical, cost-effective solutions to today's most critical energy and environmental issues and challenges. Its research portfolio consists of a wide array of strategic energy and environmental solutions, including clean coal technologies, CO_2 sequestration, energy and water sustainability, hydrogen technologies, air toxics and fine particulate, mercury measurement and control, alternative fuels, wind energy, biomass, water management, flood prevention, global climate change, waste utilization, energy-efficient technologies, and contaminant cleanup.

The EERC's business partners range in size from large multinational corporations to regional utilities to small local businesses. Its government partners include not only federal agencies such as the U.S. Department of Energy, the U.S. Environmental Protection Agency, the U.S. Department of Defense, and the U.S. Department of Agriculture, but also state and local government entities.

U.S. Department of Energy (DOE)

The Department of Energy's overarching mission is to advance the national, economic, and energy security of the United States. In order to do this, it promotes scientific and technological innovation, while working to ensure the environmental cleanup of the national nuclear weapons complex. Strategic goals to achieve the mission are designed to deliver results along five strategic themes, including:

- Energy security. The DOE's philosophy is that America's energy security should be achieved through the production of reliable, clean, and affordable energy.

- Nuclear security. Ensuring America's nuclear security is also a critical component of DOE's working agenda.

- Scientific discovery and innovation. The DOE works to strengthen scientific discovery, economic competitiveness, and to improve the quality of life in the United States through innovations in science and technology.

- Environmental responsibility. The DOE helps to protect the environment by providing a responsible resolution to the environmental legacy of nuclear weapons production.

- Management excellence. The DOE believes in enabling its mission through sound management.

National Renewable Energy Laboratory (NREL)

The National Renewable Energy Laboratory (NREL) is the nation's primary laboratory for renewable energy, and energy efficiency research and development. NREL's mission and strategy are focused on advancing the U.S. Department of Energy's and our nation's energy goals. It began operating in 1977 as the Solar Energy Research Institute. In September of 1991, it was designated a national laboratory of the U.S. Department of Energy (DOE), and its name changed to NREL.

The laboratory's scientists and researchers support critical market objectives to accelerate research from scientific innovations to market-viable alternative energy solutions. The laboratory thereby directly contributes to our nation's goal for finding new renewable ways to power our homes, businesses, and cars. At the core of this strategic direction are NREL's research and technology development areas, including an understanding of renewable resources for energy, the conversion of these resources to renewable electricity and fuels, and ultimately to the use of renewable electricity and fuels in homes, commercial buildings, and vehicles.

11. Search the information pages of several federal governmental agencies and locate the applicable policies regarding the operation of solar power generating systems.

   - Federal solar cell power legislation

   - National solar data

12. Use Table 3-14 to organize the specified details about any federal legislation regarding the use of solar cell power installations and/or equipment. Use Table 3-15 to organize the specified details of federal solar data. Try to locate data from at least two differing seasonal periods for each selected location. A helpful source of information can be found at the World Radiation Data Centre at: *http://wrdc.mgo.rssi.ru/.*

Table 3-14: Federal Solar Cell Power Legislation

AGENCY	LEGISLATION/CODE	DATE	TITLE	DETAILS

Table 3-15: Federal Solar Radiation Data (Wh/m^2)

LOCATION	GHR	DNR	DHR	DATE	DATA

GHR = Global horizontal radiation in Wh/m^2

DNR = Direct Normal Radiation in Wh/m^2

DHR = Diffuse Horizontal Radiation in Wh/m^2

13. This concludes the hands-on lab procedure. Have your instructor review your results before moving on to the next procedure.

Procedure 11 Questions

1. During Internet research, what must be done to locate a document containing an exact phrase?

2. What is the nation's primary laboratory for renewable energy research and development?

3. Name the college with which the Energy and Environmental Research Center (EERC) is associated.

4. What does the acronym GHR stand for?

5. What is the role played by the glass substrate in a solar power system?

PROCEDURE 12 – PV SYSTEM DESIGN

Solar

Objectives:

- Determine appropriate technology options for a given scenario.
- Match PV panel output capabilities to a specified load.
- Determine equipment needed for this project.
- Calculate cost of implementing the design solution.

Resources Needed:

- Marcraft "*Generating Clean Electrons*" Text/Lab manual
- Internet connected computer or reference materials
- Completed Procedure # 11 – Solar Power Research
- Calculator
- Pencil and paper
- Library resources

ABOUT THE AUTHOR

Charles J. Brooks (A+, Network+, i-Net+, Server+, HTI+, MCP) is currently co-owner and vice president of Education Technologies Group Inc., as well as co-owner of eITPrep, LLP, an online training company. He is in charge of research and product development at both organizations. A former electronics instructor and technical writer with the National Education Corporation, Charles taught and wrote on post-secondary EET curriculum, including introductory electronics, transistor theory, linear integrated circuits, basic digital theory, industrial electronics, microprocessors, and computer peripherals. Charles has authored several books, including the first five editions of *A+ Certification Training Guide*, *The Complete Introductory Computer Course*, and *IBM PC Peripheral Troubleshooting & Repair*. He currently also writes about networking, residential technology integration and convergence.

DISCUSSION

Read the following scenario:

> You have been contracted by the B&O Railroad company to design a stand-alone power generation system that can be used to provide power for remote signaling and control boxes. The railroad wants to place these boxes along their tracks that run through many miles of undeveloped wilderness where there is no commercially available power to work with.
>
> The signaling and control boxes contain a variety of different sensing, decision processing and control circuits. It also contains three different colored lights that are used to communicate with train engineers and railroad workers concerning train traffic in the vicinity of the boxes. Figure 3-53 shows the block diagram of the railroad's signaling and control boxes.

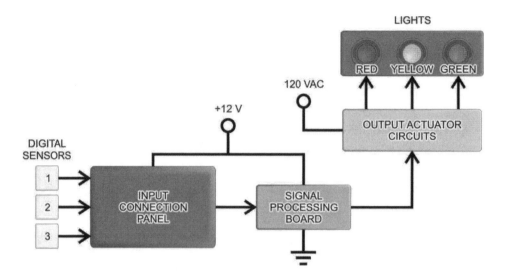

LIGHTS

Figure 3-53: The Components of the Railroad's Signaling and Control Box

The digital sensing and decision circuitry requires a 12 Vdc supply and will consume approximately 55 Watts of power on a continuous basis. The communication lights are all 750W bulbs that require 120 AC power and may have one, two or all three bulb illuminated at any time.

Your job is to design a power system to provide enough energy to meet the requirements of the railroad's signal and control box on a continuous operating basis.

Solar

Procedure

1. The railroad has contracted you to design the power supply for their remote signaling and control boxes. Under the scenario given in the discussion section, what technologies might you consider for this project? List three options on the following lines:

    _____

    _____

    _____

2. How much and what type of power is required to support the digital circuitry in the boxes?

    _____

3. How much and what type of power is required to support the signal light circuitry in the boxes?

    _____

4. How can you supply the system with power on a 7/24/365 basis?

   _____

5. Using the equipment from the hands-on procedures in this Lab Guide, determine how many PV panels would be required to supply the DC requirements of this project.

   _____

6. How can you supply the AC requirements of the project?

   _____

7. Will the Inverter module on the GT-1500 Clean Electron Generation Panel meet the requirements of the AC circuitry in the boxes? Explain your answer on the lines below:

   _____

   _____

   _____

8. Using the information from the Solar Research Lab you just completed (or from additional product research as required), locate an alternative non-grid tie inverter module that will supply the AC output requirements of this project.

   Model _____

9. What are the input requirements for the inverter you located and how many PV panels like the ones on the experiment panel be required to produce this much power?

   _____ (Amps)

   _____ (DC Volts)

   _____ (Panels)

10. How are the panels described in Question #9 configured?

    _____

11. What is the total physical size of the PV array if it is constructed using the type of PV panels on the experiment panel?

    _____

12. Did you (or can you) find a more efficient PV panel product to build this project with? If so, provide the information for it on the following lines:

_____

_____

_____

13. You will need to mount the PV array so that it can be oriented toward the sun. Did you locate a suitable mounting option for this size of array during your research? If not, find the equipment you will need and describe it, along with its price, on the following lines:

Model: _____   Cost = $: _____

14. Describe the wiring specifications you will to meet for this project.

_____

_____

_____

_____

15. List other components you will need to include in the design to provide a safe and efficient product.

_____

_____

_____

_____

16. If you are using 12 volt, deep-cycle, lead acid automobile batteries to create the battery storage pack (each rated for 600 cold cranking amps), how many batteries would be needed and in what configuration should they be wired for this project?

_____

_____

17. What is the raw cost of creating these power units considering all the components you will need to purchase for each?

Cost = $: _____

18. Using a copy of the block diagram of the railroad's system (presented at the beginning of this procedure), create a proposal document that you will present to the railroad for the project. Include all components, interconnection information and specification notes possible.

The following questions test your knowledge of the material presented in this chapter.

1. What is the purpose of a Stirling engine?

2. Define insolation.

3. What factors determine the amount of voltage developed across a solar cell?

4. Describe the differences between loads in both DC and AC circuits.

5. Which direction do roof-mounted PV panels usually face?

6. How do commercial solar farms track the position of the sun?

7. Define ampacity.

8. How should PV panels be connected to service devices requiring heavy DC current loads?

9. What are the benchmarks used by the battery industry for rating batteries?

10. List as many raw materials used in the production of light concentration components as you can.

11. What may happen when the wires to the diversion load controller are connected backwards?

12. What is the major concern when working with PV arrays featuring high current capabilities?

CHAPTER 4

Fuel Cells

OBJECTIVES

Upon completion of this chapter, you will be able to perform the following tasks:

1. Use electrolysis to generate hydrogen for fuel.

2. Connect a fuel cell for electrical generation.

3. Identify the major parts of the fuel cell.

4. Test the direct output of the fuel cell.

5. Adjust the output of the fuel cell by stacking.

6. Document fuel cell output in various configurations (serial vs. parallel).

7. Correlate power generation to hydrogen consumption (efficiency).

8. Configure, test and operate an off-grid fuel cell installation.

9. Connect fuel cells to protective/control devices.

10. Connect the fuel cell to monitoring devices.

11. Connect the fuel cell circuitry to rechargeable batteries.

12. Drive different DC loads with the fuel cell system.

13. Document battery charge/discharge rates.

14. Search for fuel cell power services.

15. Research various fuel cell power components and strategies.

16. Locate applicable fuel cell power regulations and legislation.

17. Given a scenario for a fuel cell application, determine the best options for meeting the specifications of the project.

18. Determine the Fuel Cell specifications required to meet the power requirements of the project.

19. Determine other equipment components required to complete the project as described.

20. Select components that will meet the specifications for each section of the project scenario.

21. Determine the physical size requirements for the Fuel Cells that can be used for the project.

Fuel Cells

INTRODUCTION

Fuel cells are electrochemical devices that use hydrogen and oxygen to produce electricity. In the process of converting these two elements into electricity, the fuel cell also produces heat and water. This makes fuel cells a very clean source of electrical energy. In addition, fuel cells tend to be portable units, which enables them to be used wherever they are needed. This has led to fuel cells being used to provide electrical power for buses and automobiles.

FUEL CELL OPERATION

The operation of the fuel cell is very similar to that of a battery. However, unlike a battery that is basically sealed closed, the chemical elements that create the electrical energy in a fuel cell do not run out. An external supply of hydrogen and oxygen is used to continually renew the fuel cell operations.

Figure 4-1 shows the operation of a typical fuel cell. The fuel cell consists of a membrane called the electrolyte that separates two electrode materials. The electrolyte is a thin membrane coated with a catalyst material that keeps the electrodes from interacting directly with each other. Collection plates back the electrodes and form the end of the cell and provides a path for the electrical energy to be extracted from the cell. An additional plate is added to each end to channel the hydrogen and oxygen gases to opposite sides of the cell.

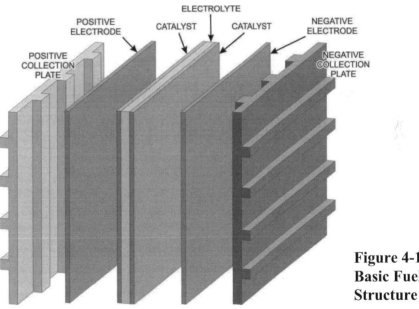

Figure 4-1: Basic Fuel Cell Structure

Hydrogen is introduced to the **anode** (negative electrode) on one side of the cell while oxygen (or air) is introduced to the **cathode** (positive electrode) on the other side of the cell. The catalyst material at the anode causes the hydrogen atom to give up its electron to become a free electron (a negatively charged particle). The hydrogen atom with the missing electron becomes a positively charged hydrogen ion. The catalyst material allows the positively charged ion to pass through the membrane to the cathode side of the cell but blocks the movement of the electron.

anode

cathode

The electrons separated from the hydrogen atoms (and their negative charges) accumulate on the cathode side of the cell while the positively charged hydrogen ions pile up on the anode side. The energy associated with these two items causes an electrical push to form on the cathode side of the cell and an electrical pull to be placed on the anode side.

The size of the charge difference between the two sides is referred to as **voltage (V)**. Voltage is an **electromotive force (EMF)** that places an electrical push and pull on the different sides of the cell. The amount of voltage (electrical push/pull) developed across the cell is determined by the type of materials used to build the fuel cell, the physical surface area of the fuel cell and the amount of hydrogen and oxygen applied to the cell.

Because the type of charge on each side of the fuel cell is always the same, the electrons are always being pushed in the same direction. Therefore, like batteries, fuel cells produce **direct current (DC)** electricity that always moves through the external circuit from the negative terminal to the positive terminal, as shown in Figure 4-2.

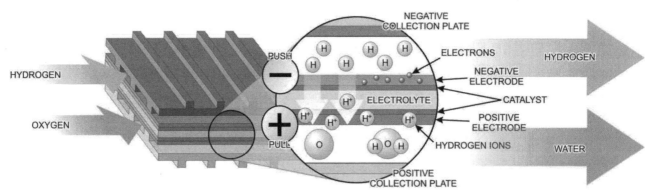

Figure 4-2: Basic Fuel Cell Operation

If an acceptable external pathway is provided for the movement of the electrons from the pushing end of the fuel cell to the pulling end, an electrical circuit is created. This concept is depicted in Figure 4-3. You can envision this as electrons hopping from one atom to the next to move around the circuit from the pushing end of the device (fuel cell) to the pulling end.

The electromotive force is applied to all of the atoms between the two ends of the conductors, which causes a flow (or current) of electrons to move through the circuit.

After traveling through the external circuit, the electron reaches the anode side of the cell where it recombines with one of the hydrogen ions. The reunited hydrogen atoms combine with oxygen atoms being introduced to the cathode side of the cell to produce H_2O (water), which is drained from the cell.

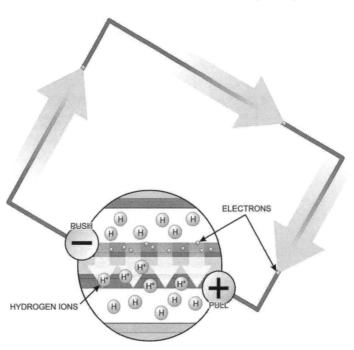

Figure 4-3: Electron Current Flow Using a Fuel Cell

Power

The power output of a fuel cell device varies with the load applied. Figure 4-4 shows a typical set of performance curves for the 11-cell fuel cell stack used on the Marcraft Clean Electron Generation panel. Notice how the power level for a given fuel cell changes with respect to the current being pulled from the device over a range of output voltages present at its output terminals.

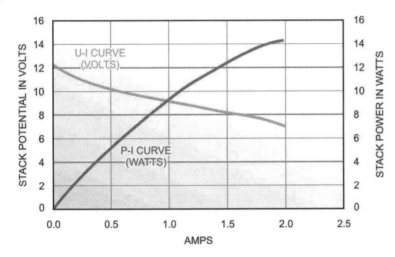

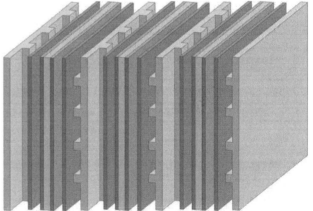

Figure 4-4: Fuel Cell Performance Curves

A single-cell fuel cell device may be capable of supplying enough power to operate a small, low power device such as a small hobby motor or a low-power LCD display. For higher power applications, multiple individual cells are connected together to form fuel cell stacks, as illustrated in Figure 4-5. Fuel cell stacks are created by placing multiple single fuel cells between the electrical collection plates. The electrical output of the individual cells are interconnected to form an internal series circuit. In this configuration the individual voltages of the cells add together to produce an output equal to the sum of the voltages generated by each cell. However, the current capabilities of the stack are limited to the capabilities of the least productive cell in the stack.

The external outputs of individual fuel cells or stacks can be combined in different serial and parallel configurations to provide different current, voltage or power requirements for a particular load. This provides much greater flexibility in meeting a particular load requirement than trying to do so with a single, fixed fuel cell stack. Figure 4-6 illustrates the advantage of using independent fuel cell stacks to provide particular load requirements.

Figure 4-5: Fuel Cell Stack

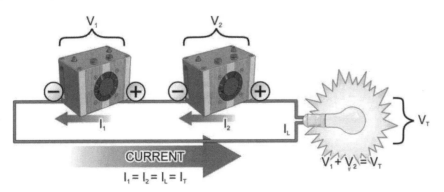

Figure 4-6: Configuring Fuel Cell Stacks

FUEL CELL TYPES

The fuel cell type described earlier represents a class of fuel cells that operate on a proton exchange basis (the hydrogen ion is made up simply of positively charged protons after losing its only electron). Because the exchange occurs through a elective membrane, fuel cells operating on this basis are more commonly referred to as PEM (proton exchange membrane) fuel cells. There are different versions of these fuel cells that employ different types of electrolyte membrane materials and may be driven by fuels other than pure hydrogen and oxygen.

Direct methanol fuel cells (**DMFCs**) employ a PEM membrane and operate in the same manner as described earlier. However, the DMFC is designed to use methanol (CH_3OH) as a fuel instead of hydrogen. The major drawback associated with DMFCs is that methanol is dangerous and corrosive to work with. They are also relatively inefficient in converting energy compared to other fuel cell types. Their main advantage is that the methanol fuel is stored and used in its liquid state.

Another technique used to build fuel cells is based on exchanging oxygen ions through a membrane. This class of fuel cells is referred to as **solid oxygen fuel cells** (**SOFC**). These fuel cells employ a membrane that is conductive to oxygen ions (instead of hydrogen ions) and allows them to migrate across the cell—while forcing the electron to pass through an external circuit.

These fuel cells have the advantage of being able to use several different fuel sources such as ethanol, methanol, natural gas, and gas derived from coal. On the other hand, these fuel cells operate at very high temperatures making them undesirable for some applications.

Alkaline fuel cells (**AFC**) employ an electrolyte of potassium hydroxide, also known as potash. These fuel cells provide excellent performance but are sensitive to the presence of carbon monoxide (CO). AFC fuel cells require a very high level of purity in their hydrogen and oxygen supplies.

Phosphoric acid fuel cell (**PAFC**) and **Molten carbonate fuel cell** (**MCFC**) types employ phosphoric acid and a molten mixture of alkali metal carbonates respectively to provide fuel cells capable of working with alternative fuel sources such as natural gas, biogas and coal gas, in addition to hydrogen and oxygen/air. PAFCs tend to be very inefficient compared to other fuel cell types, while MCFCs tend to have very high operating temperatures. Table 4-1 lists common fuel cell types and their electrolyte materials.

Direct methanol fuel cells (DMFCs)

solid oxygen fuel cells (SOFC)

Alkaline fuel cells (AFC)

Phosphoric acid fuel cell (PAFC)

Molten carbonate fuel cell (MCFC)

Table 4-1: Common Fuel Cell Types

FUEL CELL	ELECTROLYTE
Proton Exchange Membrane Fuel Cell (PEMFC)	Proton exchange membrane
Direct Methanol Fuel Cell (DMFC)	Proton exchange membrane
Solid Oxide Fuel Cell (SOFC)	Oxide ion conducting ceramic
Alkaline Fuel Cell (AFC)	Potassium hydroxide (KOH) solution
Phosphoric Acid Fuel Cell (PAFC)	Phosphoric Acid

Fuels

The basic fuel for driving fuel cell operation is hydrogen. Oxygen is also introduced as an oxidant (a substance that easily gains electrons in a chemical reaction). However, some fuel cell types can be operated from hydrocarbon and alcohol fuels and chlorine oxidants. Hydrocarbons used with other fuel cell types include:

- Natural gas (Methane)

- Biogas (gases produced from organic material in the absence of oxygen)

- Coal gas (Gaseous fuel made from coal)

- Diesel fuel (Fuel derived from petroleum and includes biodiesel and biomass)

- Methanol (CH_3OH – also known as wood alcohol or methyl alcohol)

- Hydrides (Negative hydrogen ions)

Table 4-2 describes the fuel types associated with common fuel cell types.

FUEL CELL	FUEL OXYDANT
Proton Exchange Membrane Fuel Cell (PEMFC)	H_2 O_2, *Air*
Direct Methanol Fuel Cell (DMFC)	CH_3OH O_2, *Air*
Solid Oxide Fuel Cell (SOFC)	Natural gas, biogas, coal gas, H_2 O_2, *Air*
Alkaline Fuel Cell (AFC)	H_2 O_2
Phosphoric Acid Fuel Cell (PAFC)	Natural gas, biogas, H_2 O_2, *Air*
Molten Carbonate Fuel Cell (MCFC)	Natural gas, biogas, coal gas, H_2 O_2, *Air*

Table 4-2: Common Fuel Cell Fuels

Heat Generation

Fuel cells are also classified by the amount of heat they generate (operating temperature). The process of generating free electrons and ions in the fuel cell creates large amounts of heat. The process of converting $2H_2O$ and O_2 into $2H_2O$ (Written as $2H_2 + O_2 \rightarrow 2H_2O$) produces large amounts of heat.

Low-end, low-power fuel cell types generally operate at temperatures below 40° C. These units typically produce up to 50 watts of power. Mid range, medium power fuel cell types produce between 100 Watts and 1 Megawatts (1 MW) and operate at temperatures between 80 and 300° C. High output, high temperature fuel cells operate at between 150 and 1100° C and produce between 10 MW and 100MW. Table 4-3 describes the operating temperature ranges of common fuel cell types.

Table 4-3: Common Fuel Cell Temperature Ranges

FUEL CELL	OPERATING TEMPERATURE
Proton Exchange Membrane Fuel Cell (PEMFC)	Room temperature to 80° C
Direct Methanol Fuel Cell (DMFC)	Room temperature to 130° C
Solid Oxide Fuel Cell (SOFC)	800 - 1000° C
Alkaline Fuel Cell (AFC)	Room temperature to 90° C
Phosphoric Acid Fuel Cell (PAFC)	160 - 220° C
Molten Carbonate Fuel Cell (MCFC)	620 - 660° C

ELECTROLYSIS

One method of generating hydrogen and oxygen to drive a PEM cell is through a process known as electrolysis. Electrolysis separates the elements of chemically bonded compounds from each other by passing an electric current through them. In the case of PEM fuel cells, we can break a water molecule (H_2O) into its base elements—hydrogen and oxygen—by passing a current through it.

Electrolyzer

Sodium Bicarbonate ($NaHCO_3$)

The Marcraft **Electrolyzer**, depicted in Figure 4-7, employs a distilled water and **Sodium Bicarbonate** (baking soda—**NaHCO₃**) electrolyte solution to conduct the electrolysis process. The Potassium Carbonate makes the water more conductive to carrying electrical current—distilled water is not a good conductor of electricity—however, dirty water or salt water is conductive.

NOTE

It is also possible to run the Marcraft electrolyzer on a distilled water and Potassium Carbonate (K_2CO_3) electrolyte solution. However, this solution presents a few potential safety concerns to deal with in the procedural portions of this chapter. These concerns are discussed in the "Safety Precautions" section later in this chapter.

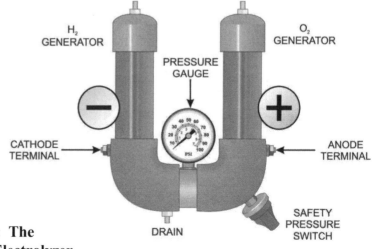

Figure 4-7: The Marcraft Electrolyzer

The solution is placed in the U-shaped vessel and a direct current is passed through the solution from the cathode (-) to the anode (+) connections. The anode and cathode connection terminals, which are made of stainless steel, are active participants in the electrolysis process and slowly get used up. Stainless steel is a relatively long lasting electrode material, however, the electrodes can also be made of iron, carbon, platinum and titanium.

Figure 4-8 shows the molecular relationships the make up baking soda (NaHCO$_3$). Each molecule consists of:

- One Sodium (Na) atom

- One Hydrogen (H) atom

- One Carbon (C) atom

- Three Oxygen (O) atoms

Using Potassium Carbonate (K$_2$CO$_3$) as the electrolyte gives a molecule that contains:

- Two Potassium (K) atoms

- One Carbon (C) atom

- Three Oxygen (O) atoms

As the current passes through the solution, water molecules are split into positively charged hydrogen ions (missing its electron) and negatively charged oxygen-hydrogen ions (called **hydroxide ions**). The positively charged hydrogen ions (H+) are attracted to the negative cathode terminal while the hydroxide (OH-) ions are attracted to the positive anode terminal, as shown in Figure 4-9. At the cathode terminal, the hydrogen ion picks up a free electron to return to a neutral charge condition (H). Then it bonds with another hydrogen molecule to form H$_2$, which is a gas. This gas bubbles to the surface of the solution from the cathode terminal.

NOTE

Be aware that technicians and engineers use different methods of describing current flow in circuits. Engineers use a method known as conventional current flow to describe the movement of positive charges through the circuit, while technicians employ electron current flow, which describes the movement of the electrons through the circuit.

In the previous paragraph, technicians describe the current flow as moving from the cathode to the anode of the electrolyzer. Engineers would describe it as the movement of current from the anode to the cathode. This can lead to some confusion when reading documentation if you are not aware of the background of the writer.

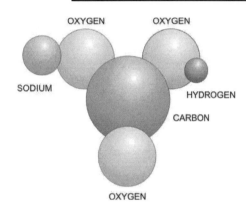

**Figure 4-8:
The Structure of
Baking Soda**

hydroxide ions

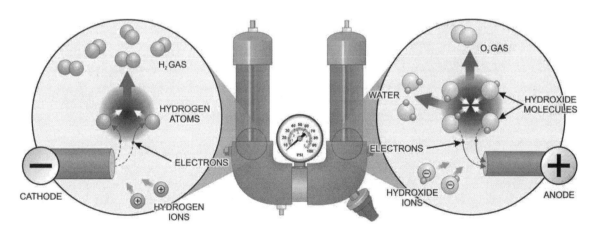

Figure 4-9: Forming Gases in the Electrolyzer

Likewise, the hydroxide molecule gives up its extra electron at the anode terminal and becomes neutral (OH). The hydroxide molecules combine with three others to form a single oxygen molecule (O_2) and two water molecules (H_2O). The O_2 molecule is a gas that bubbles to the surface from the anode terminal. Both gases are collected in the tops of the electrolyzer tubes.

The rate at which the electrolyzer produces hydrogen and oxygen is dependent on the amount of electrolyte in the solution and the voltage applied to the terminals. The more baking soda (or Potassium Carbonate) added to the solution, the more conductive it becomes. However, the more conductive the solution becomes, the more current that will be drawn out of the power source.

The Marcraft Electrolyzer can be powered by the 15/30 selectable Vdc power supply or from the trainer's photovoltaic (PV or solar) panel array. A pressure cutoff switch is placed inline with the power source's positive lead between the power source and the electrolyzer.

NOTE

The level of power derived from the PV panels on the Marcraft Clean Electron Generation panel may be too small to create hydrogen gas fast enough to keep up with the consumption rate of the fuel cells on the trainer.

---

overflow tubes

As the hydrogen and oxygen gases form at the tops of the two electrolyzer tubes, they are routed through two small **overflow tubes**. These tubes are used to collect any liquid solution that escapes from the electrolyzer to avoid contaminating the hydrogen and oxygen storage containers.

storage tubes

bubbler tubes

After passing through the overflow tubes, the hydrogen and oxygen gases are routed into a pair of water-filled **storage tubes**. As the gases fill these tubes, they force water out of the tubes and into the **bubbler tubes** above them. This arrangement enables you to visually monitor the production of the gases and to know when the tubes are filled with the gases you need to run the fuel cells.

When the storage container tubes are connected to one or more fuel cells, the pressure of the water stored in the bubbler tubes is used to feed the hydrogen gas to the fuel cell(s). This removes the need for pressure and flow control regulators required for most fuel cell applications.

Control valves are placed in the tubing system at key positions to control the flow of hydrogen and oxygen between the hydro generator's different vessels. A length of 1/4" OD plastic tubing extends from the top of the hydrogen storage tube and is terminated with a control valve. This is the connection point for supplying hydrogen to the fuel cells. Figure 4-10 shows the complete Marcraft hydrogen generation system.

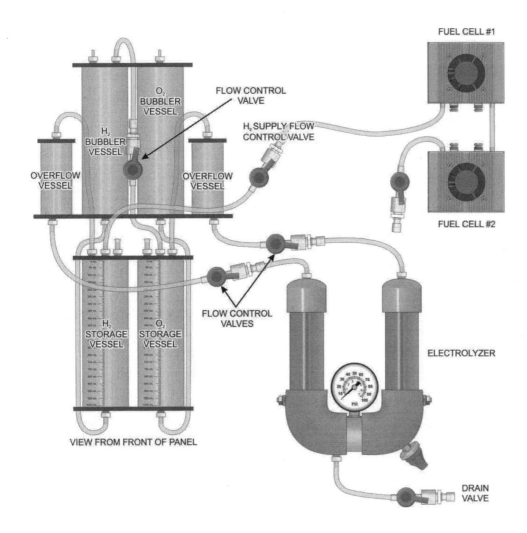

FUEL CELL #1

O₂
BUBBLER
VESSEL

FLOW CONTROL
VALVE

H₂ SUPPLY FLOW
CONTROL VALVE

H₂
BUBBLER
VESSEL

OVERFLOW
VESSEL

OVERFLOW
VESSEL

FUEL CELL #2

FLOW CONTROL
VALVES

H₂
STORAGE
VESSEL

O₂
STORAGE
VESSEL

ELECTROLYZER

PSI

VIEW FROM FRONT OF PANEL

DRAIN
VALVE

Figure 4-10: The Complete Hydrogen Generation System

SAFETY PRECAUTIONS

All fuel cell systems pose chemical, heat and electrical hazards. You must be aware of how these hazards are presented by the fuel cell system and take steps necessary to prevent injury or damage from these causes.

Electrical Hazards

The Marcraft fuel cell array consists of two 11-cell, 6.6-volt PEM fuel cells capable of producing up to 12 Watts of power each. The relationship between electrical power, current and voltage is an extended part of Ohm's Law and is expressed as:

$$P = V \times I \text{ or } I = \frac{P}{V}$$

where P is power in Watts, V is voltage in Volts, and I is current in Amperes (amps)

Therefore, a 4-volt fuel cell operating at the 4-Watt level would be delivering 1.0 amps of current to the load under full output conditions. With the two fuel cells wired in parallel, the circuit is capable of delivering up to 2.0 amps of current. In parallel circuits the source voltage is the same as the individual sources, but the current flow capabilities double. Current levels as low as 0.1 - 0.2 amps can be fatal to humans under certain circumstances. Therefore caution should always be used when working with this or any other electrical devices.

CAUTION

Current levels as low as 0.1 - 0.2 amps can be fatal to humans under the correct circumstances. Therefore caution should always be used when connecting this and other electrical devices.

---

burns

fire

conductors

Another danger associated with electrical current flow is the possibility of **burns** or **fire** related to **conductors** (wiring and devices that give up electrons easily) heating up. Even though the conductor materials give up electrons more easily than other substances, their electrons do not just fall off the atom—even conductors have some level of resistance in them. Therefore, some energy is given off as heat when current passes through the conductor.

Heat in wiring systems is often a result of too much current flowing through an undersized wire or through a bad connection. One of the keys to minimizing the amount of heat generated in wiring is to use the proper size wiring and the correct external insulation coating. A wire with a larger cross sectional area carries a given amount of current more easily than a smaller wire of the same material. There are simply more atoms across the face of the larger wire to give up the necessary number of electrons. Therefore, less heat is produced for that level of current.

Chemical Hazards

combustible

explosive

Hydrogen is both **combustible** and **explosive** when it is alone in its gaseous state. Heating or a spark in the presence of oxygen can cause hydrogen to ignite (causing a fire) or explode. Inhaling high concentration of hydrogen gas can cause an oxygen deficiency that produces symptoms that include headaches, dizziness, drowsiness, nausea and possibly unconsciousness.

Oxygen is an oxidizing agent that has major dangers associated with it, including fire and explosion hazards. Almost all materials will burn vigorously in the presence of oxygen. Even additional oxygen in the air will cause materials to ignite more easily and burn hotter then they would in normal atmospheric air. Breathing a pure oxygen atmosphere can cause damage to the cells of the human body under certain circumstances.

Therefore, you should treat these gases with caution. Never have an ignition source to the area around these gases. Also, do not directly inhale either gas as doing so can affect your blood chemistry.

NOTE

The quantities of hydrogen and oxygen gases produced on the Marcraft Clean Electron Generation panel are not large enough to produce significant damage if ignited. However, allowing either gas to ignite will create a large bang and damage the generator's holding tubes. If an ignition source is introduced to the oxygen gas in the presence of other flammable materials, such as clothing, a fire could result.

Electrolysis Hazards

The electrolysis process can also produce potentially dangerous substances depending on the exact substances used to create the hydrogen and oxygen. When sodium bicarbonate is used as the electrolyte, several other gases are formed in small amounts. These gases include hydrogen, oxygen, **carbon dioxide (CO_2)** and **carbon monoxide (CO)**. As this occurs, the baking soda is transformed into **sodium hydroxide (NaOH)**.

During electrolysis of $NaHCO_3$, the sodium ions (Na+) will rush to the electrolyzer's cathode and you will get the following chemical transformations:

- $2Na+ + 2e- + 2H_2O \rightarrow 2NaOH + H_2$ – Two sodium ions and two free electrons along with two water molecules produces two molecules of sodium hydroxide and two hydrogen gas molecules.

- $HCO_3- + H_2O \rightarrow H_2CO_3 + OH-$ – A bicarbonate ion interacts with a water molecule to form a carbonic acid ion (H_2CO_3-) and a hydroxide ion with a negative charge.

- $H_2CO_3 \rightarrow H_2O + CO_2$ – The carbonic acid molecule breaks down into a water molecule and a carbon dioxide molecule.

- $CO_2 + 2H+ + 2e- \rightarrow CO + H_2O$ – The carbon dioxide combines with two positively charged hydrogen ions and two free electrons to form a carbon monoxide molecule and a water molecule.

- $CO + 2H+ + 2e- \rightarrow C + H_2O$ – Finally, the carbon monoxide molecule combines with two positively charged hydrogen ions and two free electrons to form a carbon molecule and a water molecule.

| carbon dioxide (CO_2) |
| carbon monoxide (CO) |
| sodium hydroxide (NaOH) |

WARNING

On the oxygen side of the electrolyzer, you are also producing CO_2 (30%) and CO (4%) gases. Refer to the Safety Precautions—Chemical Hazards section for more information about these gases, their dangers and their presence with the Marcraft Clean Electron Generation panel.

At sufficient levels of intake over time, CO_2 gas can be dangerous for humans. The **Occupational Safety and Health Administration (OSHA)** has set a standard for the safe level of CO_2 gas as 5,000 **parts per million (PPM)** in the atmosphere. The normal Short Term Exposure Limit under the OSHA is 15,000 ppm.

| Occupational Safety and Health Administration (OSHA) |
| parts per million (PPM) |

When carbon monoxide gas is inhaled, it enters the blood stream through the lungs, displaces oxygen in the blood and interrupts the delivery of oxygen to the heart, brain and other major organs of the body.

- At 200 ppm (parts per million) a healthy person should begin to get a slight headache after 2 to 3 hours.

- At 400 ppm, a person will develop a frontal headache after 1 to 2 hours of exposure, developing into a widespread headache in about 3 hours.

- At 800 ppm, the person will develop dizziness, vomiting, and convulsions within 45 minutes and develop into lack of sensibility after about 2 hours of exposure.

These gases are not produced in sufficient quantities on the Marcraft Clean Electron Generation panel to produce significant danger of exposure. The total amount of CO and CO_2 produced depends on the amount of baking soda used to create the electrolyte solution.

If anyone appears to have the symptoms associated with CO poisoning described above, move that person to a location where they can receive fresh air. Take steps to ventilate the area such as opening doors and windows. Commercially available carbon monoxide detectors can be used to monitor the area around the panel and identify the presence of unacceptable levels of CO.

CAUTION

When the oxygen side of the Marcraft electrolyzer is vented from the storage tube, the oxygen gas will leave the tube first because it is lighter than the other compounds. The carbon monoxide, and then the carbon dioxide gases should follow in order.

Sodium Hydroxide

Care should also be taken when removing the spent electrolyte from the electrolyzer. In the process of generating hydrogen and oxygen, the baking soda electrolyte solution in the electrolyzer is reduced to NaOH (**Sodium Hydroxide** also known as caustic soda or lye), which is a caustic chemical.

Sodium Chloride (NaCL)

CAUTION

It is also possible to drive the electrolyzer using other electrolyte solutions such as table salt (**Sodium Chloride—NaCL**). This particular combination produces chlorine gas along with the hydrogen and oxygen. Chlorine gas is very dangerous, so this electrolyte solution is not recommended for use in creating hydrogen through electrolysis. Likewise, you should always validate the chemical reactions involved in any electrolysis process before implementing it as the results can easily turn out to be unhealthy or deadly.

Pressure Hazards

The Marcraft electrolyzer is equipped with a pressure switch that limits the pressure that can be developed inside the electrolyzer. Without this safety switch the process will continue inside the vessel and can reach unsafe pressure levels if the gases are not vented or used up.

CAUTION

Do not operate the electrolyzer without the pressure switch installed and wired into the power supply circuit, as this will allow the electrolysis process to continue until the pressure inside the vessel reaches an unsafe level. Allowing the electrolyzer to run in this uncontrolled manner can eventually cause the vessel to explode.

The switch is designed to create an open circuit when a pressure of 7 PSI (pounds per square inch) is reached. The switch is wired in series with the positive lead of the power source so that the path for current flow is interrupted when the pressure reaches this level. The electrolyzer should not be used without this switch in place.

PROCEDURE 13 – INTRODUCTION TO FUEL CELLS

Fuel Cells

In this lab procedure you will operate a hydrogen generation system to create the hydrogen required to drive the fuel cell operation. You will also identify the key components of a fuel cell-based electrical generation system, correctly connect fuel cells together for use, and test the basic operation of the fuel cell system.

Resources Needed:

- PEM Fuel Cells (2)
- Electrolyzer
- 1/4" OD Plastic Tubing
- DC Power Adapter (30 Volt – 0.75Amp or higher)
- Sodium Bicarbonate (Baking Soda)
- Potassium Carbonate (optional)
- Distilled Water
- Temporary Hydrogen Storage Cylinder (optional)
- Marcraft Green Electron Generation Experiment Panel
- Hand-held Digital Multimeter
- Clock, Timer or Watch with minutes and seconds capability

As with any electrical system, one of the keys to installing a fuel cell generation system is to read and understand its documentation. Locate and record the following information from the Instruction Manual and Reference Information booklet:

1. Obtain the Fuel Cell's User's Manual from your Instructor and verify that all of the fuel cell parts are present in your work area.

2. According to the User's Manual documentation, what action should be taken to " rejuvenate" the fuel cell after it has been in storage for some time?

    _____

    _____

3. According to the User's Manual documentation, what is the maximum power output for the 11-cell version of these fuel cells?

    _____

4. According to the User's Manual documentation, what is the rated output voltage of the 11-cell fuel cell stack?

    _____

5. According to the power curves for these fuel cells, what is the maximum current production of these 11-cell fuel cell stacks?

_____

6. What is the expected operating temperature for the 11-cell fuel cell stack under basic operation?

_____

7. What is the maximum suggested fuel supply (hydrogen) pressure for these fuel cells?

_____

8. According to the Power Curves for these Fuel Cells, what is the expected voltage level for the cell if a load is pulling 1 amp of current from it?

_____

9. According to the Power Curves for these Fuel Cells, what is the expected power delivery for the cell if a load is pulling 1 amp of current from it?

_____

10. According to the User's Manual documentation, what occurs when the load exceeds 12 watts?

_____

_____

11. Ideally, how much hydrogen should be consumed (hydrogen flow) by each fuel cell at maximum output?

_____

12. At full power, what would the expected efficiency of the stack be?

_____

Charging the Electrolyzer

Fuel Cells

The first step in preparing the fuel cell system for operation is to generate the hydrogen needed to power the cells. The first step in this process is to prepare and install the electrolyte solution.

1. Make sure that the two tubes at the top of the electrolyzer are disconnected from the tubes coming from the H_2 and O_2 overflow vessels on the backside of the experiment panel. Refer to Figure 4-11.

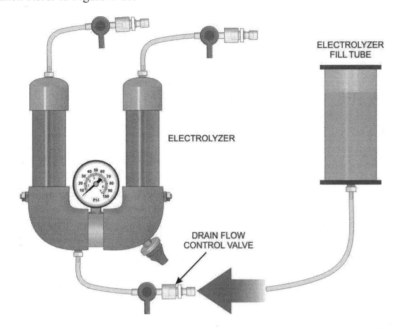

ELECTROLYZER FILL TUBE

ELECTROLYZER

DRAIN FLOW CONTROL VALVE

Figure 4-11: Preparing to Add Electrolyte to the Electrolyzer

2. Make sure the two Flow Control valves at the top of the electrolyzer are closed and the Flow Control valve at the bottom of the electrolyzer is closed. Refer to Figure 4-11.

3. Obtain the electrolyzer's Fill bottle and pour 400 mL of distilled water into it, being sure the drain tube is held above the Fill bottle.

4. Measure 4 level tsps (teaspoons) of baking soda into the Fill bottle and stir to mix thoroughly until the baking soda has been completely dissolved.

5. Connect the Fill bottle drain tube valve to the open end of the Drain Flow Control valve on the bottom of the electrolyzer and rotate the (luer) nut to lock the tube valves together as illustrated in Figure 4-11.

6. Open the two Flow Control valves at the top of the electrolyzer.

7. While holding the Fill bottle above the top of the electrolyzer, open the Flow Control valve on the bottom of the electrolyzer so that gravity forces the electrolyte solution to drain from the Fill bottle into the electrolyzer (the Fill bottle must remain above the top of the electrolyzer for this to occur).

8. After all of the solution has drained into the electrolyzer, close the Drain Flow valve on the bottom of the electrolyzer.

9. Rotate the (luer) nut to unlock the valve tube and remove the tube that connects to the electrolyzer Drain Flow Control valve coming from the bottom of the Fill bottle.

10. Close the H_2 and O_2 Flow Control valves on the top of the electrolyzer, as shown in Figure 4-12.

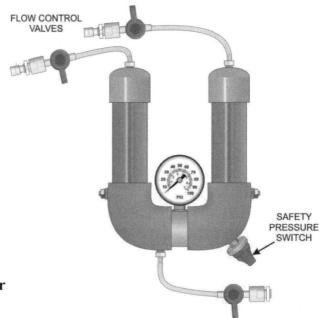

Figure 4-12: Preparing the Electrolyzer for Testing

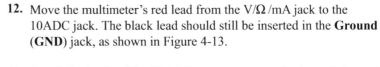

11. Remove the red wire that runs between the upper left lug of the Fuel Cell Power connection block and the Safety Pressure Switch.

12. Move the multimeter's red lead from the V/Ω/mA jack to the 10ADC jack. The black lead should still be inserted in the **Ground (GND)** jack, as shown in Figure 4-13.

13. Attach the leads of the 30VDC power source to the lower left terminals of the Fuel Cell Power connection block, as shown in Figure 4-14. The white wire with printing coming from the power source is negative and the white wire without printing is positive wire. Do NOT plug the power source into the commercial AC power source (outlet) at this time.

14. Secure the meter's common (black) lead under the top terminal across from the positive lead of the power source.

15. Connect the multimeter's (red) lead to the open terminal on the safety pressure switch. This places the multimeter directly in the power supply line, which forces all of the current being supplied to the electrolyzer to pass through the multimeter—this is how current measurements must be made—in series with the current flow being measured.

16. Set the multimeter's function selector to measure 10ADC.

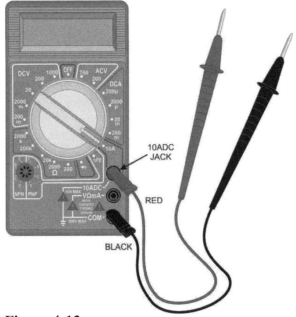

Figure 4-13: Attaching the Meter Leads for Measuring 10A DC

The electrolyzer is now charged, wired and ready for initial operational testing. Have your instructor check your work to this point before proceeding to the electrolyzer testing process.

Testing the Electrolyzer

Fuel Cells

Because the Safety Pressure Switch is preset by the manufacturer, obtaining desired results during the following procedure of testing the electrolyzer may not be possible. In order to complete the test, the Safety Pressure Switch will need to be adjusted so that a visual reading on the electrolyzer Pressure Gauge can be obtained.

1. Refer to Figure 4-14 and locate the Safety Pressure Switch on the Green Electron Generation Experiment Panel.

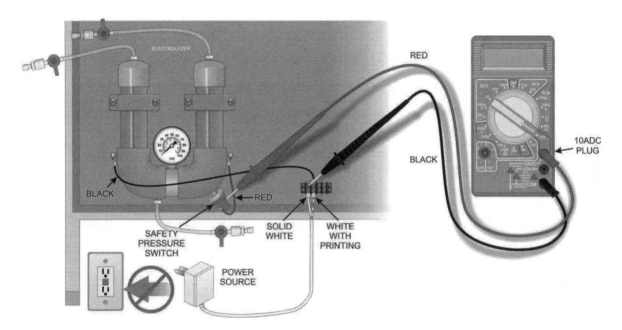

2. On the bottom of the Safety Pressure Switch remove the rubber plug using a small flat head screwdriver to pry out the plug from the Safety Pressure Switch.

3. Using a 7/32" Allen wrench, turn the set screw clockwise (CW) until the screw bottoms out or resistance is felt.

4. When the screw is bottomed out, without allowing the safety pressure switch to turn, turn the set screw counter-clockwise (CCW) 6 1/2 turns.

5. Remove the Allen wrench and replace the rubber plug on the Safety Pressure Switch.

6. Turn the multimeter On and plug the power source into the 120 Vac outlet. Note the time when the power source is plugged in on the following line:

    Time: _____

7. Record the amount of current that initially flows through the electrolyzer on the following line:

    _____

Figure 4-14: Electrolyzer Test Wiring

8. Does the multimeter show positive or negative current flow is occurring? What does this mean as far as current flowing through the electrolyzer?

_____   _____

NOTE: If no current flow is showing on the multimeter, remove the power source from the outlet and check the wiring and the electrolyte.

9. Observe the reading on the electrolyzer's pressure gauge as it generates hydrogen and oxygen. The safety pressure switch should stop the electrolysis process when the pressure in the vessel reaches approximately 10 psi, and the multimeter stops showing current flow. Record the time when the multimeter stops showing current flow, and the vessel reaches the approximate 10 psi on the following line:

Time: _____

CAUTION

If the electrolyzer does not cut off by the time the pressure reaches 10 psi, disconnect the power source from the electrolyzer (and from the AC source).

---

10. Calculate the amount of time that was required for the process to complete and record the answer on the following line:

Time: _____

11. Check the reading on the multimeter to verify that current flow to the electrolyzer has been stopped.

12. Unplug the power source from the outlet.

13. Obtain an open vessel (such as a beaker, cup or pan) to drain the electrolyte from the electrolyzer and place it under the electrolyzer's drain valve.

14. Slowly open the flow control valves on the top of the hydrogen and oxygen tubes to vent the gases into the air.

15. Open the drain valve to empty the electrolyte into the open vessel, and dispose of the drained solution.

16. Fill the Fill bottle with tap water, connect it to the valve on top of either the hydrogen or oxygen tubes and use only enough of the water to rinse any residue out of the electrolyzer into the open vessel. You may shake the experiment panel gently to make sure all of the solution has drained out of the electrolyzer.

17. Close all three electrolyzer valves, and dispose of all water and electrolyte from both containers.

Creating a Stronger Electrolyte

1. Open all electrolyzer valves and prepare an electrolyte solution consisting of 400 mL of distilled water and 6 level tsp of baking soda, as in Steps 2 through 10 in the "Charging the Electrolyzer" procedure.

NOTE: Leave the 6 tsp solution in the electrolyzer for the remaining procedures in this Lab exercise.

2. Repeat Steps 6 through 12 in the "Testing the Electrolyzer" procedure and compare the outcomes of both procedures on the following lines:

Time: _____

_____

_____ _____

Time: _____

Time: _____

Fuel Cells

Preparing the Electrolyzer System for Operation

Completing the following steps is a one time operation. Once completed, the process does not need to be performed, unless the storage vessels and system are first drained of all liquids.

1. Disconnect the multimeter leads from the safety pressure switch and the Fuel Cell Power connection block terminal.

2. Reinstall the red 12 AWG wire that runs between the Fuel Cell Power connection block and the open safety pressure switch terminal.

3. Obtain the Fill bottle and fill it with tap water.

4. Disconnect the Flow Control valve fittings from both sides of the electrolyzer, as shown in Figure 4-15.

5. Connect the Fill bottle drain valve to the Inlet connector on top of the H$_2$ Bubbler vessel. Refer to Figure 4-15.

6. Repeat Steps 3 and 5 to completely fill the H$_2$ Storage vessel with tap water.

NOTE: It is important that the H$_2$ Storage vessel contain exactly 1 liter of tap water, no more and no less, for proper operation.

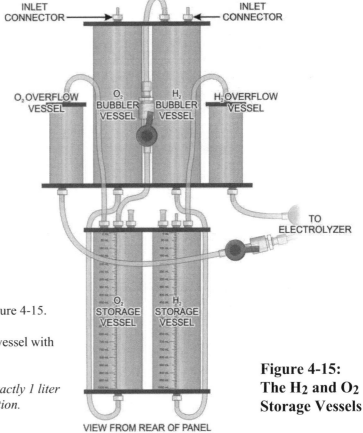

Figure 4-15: The H$_2$ and O$_2$ Storage Vessels

7. Modify Steps 3 through 6 to fill the O_2 Storage vessel with tap water.

NOTE: It is important that the O_2 Storage vessel is completely full of tap water for proper operation.

8. Reconnect the Flow Control valve tubing to both sides of the electrolyzer.

Fuel Cells

Investigating the Overflow, Bubbler and Hydrogen/Oxygen Storage Vessels

1. Locate the 1/4" OD tubing at the bottoms of both Overflow vessels that act as drain hoses.

2. Locate the flow control valves at the end of the tubes coming from the top of each side of the electrolyzer tubes, and make sure the valves are in the closed position.

3. Make sure the Overflow vessels are connected to the electrolyzer tube flow control valves, as illustrated in Figure 4-16.

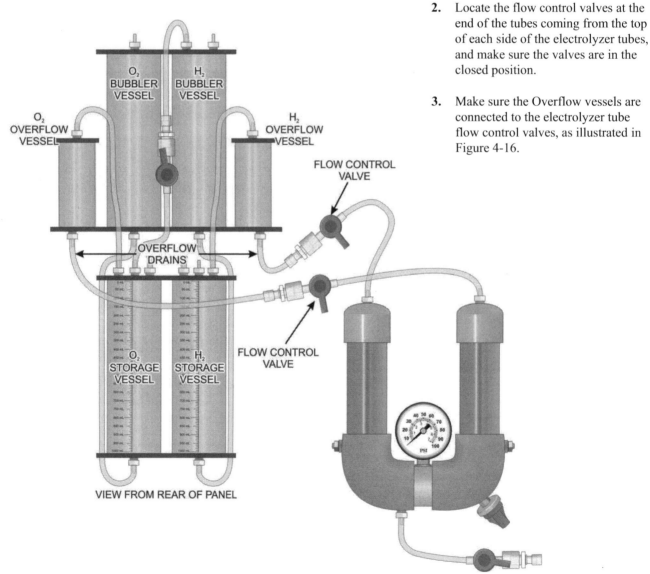

Figure 4-16: Overflow Vessel Plumbing

4. Verify the presence of the 1/2" OD tubing running between the top of the Overflow vessels and the Inlet connectors of the Storage vessels, as illustrated in Figure 4-17.

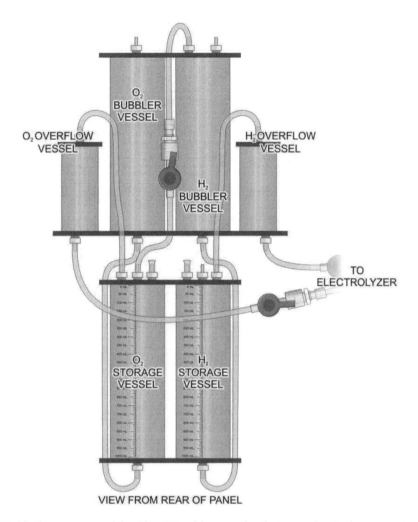

VIEW FROM REAR OF PANEL

**Figure 4-17:
Complete Bubbler
Vessel Plumbing**

5. Verify the presence of the 1/4" OD tubing running between the Outlet connector on the O_2 Storage vessel to the Inlet connector on the H_2 Bubbler vessel.

6. Locate and verify the Flow Control valve, between the H_2 Bubbler vessel and the O_2 Storage vessel, is in the **Off** position, as shown in Figure 4-17.

7. Locate and verify the Flow Control valve attached to the Outlet connector on the H_2 Storage vessel is closed. This is the valve that will be used to control the flow of hydrogen to the fuel cells in the following procedures.

The Electrolyzer is now ready to generate a hydrogen supply for use with the fuel cells. Have your instructor check your system before moving on to actually generate a hydrogen supply.

Fuel Cells

Generating a Hydrogen Supply

1. Refer to Figure 4-18 and confirm the following conditions are correct on the panel:

    *   The flow control valves on the tops of the electrolyzer tubes are open.

    *   The flow control valve between the O_2 Storage vessel and the H_2 Bubbler vessel is closed.

    *   The flow control valve on the Outlet of the H_2 Storage vessel is closed.

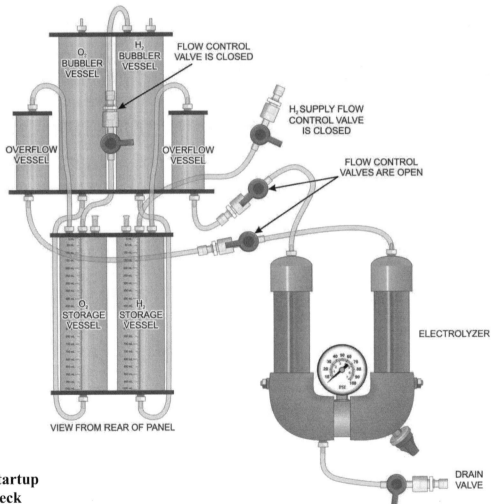

**Figure 4-18:
Electrolyzer Startup
Conditions Check**

2. Plug the Fuel Cell power source into the AC outlet.

NOTE: The electrolyzer should begin to generate hydrogen and oxygen gas bubbles that flow through the Overflow vessels to the H_2 and O_2 Storage vessels. As the gases collect in the Storage vessels, the water from those vessels should be forced up and into the Bubbler vessels above them.

3. Note the time when the power source is plugged in on the following line:

Time: _____

4. If possible, continue to monitor the hydrogen production process for approximately 2 hours or until 200 mL of hydrogen has been generated in the H_2 Storage vessel. Record the time on the following line: **

Time: _____

*NOTE: **Typically the Marcraft Electrolyzer can be expected to generate a little over 100 mL of hydrogen an hour using the 6 tsp baking soda solution. It may take up to 10 hrs to generate a complete liter of hydrogen gas. If this time frame is too long for your lab period, unplug the electrolyzer power source and close the flow control valves when it reaches a convenient hash mark on the hydrogen Storage vessel. To resume generating hydrogen to obtain a sufficient amount, open the electrolyzer flow control valves and plug in the power source. You should need about 120 minutes and about 500 mL of hydrogen to complete the following introductory fuel cell testing procedure.*

5. Remove the power supply from the AC outlet and calculate the amount of time that was required for the process to generate the above amount of hydrogen, and record the time on the following line:

Time _____

6. On the following lines, record the amount of hydrogen and oxygen gasses that has been generated in the H_2 and O_2 Storage vessels as indicated by the scale on the H_2 Storage vessel:

Hydrogen: _____

Oxygen: _____

7. Use the formula for volume in a cylinder to calculate the approximate amount of each gas generated:

$$V = \pi r^2 h$$

where $\pi = 3.14$, the radius of the inside of these tubes is 3.75 cm, and h is the height of the gas generated in the Storage vessels in centimeters. (Use a ruler to measure the height of the H_2 and O_2 in the vessels.)

Hydrogen: _____

Oxygen: _____

The Electrolyzer system is now ready to provide hydrogen to the fuel cells. Have your instructor check your system before moving on to test the fuel cells on the Clean Electron Generation panel.

Fuel Cells

Testing the Individual Fuel Cells

1. Verify and confirm that there is no load on either of the fuel cells. If necessary, remove any wired connections from the right side of the fuel cell terminal blocks.

2. Verify and confirm that the H_2 supply tubing is free of any liquid. If necessary, remove the tubing from the input port of Fuel Cell #1 and briefly open the Flow Control valve to expel any liquid, then close the valve.

3. Remove the tubing that runs from the exit port of Fuel Cell #1 and the input port of Fuel Cell #2 and set it aside.

4. Move the tubing connected to the exit port of Fuel Cell #2, as shown in Figure 4-19.

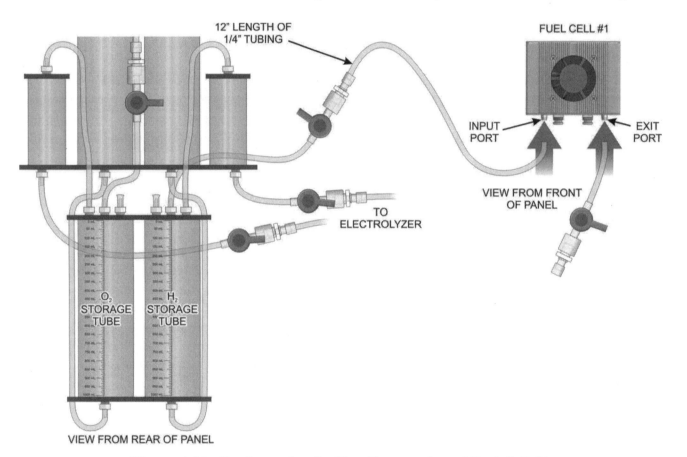

Figure 4-19: Configuration for Test Preparation of Fuel Cell #1

5. Move the multimeter's red lead back to the $V/\Omega/mA$ jack from the 10ADC jack and set the multimeter to its 20 DCV setting. The black lead should still be inserted in the Ground (GND) jack.

6. Place the leads of the meter across the terminal of the Fuel Cell #1.

7. Observe and record the hydrogen level in the H₂ Storage vessel on the following line:

    Level:_____

8. Close the electrolyzer Flow Control valves and open the Flow Control valve between the O₂ Storage vessel and the H₂ Bubbler vessel.

NOTE: In the next step, if there is not an immediate indication on the meter of a voltage increase, perform the following procedure to remove any blockage in the fuel cell that may be occurring.

- *Completely close the Flow Control valve at the exit port of the fuel cell.*

- *Quickly turn the valve so it is completely open.*

- *When the voltage begins to increase, close the Flow Control valve.*

This will remove any blockage allowing hydrogen to flow into Fuel Cell #1.

9. Open the H₂ Supply Flow Control valve to allow hydrogen to flow into Fuel Cell #1.

10. Observe and record the voltage reading that immediately rises to and appears on the multimeter on the following lines:

    _____

11. Monitor the voltage and the H₂ Storage vessel level for 2 minutes and close the H₂ Flow Control valve to stop the flow of hydrogen to Fuel Cell #1 and record the results on the following line:

    _____

    _____

12. Close the H₂ Flow Control valve to stop the flow of hydrogen to Fuel Cell #1.

13. As there is no load attached to Fuel Cell #1, the hydrogen should be retained in the fuel cell, however it will leak out over a period of time. From the observations in Steps 11 and 12, check the scale and record the amount of hydrogen that was used by Fuel Cell #1 on the following line:

    _____

14. Remove the 3" length of tubing with Flow Control valve from the exit port of Fuel Cell #1 and reinstall it on the exit port of Fuel Cell #2, as shown in Figure 4-20.

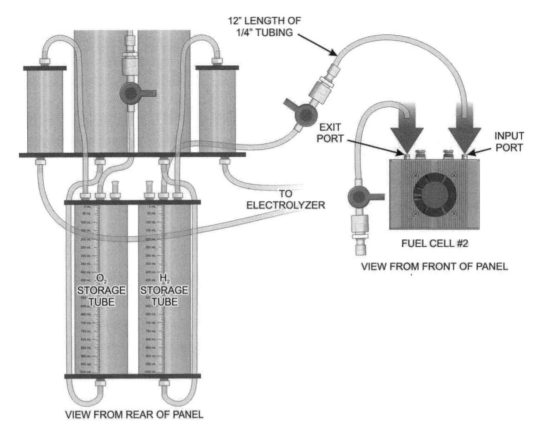

12" LENGTH OF
1/4" TUBING

EXIT
PORT

TO
ELECTROLYZER

INPUT
PORT

FUEL CELL #2

VIEW FROM FRONT OF PANEL

O₂
STORAGE
TUBE

H₂
STORAGE
TUBE

VIEW FROM REAR OF PANEL

**Figure 4-20:
Configuration for
Test Preparation of
Fuel Cell #2**

15. Remove the tubing from the input port of Fuel Cell #1 and insert it into the input port of Fuel Cell #2.

16. Place the multimeter across the terminals of the Fuel Cell #2.

17. Observe and record the amount of hydrogen in the H_2 Storage vessel on the following line:

_____

NOTE: In the next step, if there is not an immediate indication on the meter of a voltage increase, perform the following procedure to remove any blockage in the fuel cell that may be occurring.

- *Completely close the Flow Control valve at the exit port of the fuel cell.*
- *Quickly turn the valve so it is completely open.*
- *When the voltage begins to increase, close the Flow Control valve.*

This will remove any blockage allowing hydrogen to flow into Fuel Cell #2.

18. Open the H_2 Supply Flow Control valve to allow hydrogen to flow into Fuel Cell #2.

19. Observe and record the voltage reading that immediately rises to and appears on the multimeter on the following line:

Fuel Cell #2: _____ (Volts)

20. Monitor the voltage and the H_2 Storage vessel level for 2 minutes and close the H_2 Flow Control valve to stop the flow of hydrogen to the Fuel Cell #2 and record the results on the following lines:

_____

_____

21. Close the H_2 Supply Flow Control valve to stop the flow of hydrogen to Fuel Cell #2.

22. As there is no load attached to Fuel Cell #2, the hydrogen should be retained in the fuel cell, however it will leak out over a period of time. From the observations in Steps 18 and 19, record the amount of hydrogen that was used by Fuel Cell #2 on the following line:

_____

23. Restore the original tubing configuration by reinstalling the tubing between the exit port of Fuel Cell #1 and the input port of Fuel Cell #2.

This completes the preliminary tests of the fuel cells. Have your instructor check your findings before moving forward to configure the fuel cells on the Clean Electron Generation panel for use.

Configuring Fuel Cells

Fuel Cells

Fuel cells are DC power sources and can be considered hydrogen-controlled batteries. Like batteries, solar cells and panels can be connected together to provide different voltage and current capabilities to fit different load/installation requirements. When fuel cells are connected in series (positive terminals are connected to negative terminals in a daisy-chain connection) as illustrated in Figure 4-21, the voltage level provided to an external load is equal to the sum of all the individual fuel cell voltages.

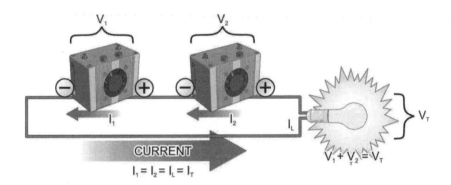

Figure 4-21: Series Connected Fuel Cells

In this configuration, the same current flows through all the fuel cells and the load. This arrangement enables multiple fuel cells to be combined to provide power to a piece of equipment that requires a higher voltage source—such as using four 6-volt fuel cells to provide a 24 Vdc source for a portable device with this input requirement.

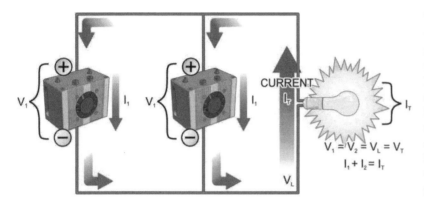

When fuel cells are connected in parallel (positive terminals are connected to positive terminals and negative terminals are connected to negative terminals) as illustrated in Figure 4-22, the voltage level is the same as the lowest individual fuel cell's output (all of the fuel cells in such an array should have the same stated voltage ratings). However the current delivery capabilities of parallel fuel cells is equal to the sum of the currents produced by each of the cells. This is helpful in situations where devices that require heavy DC current loads need an acceptable source of power.

Figure 4-22: Parallel Connected Fuel Cells

Fuel Cells

Setting Up the Hydrogen Source

Perform the following steps only if the fuel cells are not properly configured, as depicted in Figure 4-23. If the fuel cells are properly configured, proceed to the "Establishing Fuel Cell Electrical Configurations" procedure.

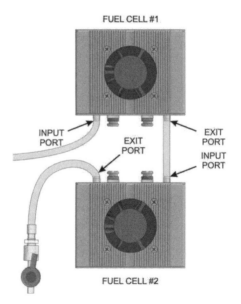

Figure 4-23: Fully Configured Hydrogen Source Plumbing

1. Confirm that the tubing from the hydrogen supply is in the input port of Fuel Cell #1.

2. Remove any tubing from the hydrogen exit port on Fuel Cell #1 and install a short piece of 1/4" OD tubing between the exit port of Fuel Cell #1 and the input port of Fuel Cell #2.

3. Remove the plug from the exit port of Fuel Cell #2 and set it aside. Insert the open end of the 3" length of tubing with the Flow Control valve from the previous procedure. This arrangement is depicted in Figure 4-23.

Establishing Fuel Cell Electrical Configurations

Fuel Cells

1. At the Fuel Cell Configuration connection block, form a series connection by attaching a jumper wire between the positive (+) terminal of Fuel Cell #1 to the negative (-) terminal of Fuel Cell #2.

2. Set the hand-held multimeter to its 20 DCV setting.

3. At the Fuel Cell Configuration connection block, connect the black lead of the multimeter to the negative terminal of Fuel Cell #1 and the red lead to the positive terminal of Fuel Cell #2, as illustrated in Figure 4-24.

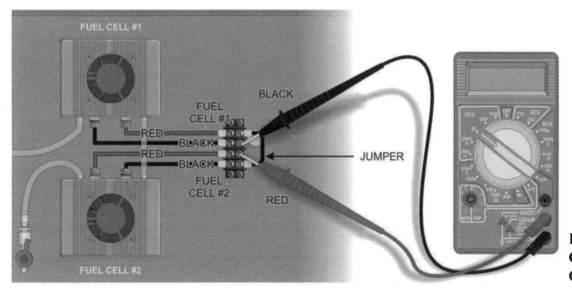

Figure 4-24: Connecting Fuel Cells in Series

NOTE: In the next step, if there is not an immediate indication on the meter of a voltage increase, perform the following procedure to remove any blockage in the fuel cells that may be occurring.

- *Completely close the Flow Control valve at the exit port of the fuel cell.*

- *Quickly turn the valve so it is completely open.*

- *When the voltage begins to increase, close the Flow Control valve.*

This will remove any blockage allowing hydrogen to flow into Fuel Cell #1 and Fuel Cell #2.

4. Open the flow control valve in the hydrogen supply line and record the total voltage level provided by the 2 series connected fuel cells on the following line:

_____

5. Close the H_2 Supply Flow Control valve to stop the flow of hydrogen to the fuel cells.

6. How does this value relate to the individual voltages of Fuel Cell #1 and Fuel Cell #2 measured in Step 16 of the "Testing the Individual Fuel Cells" procedure?

_____

7. Remove the multimeter leads from the connection block terminals for Fuel Cell #1 and Fuel Cell #2.

8. Remove the black jumper wire from the positive (+) terminal of Fuel Cell #1 to the negative (-) terminal of Fuel Cell #2.

9. At the Fuel Cell Configuration connection block, form a parallel fuel cell connection by attaching a red jumper wire between the positive (+) terminal of Fuel Cell #1 to the positive (+) terminal of Fuel Cell #2.

10. Attach a black jumper wire between the negative (-) terminal of Fuel Cell #1 and the negative (-) terminal of Fuel Cell #2.

11. Connect the red lead of the multimeter to thepositive (+) terminal of Fuel Cell #1 and the black lead to the negative (-) terminal of Fuel Cell #2 at the Fuel Cell Configuration connection block, as illustrated in Figure 4-25.

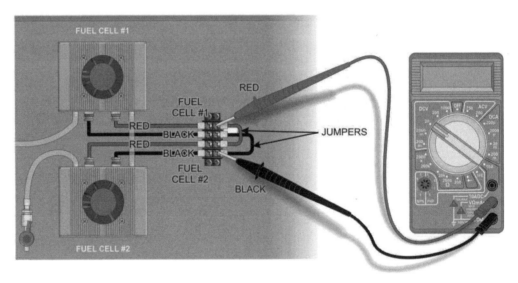

**Figure 4-25:
Connecting Fuel
Cells in Parallel**

NOTE: In the next step, if there is not an immediate indication on the meter of a voltage increase, perform the following procedure to remove any blockage in the fuel cells that may be occurring.

- _Completely close the Flow Control valve at the exit port of the fuel cell._
- _Quickly turn the valve so it is completely open._
- _When the voltage begins to increase, close the Flow Control valve._

This will remove any blockage allowing hydrogen to flow into Fuel Cell #1 and Fuel Cell #2.

12. Open the flow control valve in the hydrogen supply line and record the total voltage level provided by the 2 parallel connected fuel cells on the following line:

_____

13. Close the H_2 Supply Flow Control valve to stop the flow of hydrogen to the fuel cells.

14. How does this value relate to the individual voltages of the Fuel Cell # 1 and Fuel Cell #2 measured in Step 16 of the "Testing the Individual Fuel Cells" procedure?

15. Remove the multimeter leads from the connection block terminals for Fuel Cell #1 and Fuel Cell #2, and turn off the multimeter.

16. Close the Flow Control valves on the hydrogen supply line and the tubing between the H_2 Bubbler vessel and the O_2 Storage vessel.

This completes the procedures for testing the basic fuel cell configurations. Leave the system configured as it is now for the next procedure, "Advanced Fuel Cell Operations".

Procedure 13 Questions

1. How many 6V, 12W fuel cells would be needed to supply a load that requires a 48-volt supply that can push at least 2.5 amps of current? How should these fuel cells be configured?

2. What is the approximate daily power output of your 2-unit fuel cell array provided the electrolyzer can produce enough hydrogen to operate at maximum output for the entire period?

3. How did changing the electrolyte ratio from 1 tsp/100 mL to 1.5 tsp/100 mL affect the operation of the electrolyzer?

4. Why do you need to make sure the flow control valve on the outlet side of the H_2 Bubbler vessel is open while generating hydrogen?

5. What are the symptoms of carbon monoxide poisoning? How long do they normally take to manifest themselves in humans?

6. What is the outcome of connecting 8, 6-volt fuel cell stacks in series with each other?

7. Given the measured H_2 generation rate of your electrolyzer and the consumption rate of your fuel cell stacks, is it possible to operate the fuel cells directly from the H_2 generator?

8. What type of hazards are associated with working around hydrogen gas?

9. If the electrolyzer were powered by the 24V, 0.6 amp PV panels on the experiment panel, how would the performance of the electrolyzer be affected?

ADVANCED FUEL CELL OPERATIONS

Transportation systems have developed as one of the most interesting application areas for fuel cells. The idea of creating hydrogen-powered buses, automobiles and two-wheeled vehicles has driven the most fuel cell development efforts. All of the major automobile manufacturers have been exploring fuel cell technology to produce a commercialized, fuel cell power vehicle.

Larger fuel cell systems are used as emergency power generation devices for hospitals, offices, schools and utility plants. These devices must be large enough to supply emergency services for these institutions during power failures. Smaller fuel cells are used to provide power to portable devices. These fuel cell systems offer a lightweight, improved-duration alternative to batteries for portable computers and devices.

Fuel cells are sometimes used in conjunction with other alternative energy sources to supply power in remote locations, such as cogenerating power for signaling and sensing control systems on railroads, where the equipment is located away from commercial power sources. This can include using photovoltaic (solar) panels to drive fuel cell-based electrolyzers that in turn generate hydrogen from stored water. The generated hydrogen is then used to drive other fuel cells when additional energy is required.

Motors

Using fuel cells in transportation applications typically requires that the fuel cell supply electrical energy to an electric motor. This motor is typically a DC motor. A DC motor is an electromechanical device that converts electrical energy into rotational mechanical force. These devices are very similar in construction and operation to DC generators like those you will (or already have) work with in the Wind Turbine labs in Chapter 2. A simple DC motor is depicted in Figure 4-26.

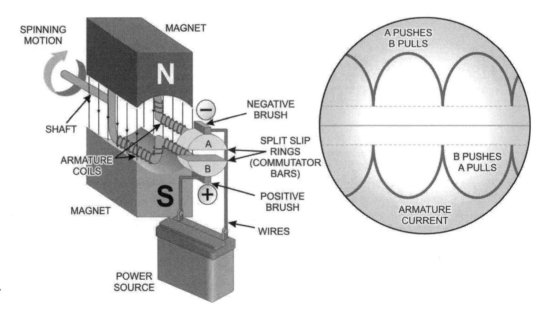

Figure 4-26: The Operation of a Simple DC Motor

The DC motor operates according to the principles of magnetic attraction and repulsion—like charges repel each other and unlike charges attract each other. The DC **motor** is made up of two basic parts—a central armature (or rotor) with armature coils driven by an external voltage source and magnetic field poles (or stators). In this example the field poles are represented by permanent magnets. These poles can also be created using electromagnetic coils.

motor

The external voltage source creates a current flow through the armature coils, which produce electromagnetic fields. These magnetic fields interact with the magnetic fields surrounding the field poles and cause the rotor to move to align the armature fields with the field pole fields. The polarity of the fields developed by the armature coils depends on the direction that current flows through the coils. This is determined by the polarity of the external voltage source.

As the rotor moves to align the fields in the motor, the split ring configuration on the commutator changes sides and reverses the direction of current flow through the coils. This change causes the armature coils to be repelled by the field pole they have just arrived at and to begin seeking the opposite polarity pole on the other side of the motor.

Real DC motors typically contain multiple commutator segments and armature coils. This makes the operation of the motor smoother and lessens the need for inertia to drive the armature to the next field pole.

PROCEDURE 14 – EXAMINING THE FUEL CELL CONTROL PANEL

Fuel Cells

In this set of procedures, you will use the fuel cell stack to provide power for a number of different load types. You will also perform activities to define the operating parameters of these fuel cells in different applications, such as transportation applications, driving resistive loads, and charging batteries. You will also experiment with different fuel cell stack configurations to determine which configuration best fits a particular application.

Fuel cell arrays generate an output whenever hydrogen and oxygen are applied to them. After the hydrogen is introduced to the cell there is no practical way to shut down its internal operation until the hydrogen is used up. Therefore, every fuel cell installation must have a set of control devices that can be used to separate the devices from the rest of the electrical system. The most basic fuel cell control panel should contain at least an ammeter, a fuse or a circuit breaker, and a disconnect switch.

These components are typically wired in series in the positive lead of the fuel cell generating system. Figure 4-27 is a suggested schematic diagram (symbolic wiring diagram) for a fuel cell installation designed to charge a set of storage batteries.

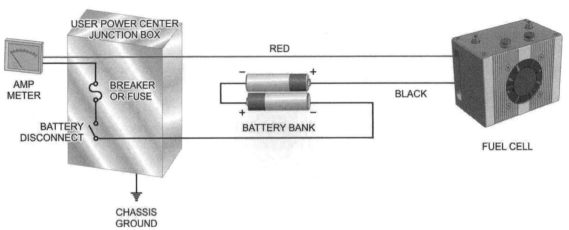

Figure 4-27: Fuel Cell System Control Panel Wiring

The control panel for a fuel cell installation typically contains a fuse or circuit breaker that protects the technician, the operator and the circuitry from damage due to short circuits or excessive rotational speeds. A circuit breaker acts as a piece of wire, providing a path for current flow through itself until the current flow level reaches a designated level. If that level is exceeded, the circuit breaker becomes an open circuit to stop the current from flowing through it.

Circuit breakers and fuses must be properly sized to safely handle the maximum amount of current that the system is designed to supply, and then break the circuit (cause an open circuit) to interrupt the flow of electrons until the over current condition can be removed or repaired. In doing so the circuit breaker or fuse protects wiring, devices and personnel from damage and injury.

Other common control mechanisms include a Battery Disconnect switch. The Disconnect Switch disconnects the output of the fuel cells from the storage battery, grid or inverter circuitry so that these elements can be serviced safely, without power that is being generated by the fuel cell.

The Disconnect Switch is a Single-Pole, Single-Throw (SPST) switch—there is one *pole* (the circle with the movable contact attached to it—and one *throw*—possible connection point. This representation of the SPST switch shows that it is a normally open switch—when the switch is in its "normal" position, there is no path for current to flow through the switch—when the switch is flipped to the active position (the movable contact swings into contact with the circle representing the throw position, creating a path for current flow through the switch.

Like fuses and breakers, switches, devices and wiring must be rated to handle the maximum designed current levels for their positions in the system. Switches are rated according to both voltage and maximum current handling capabilities. Therefore, a switch designed for operation in a 12 Vdc 15A automobile application would not be used in a 120 Vac 15A residential wiring environment. Doing so will potentially present both a damage and an injury situation.

From the control panel, the wiring may continue on to a set of storage batteries (as shown in the figure), to a DC-to-AC inverter, or to a connection into the commercial power grid. These options are explored in the next lab procedure.

Resources Needed:

- PEM Fuel Cells (2)
- Electrolyzer
- 1/4" OD Plastic Tubing
- DC Power Adapter (30 Volt – 0.75Amp or higher)
- Potassium Carbonate
- Distilled Water
- Temporary Hydrogen Storage Cylinder
- Marcraft Green Electron Generation Experiment Panel
- Hand-held Digital Multimeter
- Clock, Timer or Watch with minutes and seconds capability
- Rechargeable AA batteries (2)
- Jumper Wires (12 AWG red, black)

1. Set the multimeter to its lowest *resistance range* (used for checking Continuity of a device or circuit).

2. Place the meter's leads on the opposite terminals of the Disconnect Switch. On the following lines, record the reading obtained from the multimeter with the switch in the up and down positions:

   Switch Up: _____

   Switch Down: _____

   (These answers may be reversed depending on the orientation of the switch)

3. With the fuse removed from the fuse holder, place the multimeter leads on opposite terminals of the fuse holder. Record the resistance measurement on the following lines. Move the leads to the opposite terminals and record the meter reading in this direction:

   _____

   _____

4. Install the fuse in the fuse holder and repeat the activities in Step 3. Record the resistance measurements on the following lines:

   _____

   _____

5. Place the multimeter on its lowest resistance range and connect the leads on opposite terminals of the fuel cell's ammeter. Record the resistance measurement on the following lines. Move the leads to the opposite terminals and record the multimeter reading in this direction:

   _____

   _____

Fuel Cells

Configure the Fuel Cells for Operation

To begin the hands on procedures in this lab, you will wire the two fuel cells in parallel. In other portions of the procedure you will be asked to change this configuration to create series connected fuel cells to evaluate the performance of the stack under different load conditions and types.

1. Use two spade lug connectors to connect the two fuel cells in parallel with each other. This requires that you connect a red jumper wire between the positive terminals at the Fuel Cell Configuration connection block, as illustrated in Figure 4-28.

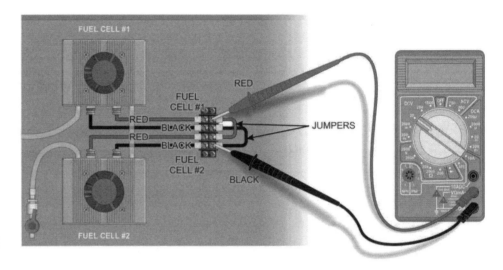

**Figure 4-28:
Connecting the Two
Fuel Cells in Parallel**

2. Use the same process described in Step #1 to connect a black jumper wire between the two fuel cells' negative terminals.

Fuel Cells

Create the Fuel Cell Control Panel

In this section of the hands on procedure you will create a control panel for the fuel cell stack. This involves wiring protection and control devices into the positive lead of the fuel cell stack circuit that will be used to drive external loads.

1. Prepare and install a short red 12 AWG jumper wire to run between the Fuel Cell #1 top-right positive (+) terminal of the Fuel Cell Configuration connection block and the (+) terminal on the Fuel Cell Stack Ammeter. (The positive (+) terminal on the ammeter is on the left as you look at the backside of the ammeter.)

2. Prepare and install a short red 12 AWG jumper wire to run between the open negative (-) terminal of the Fuel Cell Stack Ammeter and the upper spade terminal on the fuse holder. (The negative (+) terminal on the ammeter is on the right as you look at the backside of the ammeter.)

3. Prepare and install a short red 12 AWG jumper wire to run between the open terminal on the fuse holder and the top terminal on the Fuel Cell Stack's Disconnect switch.

4. Route the free end of a red 12 AWG wire through the top most hole (looking from the front of the panel) in the Clean Electron Generation Panel above the Fuel Cell Control Panel connection block.

5. Crimp a fork lug connectors to one end of the red wire and secure it to the open left-center connection terminal on the top row of the Fuel Cell Control Panel connection block.

6. Crimp a spade connector to the free end of the red jumper wire and connect it to the open terminal on the Fuel Cell Stack Disconnect switch. This completes the positive side wiring for the Fuel Cell Stack.

7. Install a black 12 AWG jumper between the Fuel Cell #2 negative (-) terminal of the Fuel Cell Configuration connection block and left-most terminal on the top row of the Fuel Cell Control Panel connection block, as depicted in Figure 4-29.

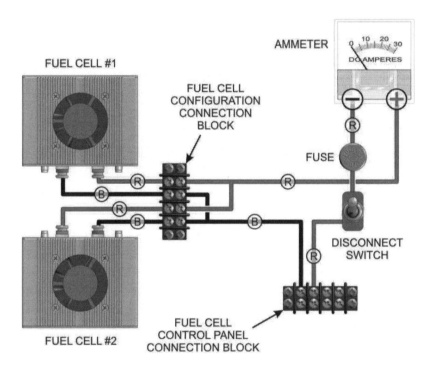

**Figure 4-29:
Control Panel
Connection Block
Wiring**

8. Verify your wiring against the schematic wiring diagram in the figure. Check off the leads on the drawing as you verify the connection pathway between each device.

Generate Hydrogen and Start the Fuel Cells

The first step in preparing the fuel cell system for operation is to generate the hydrogen needed to power the cells. On the Marcraft Clean Electron Generation panel this is accomplished with an electrolyzer. The electrolyzer is capable of generating about 100 mL of hydrogen per hour. You may need to generate a supply of hydrogen in advance to perform all of the following procedures.

Fuel Cells

Charge the Electrolyzer

If the electrolyzer was charged in Lab Procedure 13 and it was not disposed of, it will not be necessary to perform the following electrolyzer charging again. Proceed to the "Generating a Hydrogen Supply".

1. Make sure that the two tubes at the top of the electrolyzer are disconnected from the tubes coming from the H₂ and O₂ overflow vessels on the backside of the experiment panel. Refer to Figure 4-30.

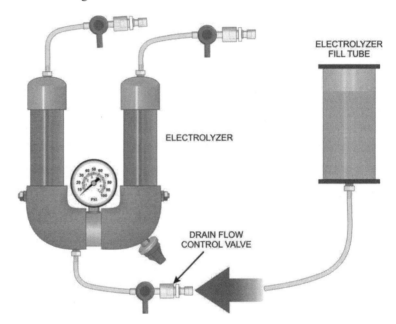

Figure 4-30: Preparing to Add Electrolyte to the Electrolyzer

2. Make sure the two Flow Control valves at the top of the electrolyzer are closed and the Flow Control valve at the bottom of the electrolyzer is closed. Refer to Figure 4-30.

3. Obtain the electrolyzer's Fill bottle and pour 400 mL of distilled water into it, being sure the drain tube is held above the Fill bottle.

4. Measure 6 level tsps (teaspoons) of baking soda into the Fill bottle and stir to mix thoroughly until the baking soda has been completely dissolved.

5. Connect the Fill bottle drain tube valve to the open end of the Drain Flow Control valve on the bottom of the electrolyzer and rotate the (luer) nut to lock the tube valves together as illustrated in Figure 4-30.

6. Open the two Flow Control valves at the top of the electrolyzer.

7. While holding the Fill bottle above the top of the electrolyzer, open the Flow Control valve on the bottom of the electrolyzer so that gravity forces the electrolyte solution to drain from the Fill bottle into the electrolyzer (the Fill bottle must remain above the top of the electrolyzer for this to occur).

8. After all of the solution has drained into the electrolyzer, close the Drain Flow valve on the bottom of the electrolyzer.

Generating a Hydrogen Supply

Fuel Cells

This procedure is only needed if a sufficient amount of H_2 is not available. It is recommended that at least 200 to 500 mL of H_2 be available during this lab to complete the following test procedures.

NOTE: Typically the Marcraft Electrolyzer can be expected to generate a little over 100 mL of hydrogen per hour using the 6 tsp potassium bicarbonate solution. It may take up to 10 hrs to generate a complete liter of hydrogen gas. If this time frame is too long for your lab period, unplug the electrolyzer power source and close the Flow Control valves on the tops of the electrolyzer tubes when it reaches a convenient hash mark on the H_2 Storage vessel. You can resume generating hydrogen by opening the Flow Control valves on the tops of the electrolyzer tubes and plug in the power source. You should need about 120 minutes and about 500 mL of hydrogen to complete the following fuel cell testing procedures.

If at any time hydrogen is needed, it can be generated by using the following steps:

(Refer to Figure 4-31.)

1. Close the Flow Control valve on the tubing between the H_2 Bubbler vessel and the O_2 Storage vessel.

2. Close the H_2 Supply Flow Control valve.

3. Open the two electrolyzer Flow Control valves.

4. Plug the fuel cell power source into the AC outlet.

The electrolyzer should begin to generate hydrogen and oxygen gas bubbles that flow through the Overflow vessels to the H_2 and O_2 Storage vessels. As the gases collect in the Storage vessels, the water from those vessels should be forced up and into the Bubbler vessels above them.

5. When a sufficient amount of hydrogen has been generated, remove the power source from the AC outlet and close the electrolyzer Flow Control valves.

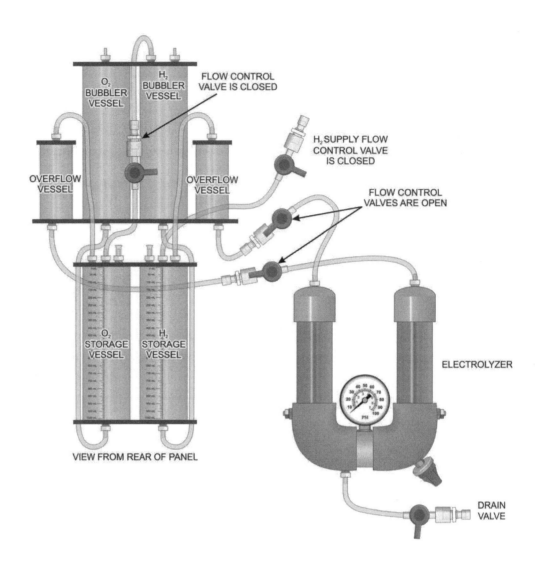

Figure 4-31:
Electrolyzer Startup
Conditions Check

Fuel Cells

Starting the Fuel Cell Stack

1. Connect the multimeter across the output terminals (the two, top-left terminals) of the Fuel Cell Control Panel connection block, as illustrated in Figure 4-32. Make sure the multimeter is configured with the red measuring lead in the V/Ω/mA jack and that it is set to measure up to 20 Vdc.

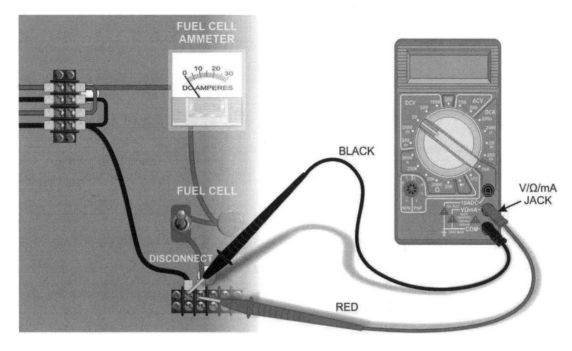

Figure 4-32: Connecting the Meter to the Fuel Cell Output Terminals

2. Make certain that the multimeter is turned **On**.

3. Open the Flow Control valve between the O_2 Storage vessel and the H_2 Bubbler vessel.

4. Move the Fuel Cell Disconnect Switch to the **ON** position.

In the next step, if there is not an immediate indication on the multimeter of a voltage increase, perform the following steps to remove any blockage in the fuel cells that may be occurring:

- Completely close the Flow Control valve at the exit port of the fuel cell.

- Quickly turn the valve so it is completely open.

- When the voltage begins to increase, close the Flow Control valve.

This will remove any blockage allowing hydrogen to flow into fuel cells.

5. Open the H_2 flow control valve to allow hydrogen to flow into the fuel cell stack.

6. Observe and record the current and voltage produced at the Fuel Cell Control Panel's electrical output terminals. The voltage level should rise slowly to its maximum open circuit potential. Record the voltage and current levels being produced by the fuel cell stack after 1 minute of operation on the following lines:

Voltage: _____

Current: _____

7. Turn the Fuel Cell Disconnect Switch to the **OFF** position.

8. Close the H_2 Flow Control valve to stop the flow of hydrogen to the fuel cell stack.

Fuel Cells

Determining Fuel Cell Power Output

In this section of the procedure, you will create different load resistance values across the Fuel Cell Load connection block and measure current and voltage across the resistances to calculate power and gas usage.

1. Make certain that the multimeter leads are configured to measure V/Ω /mA and set the function selector switch to measure resistance—using the 200kΩ range.

2. Verify that there is nothing connected to the potentiometer output at the Fuel Cell Load connection block terminals (the two lower right hand terminals), as illustrated in Figure 4-33.

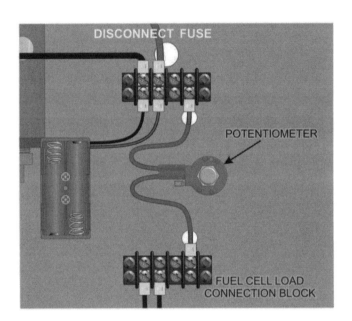

**Figure 4-33:
Potentiometer
Open Circuit**

3. Turn on the multimeter and place the multimeter leads on opposite sides of the potentiometer as depicted in Figure 4-34. This figure shows the proper method of taking a resistance reading of a device or circuit—the meter must be placed in parallel with the device or circuit being measured and no current paths can be allowed to exist except the one that runs through the meter and the device/circuit.

NOTE: To measure resistance with a multimeter, the meter function must be set to measure resistance, the test leads must be across the component being measured and other paths of current must be removed from the component so that only the current supplied by the meter is used and there are no other paths for this current than directly through the component.

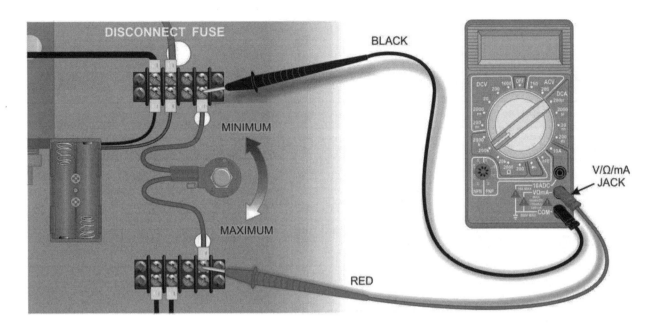

Figure 4-34:
Measuring Resistance

4. Adjust the potentiometer to its maximum resistance setting (refer to Procedure 1) and record the value on the following line:

Maximum Resistance: _____

5. Adjust the potentiometer to its approximate mid range resistance setting and record the value on the following line:

Mid-Range Resistance: _____

6. Adjust the potentiometer to its minimum resistance setting and record the value on the following line:

Minimum Resistance: _____

You will now wire the Fuel Cell Load Panel for taking load measurements under different resistance loads.

7. With the potentiometer still in the minimum resistance setting, place a short jumper wire across the two lower right terminals on the Fuel Cell Load connection block.

8. Install a black 12 AWG jumper between the right-center terminal on the bottom row of the Fuel Cell Control Panel connection block and the top row right-center terminal on the Fuel Cell Load connection block.

9. Install a short red 12 AWG jumper between the top row left-center terminal and the top right-most terminal on the Fuel Cell Control Panel connection block.

10. Install a short black 12 AWG jumper between the top row left-most terminal and the top right-center terminal of the Fuel Cell Control Panel connection block, as shown in Figure 4-35.

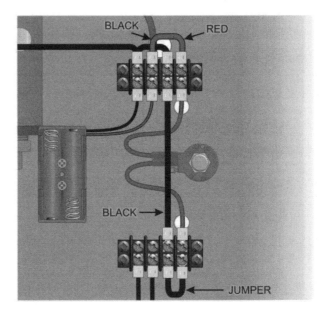

Figure 4-35:
Jumpers
Installed

11. Set the multimeter function selector switch to measure voltage using the 20 Vdc setting.

12. Move the Fuel Cell Disconnect Switch to the **ON** position.

In the next step, if there is not an immediate indication on the multimeter of a voltage increase, perform the following steps to remove any blockage in the fuel cells that may be occurring:

- Completely close the Flow Control valve at the exit port of the Fuel Cell #2.

- Quickly turn the valve so it is completely open.

- When the voltage begins to increase, close the Flow Control valve.

This will remove any blockage allowing hydrogen to flow into fuel cells.

13. Open the H_2 flow control valve to allow hydrogen to flow into the fuel cell stack.

14. Observe the current and voltage produced at the Fuel Cell Control Panel connection block output terminals. The voltage level should rise slowly to its maximum open circuit potential. Record the voltage and current levels being produced by the fuel cell stack after 1 minute of operation on the following lines:

Voltage: _____

Current: _____

15. Use Ohms Law for power to calculate the amount of power being consumed by the load and record your answer on the following line:

Power: _____

16. Reset the potentiometer to its mid range resistance setting (2.4kΩ).

17. Observe and record the current and voltage produced at the Fuel Cell Control Panel connection block output terminals on the following lines:

Voltage: _____

Current: _____

18. Use Ohms Law for power to calculate the amount of power being consumed by the load and record your answer on the following line:

Power: _____

19. Reset the potentiometer to its maximum resistance setting (5.1kΩ).

20. Observe and record the current and voltage produced at the Fuel Cell Control Panel connection block output terminals on the following lines:

Voltage: _____

Current: _____

21. Use Ohms Law for power to calculate the amount of power being consumed by the load and record your answer on the following line:

Power: _____

22. Turn the Fuel Cell Disconnect Switch to the **OFF** position.

23. Close the H_2 flow control valve to stop the flow of hydrogen to the fuel cell stack.

24. Turn the multimeter **Off** and remove the leads from the two Fuel Cell Control Panel connection blocks.

25. Remove the black jumper wire from the right two terminals on the bottom row of the Fuel Cell Load connection block.

Supplying Electrical Loads from Fuel Cells

Fuel Cells

When the fuel cells are wired in series with each other, their individual voltages add together to provide a greater push on the conductors and loads in the external circuit. However, this creates a single pathway for current to flow through all the fuel cells. This limits the current output that the fuel cell stack can deliver to a given load.

Remember that the materials used to make fuel cells also possess some resistance to giving up electrons. This is known as the fuel cell's internal resistance and creates an internal opposition to current flowing through the cell when the load requires additional external current flow. This is described in Ohm's Law for current, voltage and resistance:

$$I = \frac{V}{R}$$

where I is current in Amperes, V is voltage in Volts and R is resistance in Ohms.

An alternative to serial connections is to wire the fuel cells in parallel with each other. In this configuration, each fuel cell represents an independent path for current flow, which is added with the current flows from the other fuel cells and delivered to the external conductors and the load. In this arrangement the push applied to the external circuitry and load is not the sum of the battery voltages, but is equal to the voltage of the individual cells that make up the stack.

1. Confirm that the wires from the Fuel Cell Light to the lower-left terminals of the Fuel Cell Load connection block are connected. (The polarity of the light does not matter as it will operate the same in either direction.)

2. Add jumper wires between the battery connection at the two lower left-most terminals of the Fuel Cell Control Panel connection block and the light connections at the two top-left terminals of the Fuel Cell Load connection block.

NOTE: Make certain there are no batteries installed in the battery charging pack at this time.

3. Move the Fuel Cell Disconnect Switch to the **ON** position.

NOTE: In the next step, if the Fuel Cell Light does not illuminate, perform the following steps to remove any blockage in the fuel cells that may be occurring:

- *Completely close the Flow Control valve at the exit port of the fuel cell.*

- *Quickly turn the valve so it is completely open.*

- *When the voltage begins to increase, close the Flow Control valve.*

This will remove any blockage allowing hydrogen to flow into fuel cells and the Fuel Cell Light will turn on.

4. Open the H_2 flow control valve to allow hydrogen to flow into the fuel cell stack.

5. Allow 5 seconds to pass, then close the H_2 Flow Control valve to stop hydrogen flow into the fuel cell stack.

6. On the following line, record the time when the H_2 Flow Control valve was closed:

   Close Time: _____

7. Note the intensity of the light as time passes. Record your observations after 2 minutes of operation on the following line:

   _____

8. Turn the Fuel Cell Disconnect Switch to the **OFF** position.

Reconfigure the Fuel Cell Stack for Series Operation

Fuel Cells

1. Remove all connectted wires from the outputs of Fuel Cells #1 and #2 at the right-hand side of the Fuel Cell Configuration connection block.

2. Form a series fuel cell connection by attaching a jumper wire between the positive (+) terminal of Fuel Cell #2 and the negative (-) terminal of Fuel Cell #1, as illustrated in Figure 4-36.

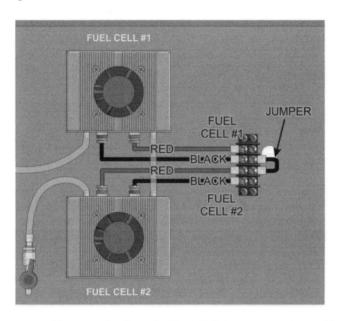

**Figure 4-36:
Connecting Fuel
Cells in Series**

3. Reconnect the red jumper wire from the Fuel Cell Ammeter to the positive terminal of Fuel Cell #1 and the black lead from the Fuel Cell Control Panel connection block to the negative terminal of Fuel Cell #2.

4. Move the Fuel Cell Disconnect Switch to the **ON** position.

NOTE: In the next step, if the Fuel Cell Light does not illuminate, perform the following steps to remove any blockage in the fuel cells that may be occurring:

*   *Completely close the Flow Control valve at the exit port of the fuel cell.*

*   *Quickly turn the valve so it is completely open.*

*   *When the voltage begins to increase, close the Flow Control valve.*

This will remove any blockage allowing hydrogen to flow into fuel cells and the Fuel Cell Light will turn on.

5. Open the H_2 flow control valve to allow hydrogen to flow into the fuel cell stack.

6. Allow 5 seconds to pass then close the H_2 flow control valve to stop hydrogen flow into the fuel cell stack.

7. On the following line, record the time when the H_2 flow control valve was closed:

   Close Time: _____

8. Note the intensity of the light as time passes. Record your observations after 1 minute of operation on the following line:

   _____

9. Turn the Fuel Cell Disconnect Switch to the **OFF** position.

10. On the following lines, explain how the illumination of the Fuel Cell Light was different from the previous procedure. Why?

    _____

    _____

    _____

11. Remove the two jumper wires between the battery connection at the two lower left-most terminals of the Fuel Cell Control Panel connection block and the two top-left terminals of the Fuel Cell Load connection block.

    This concludes the Configuration procedures of the "Advanced Fuel Cell Operation" lab. Have your instructor check your progress. Also check the volume of hydrogen remaining in your storage vessel. Determine whether you will need to generate more hydrogen before moving on to the final procedure of this lab.

Fuel Cells

Using Fuel Cells in Transportation

As mentioned earlier, one of the leading applications for fuel cells is in the area of transportation. In this section you will use the output from the fuel cell stack to drive an electric motor.

You can place a variable resistance in line with the motor to control its speed. In this procedure you will be using a variable resistance called a potentiometer to control the amount of current supplied to the motor. This variable resistance is a second load in the circuit that uses a proportional amount of the electrical push/pull applied to the circuit—it takes some of the voltage and current from the motor. The amount of voltage applied to the variable resistance is referred to as its voltage drop. Figure 4-37 depicts the schematic representation of the motor's potentiometer control circuit.

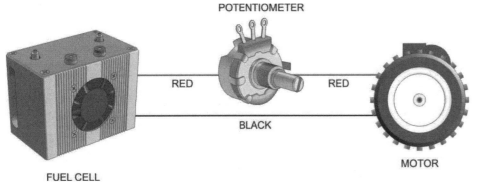

Figure 4-37: Motor Control Circuitry

The direction of the DC motor is controlled by the direction of current flow through the motor. Of course this is controlled by the polarity of the voltage applied to the motor input. In a vehicle this can be accomplished manually through a switch, or electronically using switching circuitry. In this procedure you will control the direction of the motor by switching the polarity of the input applied to the motor.

1. Locate the model race car kit and obtain only the race car chassis with wheel and motor, as shown in Figure 4-38. (If the body is attached, carefully remove it and return it to the kit box.

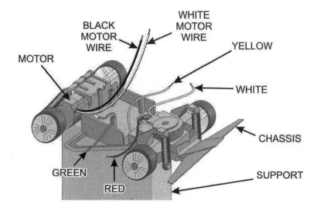

Figure 4-38: Race Car

2. Place the race car chassis on a support, so that it is suspended and the wheels are free to turn without the chassis moving.

3. Obtain 12" lengths of red and black 12 AWG wire. On one end of the red wire attach a red male spade connector and on one end of the black wire attach a red female spade connector.

4. On the opposite end of the red and black wires attach red fork connectors.

5. On the white wire from the race car motor attach a red female spade connector and on the black wire from the motor attach a red male connector.

6. Connect the red wire male spade connector to the white motor wire female spade connector and the black wire female spade connector to the black motor wire male spade connector.

7. Connect the black 12 AWG wire fork connector to the bottom row right-center terminal on the Fuel Cell Load connection block and the red 12 AWG wire fork connector to the bottom row right-most terminal on the Fuel Cell Load connection block.

The wiring of the Fuel Cell Motor section should appear as shown in Figure 4-39.

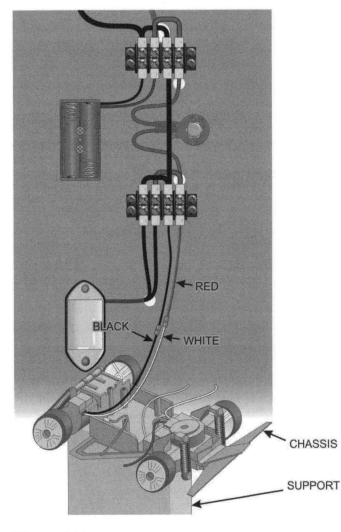

← RED

BLACK → ← WHITE

← CHASSIS

← SUPPORT

Figure 4-39:
Race Car Wiring

8. Make certain the Motor Speed Control potentiometer is in the **Maximum** or **On** position, the potentiometer shaft rotated fully counter clockwise (CCW).

9. Move the Fuel Cell Disconnect Switch to the **ON** position.

In the next step, if there is not an immediate indication of the wheels on the race car turning, perform the following steps to remove any blockage in the fuel cells that may be occurring:

- Completely close the Flow Control valve at the exit port of the Fuel Cell #2.

- Quickly turn the valve so it is completely open.

- When the voltage begins to increase, close the Flow Control valve.

This will remove any blockage allowing hydrogen to flow into fuel cells and run the race car motor, turning the wheels.

10. Open the H_2 flow control valve to allow hydrogen to flow into the fuel cell stack, and begin turning the motor and spinning the rear wheels.

11. Describe the relative speed of the motor and the direction in which it is turning:

   Full On Speed: _____

   Full On Direction: _____

12. Use the mulitmeter to measure the voltage developed across the motor speed control potentiometer and then across the motor, as illustrated in Figure 4-40. Record the voltages on the following lines:

   Full On Control Voltage: _____

   Full On Motor Voltage: _____

13. Rotate the Motor Speed Control potentiometer to the mid range resistance setting and observe the actions of the motor. Record the action of the motor and the direction in which it is turning:

   Half On Speed: _____

   Half On Direction: _____

   Half On Control Voltage: _____

   Half On Motor Voltage: _____

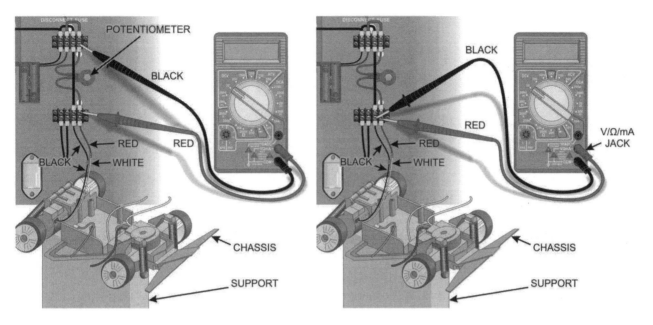

14. Rotate the Motor Speed Control potentiometer to full **Off** and observe the actions of the motor. Record the action of the motor:

    Full Off Operation: _____

    Full Off Control Voltage: _____

    Full Off Motor Voltage: _____

15. Reverse the positions of the DC motor wires connected to the Fuel Cell Load connection block and repeat Steps 9 through 14 and record your results on the following lines:

    Full On Speed: _____

    Full On Direction: _____

    Full On Control Voltage: _____

    Full On Motor Voltage: _____

    Half On Speed: _____

    Half On Direction: _____

    Half On Control Voltage: _____

    Half On Motor Voltage: _____

    Full Off Operation: _____

    Full Off Control Voltage: _____

    Full Off Motor Voltage: _____

Figure 4-40: Measuring Control and Motor Voltages

16. Turn the Fuel Cell Disconnect Switch to the **OFF** position.

17. Close the H$_2$ flow control valve to stop the flow of hydrogen to the fuel cell stack.

18. Disconnect the motor wiring from the Fuel Cell Load connection block.

This concludes the Transportation procedure of the "Advanced Fuel Cell Operation" lab. Have your instructor check your progress. Also check the volume of hydrogen remaining in your storage vessel. Determine whether you will need to generate more hydrogen before moving on to the final procedure of this lab.

Fuel Cells

Charging Batteries with Fuel Cells

While other alternative energy sources, such as wind turbines and solar panels, are routinely used to recharge storage batteries, fuel cells are not typically associated with this application. However, in remote power supply operations you may find fuel cells working in conjunction with other sources to provide power under different environmental circumstances. In these applications the output of the fuel cell may be used to charge storage batteries for later operations. In this section you will use the fuel cell stack to recharge a battery pack.

Recharging batteries requires that a reverse current be forced through the batteries to reverse the internal electrochemical charging action and return the internal makeup of the batteries to their original states. This requires a reverse voltage high enough to overpower the output voltage produced by the batteries.

NOTE: The system will not be able to safely charge fully charged batteries. Make sure batteries have been at least partially discharged before performing this procedure.

1. Before installing rechargeable batteries in the battery pack, make sure that the Fuel Cell Disconnect Switch on the panel is in the **OFF** position.

2. Obtain two rechargeable AA batteries and install them in the battery pack of the Clean Electron Generation panel, as described in Figure 4-41. Make certain to install the batteries using the correct polarities.

3. The battery pack is wired so that the batteries inside are in series with each other. Calculate the total voltage of these batteries if they are charged to their full potential. Record the results of this calculation on the following line:

Calculated Battery Voltage: _____

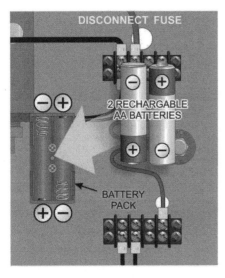

Figure 4-41: Installing Rechargeable Batteries

4. Place the multimeter across the battery connection at the two lower-left terminals of the Fuel Cell Control Panel connection block to measure the voltage level being produced by the batteries. (Because the Disconnect switch is in the **OFF** position, the only voltage that can be present at these terminals is the voltage being produced from the batteries) Record the initial battery voltage on the following line:

Initial Battery Voltage: _____

5. Move the Fuel Cell Disconnect Switch to the **ON** position.

6. Open the H$_2$ flow control valve to allow hydrogen to flow into the fuel cell stack.

7. After about 1 minute of operation, record the voltage level across the batteries and the current flow through the Fuel Cell ammeter on the following lines:

   Battery Charging Voltage (Multimeter reading): _____

   Battery Charging Current (Ammeter reading): _____

8. Periodically move the Fuel Cell Disconnect switch to the **OFF** position and check the voltage level of the batteries. If the voltage is below the initial combined voltage of the batteries, return the switch to the **On** position and continue charging the batteries.

9. When the battery voltage reaches the initial combined voltage of the batteries with the Disconnect Switch in the **OFF** position, leave the Fuel Cell Disconnect Switch in the **OFF** position.

10. Close the H$_2$ flow control valve to stop the flow of hydrogen to the fuel cell stack.

11. Connect the jumper wires between the bottom row battery connection left two terminals at the Fuel Cell Control Panel connection block and the light connections at the two top left terminals of the Fuel Cell Load connection block. You should see the lamp light dimly.

12. Monitor the battery voltage until it drops by 10 percent. At this time, remove the multimeter leads and the two jumper wires between the lower left terminals of the Fuel Cell Control Panel connection block and the upper left two terminals of the Fuel Cell Load connection block.

13. Remove the rechargeable batteries from the battery pack and store them safely.

14. Remove the black jumper wire from the top row left-most terminal on the Fuel Cell Control Panel connection block and the negative (-) terminal of Fuel Cell #2 on the Fuel Cell Configuration connection block.

15. Remove the short red jumper wire from the positive (+) terminal of Fuel Cell #2 to the negative (-) terminal of Fuel Cell #1 on the Fuel Cell Configuration connection block.

16. Remove the red jumper wire from the positive (+) terminal of Fuel Cell #1 on the Fuel Cell Configuration connection block to the positive (+) terminal on the Fuel Cell Ammeter.

17. Remove the red jumper wire from the negative (-) terminal on the Fuel Cell Ammeter and the upper spade terminal on the Fuel Cell Fuse Holder.

18. Remove the red jumper wire from the bottom terminal on the Fuel Cell Fuse Holder and the top terminal on the Fuel Cell Disconnect Switch.

19. Remove the red jumper wire from the bottom terminal on the Fuel Cell Disconnect Switch and the top row left-center terminal on the Fuel Cell Control Panel connection block.

20. Remove the power source wires from the bottom row left two terminals of the Fuel Cell Power connection block.

21. Remove the red jumper from the top row left-center terminal on the Fuel Cell Power connection block.

22. Remove the red jumper from the positive (+) terminal of the Electrolyzer and the lower outboard terminal on the Safety Pressure Switch.

23. Remove the black jumper wire from the negative (-) terminal of the Electrolyzer and the top row left-most terminal on the Fuel Power connection block.

24. Drain the solution from the Electrolyzer into a container by opening the Flow Control valve at the bottom of the Electrolyzer and the two Flow Control valves on the tops of the Electrolyzer.

25. Open the two Flow Control valves on the tops of the Bubbler vessels to remove the H_2 and O_2 gasses from the storage vessels.

26. Using appropriate containers, drain the H_2 and O_2 Storage vessels of all liquid by removing the plugs from the bottom of the H_2 and O_2 Storage vessels.

27. When all liquids have been drained from the Electrolyzer, Storage and Bubbler vessels, close all Flow Control valves.

This concludes the "Battery Charging" procedure of the "Advanced Fuel Cell Operation" lab. Have your instructor check your progress and review your results.

Procedure 14 Questions

1. Of the three energy types that electron current flow can be converted into, what type of energy is produced by the resistors in this procedure?

2. Of the three energy types that electron current flow can be converted into, what type of energy is produced by the lamp used in this procedure?

3. Of the three energy types that electron current flow can be converted into, what type of energy is produced by the motor?

4. How does the polarity of the voltage supply affect the operation of a DC motor?

5. How does the Speed Control potentiometer affect the motor circuit?

6. Describe the meter set up required to measure component resistance.

7. What happens to the motor when the amount of inline control resistance is increased?

8. What conditions are required to recharge a rechargeable battery?

PROCEDURE 15 – FUEL CELL RESEARCH

Fuel Cells

A greater number of information sources are available to modern students than ever before, making it easier for them to participate in successful scholarship. However, students must still be capable of conducting research, or at the very least developing the necessary skills to do so. Surprisingly, the ability to research a given subject continues to be underrated by many. They consider traditional avenues of research involving cardfile searching, book reading, newspaper clipping, and magazine microfilming to be boring. With so much of this information now available through Internet browsing, library terminals and home computers are often used to conduct the necessary information searches.

However, in order to avoid the unwanted exposure to overwhelming amounts of information, students require basic Internet research skills. They must acquire or strengthen the capability of locating relevant information quickly, while not wasting valuable time searching through mountains of available data. In order to effectively utilize the time spent researching fuel cell technology, the student must make effective use Internet search engines, which are available with most services. Advanced searching methods will help to zero-in on the desired information quickly.

To locate documents containing an exact phrase, type the phrase, surrounded by quotation marks, into the search field. For example, by typing *"fuel cells"* (with the quotation marks) will return documents that contain the phrase *fuel cells*, but not Web pages that contain only *fuel* or *cells*. To locate documents containing these words, but not necessarily together, type the words separated by the Boolean operator *AND* in all caps. For example, typing *fuel AND cells* (without the quotation marks) will return Web pages that contain *fuel*, *cells*, and *fuel cells*.

To locate documents containing either one word or the other, type the words separated by the Boolean operator *OR* in all caps. For example, typing *fuel OR cells* (without the quotation marks) will return documents that contain *fuel*, or *cells*, or both.

Keep in mind that certain words can be deliberately excluded from a search, as well. For example, to exclude a word from the search, type the word to be excluded into the search field, preceded by the Boolean operator *NOT* in all caps. Using this approach, typing *fuel NOT cells* (without the quotation marks) will return only documents that do contain the word *fuel*, and do not contain the word *cells*. To zero in on documents that contain two terms separated by between 10 to 25 words, type the two terms separated by the Boolean operator *NEAR*, in all caps, into the search field. If the search expression is lengthy or complicated, use parentheses to separate the different parts. For example, typing *fuel OR cells NOT (hydrogen OR stacked)* will get you entries that have the words *fuel*, or *cells*, or both, but do not have the words *hydrogen* or *stacked*.

There is no known way to completely identify, catalog, or retrieve the billions of individual files residing on the Internet. Consider the fact that thousands more have probably been added to the stack during the time you've taken to read this far. However, various data delivery services are available, including electronic mail, file transfers, Internet group memberships, interactive collaborations, and multimedia displays. In an effort to reduce the complexity of locating and retrieving the necessary information, data services use a number of Internet protocols.

Nevertheless, the student must bear responsibility for dealing with the fact that Internet addresses are frequently changed, or even removed. This makes Internet websites extremely volatile, whereby the copying and storage of useful text and graphics research material becomes an immediate concern. Once the necessary data has been successfully downloaded, it will remain available regardless of the future status of the source Internet site.

Often, the information provided on an Internet site is protected, or formatted in such a way as to prevent it from being copied. Product vendor websites use this approach to protect proprietary information. In these situations, the researcher may find it necessary to type and save the relevant text using a word processor. Third-party graphics tools may be required to capture and convert pictures and illustrations into usable picture formats when they cannot be copied directly.

Keep in mind that Internet information can be posted by anyone, for any reason. Therefore, the information you choose to use must be verified for correctness and integrity. This is in contrast to any data you gather using the traditional researching formats previously mentioned, because in those cases a certain amount of verification has already been conducted by the publishers. However, you should never assume that the information you gather from an Internet site, a newspaper, or a magazine/book article is completely accurate, or even true. When information can be verified from a variety of sources, it becomes more likely that it is accurate!

Resources Needed:

- Books

- Newspapers

- Magazines

- Computer with Internet access and graphic capture software

Fuel cell power strategies and components are vital to the creation of alternative energy resources, so your beginning research should be concerned with identifying those strategies and components, while learning how they augment the production of alternative energies.

1. Examine the following list of fuel cell power strategies. The Alternative Energy technician will need to be familiar with the categories mentioned here.

    - Fuel cell types

    - Fuel cell connections

    - Fuel cell power generation capabilities

    - Stacked fuel cell parameters

    - Hydrogen source and storage options

    - Excess energy management

2. Use Tables 4-4 through 4-10 to organize specified details about the various types of fuel cells listed. For each type described, try to locate information about its operation, its advantages, and its drawbacks.

Table 4-4: Fuel Cell Types

TYPE	DESCRIPTION	OPERATIONS	DRAWBACKS	ADVANTAGES

Table 4-5: Fuel Cell Connections

CONNECTION TYPE	DESCRIPTION	ADVANTAGES	DRAWBACKS

Table 4-6: Fuel Cell Power Generation Capabilities

TYPE	DESCRIPTION	ELECTROLYTE	POWER	EFFICIENCY

Table 4-7: Stacked Fuel Cells

INVENTOR	TITLE	DATE	DESCRIPTION	SPECIFICS

Table 4-8: Hydrogen Sources and Production

SOURCE	DESCRIPTION	ANALYSIS	DRAWBACKS

Table 4-9: Hydrogen Storage Options

OPTION	DESCRIPTION	ANALYSIS	DRAWBACKS

Table 4-10: Fuel Cell Excess Energy Management

TYPE	DESCRIPTION	POLICY	ANALYSIS

The Alternative Energy technician should also be familiar with the way in which a fuel cell system is kept from overheating. This is because energy costs and production constraints make the protection of fuel cell systems more and more imperative.

To make your remaining research time more productive, concentrate on information about cooling strategies for fuel cell systems in the areas listed below. This type of research will be of benefit for checking out ideas for the cooling of a fuel cell, including the particular requirements of the local and national governing agencies. Information gathered here will help when considering and comparing specific fuel cell cooling strategies and the disposal of its basic raw materials.

3. Examine the following list. It identifies fuel cell cooling strategies and raw material disposal schemes with which an Alternative Energy technician will most likely be working.

    - Cooling

    - Raw material disposal

4. Use Tables 4-11 and 4-12 to organize the specified details about the fuel cell cooling strategies and raw material disposal schemes listed. For each item, try to locate at least two information sources.

Table 4-11: Fuel Cell Cooling Strategies

COOLING STRATEGY	DESCRIPTION	ANALYSIS	CONCLUSION

Table 4-12: Fuel Cell Raw Material Disposal Schemes

FORMULA	MATERIAL	PURPOSE/CAUSE	REDUCTION, REUSE, RECYCLING, DISPOSAL

Residential or rural farm clients seeking to install their own fuel cell power generating systems usually require some practical information and advice on addressing the existing barriers to home and farm fuel cell projects. For example, they need to understand when and how to approach their local boards and state agencies in order to secure the necessary permits, including the necessity of building support for their proposed installations. They need to understand how to work successfully with their installer and with their local utilities in order to interconnect their fuel cell systems.

Applicable Regulations

Various local, state, or federal regulating bodies have jurisdiction over residential alternative energy sources. A completed fuel cell power installation must satisfy specific requirements; otherwise, it testifies to the ignorance of the Residential Alternative Energy technicians who installed it.

Local

Local coding authorities are often very sensitive about being ignored. This is because Residential Alternative Energy technicians usually make a great effort to strictly adhere to the federal and state regulations with which they are most familiar. This adherence is often good enough to result in the installation of a locally compliant fuel cell power system, but not always. Local codes usually involve local commercial generating structures rather than residential installations. However, these codes must also be taken into account before any installation begins! In addition, when local governments opt to run their own power generation systems, they often end up offering spare capacity to the local community. City or county restrictions have increased with the advent of residential power generating equipment, especially in communities where local governments directly control their own power production facilities. These arrangements have often resulted in the subsequent prosecution for chronic violators of local power generating regulations.

Local power generating code information can be obtained from local planning commissions or coding departments. These bodies are usually responsible for controlling the governmental utility development in the local community, including the power planning commission. Specific information about residential alternative energy installations and/or equipment requirements not addressed by state or federal codes can be gathered by contacting your local planning commission, or the city/county agencies responsible for code enforcement. For example, environmental conditions could place unique restrictions on the local use of certain fuel cell power generating equipment.

5. Examine the following list. It identifies specific areas of concern regarding fuel cell installations and/or equipment that may be strictly controlled by your local codes.

    - Local fuel cell legislation

    - Local site data and analysis

6. Use Table 4-13 to organize the specified details about any local legislation regarding the use of fuel cell power installations and/or equipment. Use Table 4-14 to organize the specified details of local fuel cell site data. Try to locate more than one source of information for each area of concern.

Table 4-13: Local Fuel Cell Power Legislation

CITY/COUNTY	LEGISLATION/CODE	DATE	TITLE	DETAILS

Table 4-14: Local Fuel Cell Data and Analysis

AGENCY	DESCRIPTION	ANALYSIS	CONCLUSION

State

State-sponsored regulations are aimed at appropriate use of state resources in the development of alternative energy sources. These guidelines normally restrict the use of state resources to legitimate government or college business, support for various departmental mandates, or carrying out institutional missions. Energy generating sources that are used to power state governmental or university offices must comply with use requirements applying to any equipment to which they connect.

State governmental jurisdictions limit the legitimate uses of their energy resources to official legislative and administrative functions. Legal interagency agreements dictate that such resources must not be used for personal, commercial, or for-profit purposes without some form of official written approval. This makes it important to understand what the legitimate usage of state resources in the production of alternative energy in your state is. This information can be located by browsing your state government's web pages.

7. Examine the following list. It identifies specific areas of concern regarding fuel cell power installations and/or equipment that may be strictly controlled by your state codes.

   - State fuel cell legislation
   - State site data and analysis

8. Use Table 4-15 to organize the specified details about any state legislation regarding the use of fuel cell installations and/or equipment. Use Table 4-16 to organize the specified details of state fuel cell site data. Try to locate more than one source of information for each area of concern.

Table 4-15: State Fuel Cell Legislation

STATE	LEGISLATION/CODE	DATE	TITLE	DETAILS

Table 4-16: State Fuel Cell Data and Analysis

AGENCY	DESCRIPTION	ANALYSIS	CONCLUSION

Federal

Alternative energy manufacturers and consumers around the world recognize certain research facilities and/or governmental agencies that have been mandated to determine the suitability of fuel cell power as a viable energy resource. As various products have recently emerged, the recognition of suitable guidelines has helped to achieve some control over the technical development explosion in this field.

The federal organizations listed here can be consulted regarding the viability of various products relating to the use of fuel cells as an alternative energy resource. The Residential Alternative Energy technician can depend on the information published by these organizations to provide guidance in the selection of appropriate equipment for a particular installation.

Energy and Environmental Research Center (EERC)

The Energy and Environmental Research Center (EERC) is a research facility located in the southeast corner of the University of North Dakota (UND) in Grand Forks. It is recognized as one of the world's leading developers of cleaner, more efficient energy and environmental technologies to protect and clean our air, water, and soil. Originally founded in 1951 as the "U.S. Bureau of Mines—Robertson Lignite Research Laboratory," it became a federal energy technology center under the United States Department of Energy in 1977, and became known as the Energy and Environmental Research Center in 1989.

The EERC is a high-tech, nonprofit branch of UND. Yet, it operates like a business; conducts research, development, demonstration, and commercialization activities dedicated to moving promising technologies out of the laboratory and into the commercial marketplace. The EERC provides practical, cost-effective solutions to today's most critical energy and environmental issues and challenges. Its research portfolio consists of a wide array of strategic energy and environmental solutions, including clean coal technologies, CO_2 sequestration, energy and water sustainability, hydrogen technologies, air toxics and fine particulate, mercury measurement and control, alternative fuels, wind energy, biomass, water management, flood prevention, global climate change, waste utilization, energy-efficient technologies, and contaminant cleanup.

The EERC's business partners range in size from large multinational corporations to regional utilities to small local businesses. Its government partners include not only federal agencies such as the U.S. Department of Energy, the U.S. Environmental Protection Agency, the U.S. Department of Defense, and the U.S. Department of Agriculture, but also state and local government entities.

U.S. Department of Energy (DOE)

The Department of Energy's overarching mission is to advance the national, economic, and energy security of the United States. In order to do this, it promotes scientific and technological innovation, while working to ensure the environmental cleanup of the national nuclear weapons complex. Strategic goals to achieve the mission are designed to deliver results along five strategic themes, including:

- Energy security. The DOE's philosophy is that America's energy security should be achieved through the production of reliable, clean, and affordable energy.

- Nuclear security. Ensuring America's nuclear security is also a critical component of DOE's working agenda.

- Scientific discovery and innovation. The DOE works to strengthen scientific discovery, economic competitiveness, and to improve the quality of life in the United States through innovations in science and technology.

- Environmental responsibility. The DOE helps to protect the environment by providing a responsible resolution to the environmental legacy of nuclear weapons production.

- Management excellence. The DOE believes in enabling its mission through sound management.

National Renewable Energy Laboratory (NREL)

The National Renewable Energy Laboratory (NREL) is the nation's primary laboratory for renewable energy, and energy efficiency research and development. NREL's mission and strategy are focused on advancing the U.S. Department of Energy's and our nation's energy goals. It began operating in 1977 as the Solar Energy Research Institute. In September of 1991, it was designated a national laboratory of the U.S. Department of Energy (DOE), and its name changed to NREL.

The laboratory's scientists and researchers support critical market objectives to accelerate research from scientific innovations to market-viable alternative energy solutions. The laboratory thereby directly contributes to our nation's goal for finding new renewable ways to power our homes, businesses, and cars. At the core of this strategic direction are NREL's research and technology development areas, including an understanding of renewable resources for energy, the conversion of these resources to renewable electricity and fuels, and ultimately to the use of renewable electricity and fuels in homes, commercial buildings, and vehicles.

9. Search the information pages of several federal governmental agencies and locate the applicable policies regarding the operation of fuel cell power systems.

- Federal fuel cell legislation

- National site data and analysis

10. Use Table 4-17 to organize the specified details about any federally applicable legislation regarding the use of fuel cell installations and/or equipment. Use Table 4-18 to organize the specified details of federal fuel cell data. Try to locate more than one source of information for each area of concern.

Table 4-17: Federal Fuel Cell Legislation

AGENCY	LEGISLATION/CODE	DATE	TITLE	DETAILS

Table 4-18: Federal Fuel Cell Data and Analysis

AGENCY	DESCRIPTION	ANALYSIS	CONCLUSION

11. This concludes the hands-on lab procedure. Have your instructor review your results before moving on to the next procedure.

Procedure 15 Questions

1. What type of fuel cell cooling strategy involves the use of aluminum fins etched with micro channels?

2. Which is the efficiency of a Direct Methanol Fuel Cell (DMFC)?

3. What is the purpose of the American Recovery and Reinvestment Act of 2009?

4. What is the major drawback for using Microbial Fuel Cell technology for medical pacemakers?

5. In which physical state can a greater amount of hydrogen be stored for a given volume?

Fuel Cells

PROCEDURE 16 – FUEL CELL SYSTEM DESIGN

<u>Objectives:</u>

- Determine appropriate technology options for a given scenario.
- Match fuel cell panel output capabilities to a specified load.
- Determine equipment needed for this project.
- Calculate cost of implementing the design solution.

<u>Resources Needed:</u>

- Marcraft "*Generating Clean Electrons*" Text/Lab manual
- Internet connected computer or reference materials
- Completed Procedure # 15 – Fuel Cell Research

- Calculator
- Pencil and paper
- Library resources

ABOUT THE AUTHOR

Charles J. Brooks (A+, Network+, i-Net+, Server+, HTI+, MCP) is currently co-owner and vice president of Education Technologies Group Inc., as well as co-owner of eITPrep, LLP, an online training company. He is in charge of research and product development at both organizations. A former electronics instructor and technical writer with the National Education Corporation, Charles taught and wrote on post-secondary EET curriculum, including introductory electronics, transistor theory, linear integrated circuits, basic digital theory, industrial electronics, microprocessors, and computer peripherals. Charles has authored several books, including the first five editions of *A+ Certification Training Guide*, *The Complete Introductory Computer Course*, and *IBM PC Peripheral Troubleshooting & Repair*. He currently also writes about networking, residential technology integration and convergence.

Discussion

Read the following scenario:

> Your company has been contacted by the Acme Toy Company to produce an alternative energy version of their popular Marcraft Remote Control Race Car. They would like to introduce either a solar powered car, or one that runs on fuel cells.
>
> Their current race car model, depicted in Figure 4-42, is powered by four 1.5 volt (AA) batteries. The separate hand held controller uses a single 9-volt battery. The chassis of the current car design is 7.5 inches long and 5.5 inches wide. The battery box is 2.5 inches by 2.5 inches.
>
> The race car is propelled by a small electric motor, which provides variable forward and reverse speeds. The maximum current draw of the motor is approximately 1.3 mA at full speed. The motor uses 4.5 volts of the total 6.0 volt battery supply. The race car's control circuitry also provides proportional left and right steering with a minimal current draw from the fourth battery.

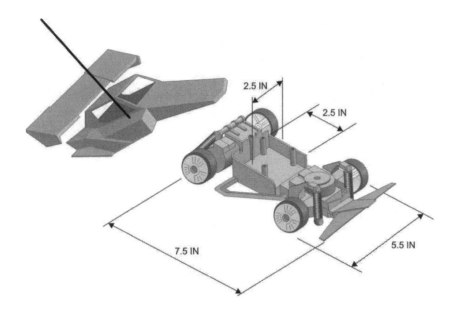

2.5 IN

2.5 IN

7.5 IN

5.5 IN

**Figure 4-42:
Race Car Chassis**

Fuel Cells

Procedure

1. How many of the PEM Fuel Cells on the Clean Electron Generation panel would be needed to deliver enough voltage to replace the four AA batteries?

   _____

2. Are the Marcraft PEM Fuel Cells physically compatible with the size of the current race car chassis?

   _____

3. How will hydrogen be applied to the fuel cells?

   _____

4. Will the current model support onboard hydrogen generation using a chemical electrolyzer? If not, is there another option for converting water into hydrogen on the chassis?

   _____

5. In your research, did you discover a fuel cell type or model that might be more compatible with the current chassis? If so, provide the manufacturer and model information on the following lines:

   Manufacturer: _____

   Model: _____

6. What is the power requirement of the current race car motor?

   _____

7. How long will your selected Fuel Cell operate on a 1 cm2 storage tank?

_____

8. Does your selected fuel cell have any temperature control requirements? If so, what are they and how will they be handled in the project.

_____

9. How will the customer obtain hydrogen to continue to operate the race car?

_____

_____

10. Can you recommend your fuel cell design over a similar solar panel design for cost and effectiveness?

_____

REVIEW QUESTIONS

The following questions test your knowledge of the material presented in this chapter.

1. What is the fuel cell membrane separating the two electrode materials called?

2. How does the anode's catalyst material affect hydrogen atoms?

3. What does the combination of hydrogen and oxygen atoms produce in a fuel cell?

4. What factor limits the current capabilities of a fuel stack?

5. What is the major drawback associated with DMFCs?

6. What type of electrolyte is used with alkaline fuel cells?

7. What is the normal operating temperature of solid oxide fuel cells (SOFCs)?

8. What is the process called that separates the elements of chemically bonded compounds from each other by passing an electric current through them?

9. During electrolysis, how is liquid solution collected that escapes from the electrolyzer?

10. According to OSHA, what constitutes a safe level for CO_2 gas in the atmosphere?

11. When does the pressure switch on the Marcraft electrolyzer engage?

12. In a fuel cell generating system, how are the ammeter, circuit breaker, and disconnect switch typically wired?

Material Data Safety Sheets

SODIUM CHLORIDE

SECTION 1: CHEMICAL PRODUCT IDENTIFICATION

Product Name: Sodium chloride
Catalog Codes: SLS3262, SLS1045, SLS3889, SLS1669, SLS3091
CAS#: 7647-14-5
RTECS: VZ4725000

TSCA: TSCA 8(b) inventory: Sodium chloride
CI#: Not applicable.
Synonym: Salt; Sea Salt
Chemical Name: Sodium chloride
Chemical Formula: NaCl

SECTION 2: COMPOSITION AND INFORMATION ON INGREDIENTS

Composition:

Name	CAS #	% by Weight
Sodium chloride	7647-14-5	100

Toxicological Data on Ingredients: Sodium chloride:

ORAL (LD50): Acute: 3000 mg/kg [Rat.]. 4000 mg/kg [Mouse].
DERMAL (LD50): Acute: >10000 mg/kg [Rabbit].
DUST (LC50): Acute: >42000 mg/m 1 hours [Rat].

SECTION 3: HAZARDS IDENTIFICATION

Potential Acute Health Effects: Slightly hazardous in case of skin contact (irritant), of eye contact (irritant), of ingestion, of inhalation.
Potential Chronic Health Effects:
CARCINOGENIC EFFECTS: Not available.
MUTAGENIC EFFECTS: Mutagenic for mammalian somatic cells. Mutagenic for bacteria and/or yeast.
TERATOGENIC EFFECTS: Not available.
DEVELOPMENTAL TOXICITY: Not available.
Repeated or prolonged exposure is not known to aggravate medical condition.

SECTION 4: FIRST AID MEASURES

Eye Contact:
Check for and remove any contact lenses. In case of contact, immediately flush eyes with plenty of water for at least 15 minutes. Cold water may be used. Get medical attention.
Skin Contact:
Wash with soap and water. Cover the irritated skin with an emollient. Get medical attention if irritation develops. Cold water may be used.
Serious Skin Contact: Not available.
Inhalation:

If inhaled, remove to fresh air. If not breathing, give artificial respiration. If breathing is difficult, give oxygen. Get medical attention if symptoms appear.
Serious Inhalation: Not available.
Ingestion:
Do NOT induce vomiting unless directed to do so by medical personnel. Never give anything by mouth to an unconscious person. Loosen tight clothing such as a collar, tie, belt or waistband. Get medical attention if symptoms appear.
Serious Ingestion: Not available.

SECTION 5: FIRE AND EXPLOSION DATA

Flammability of the Product: Non-flammable.
Auto-Ignition Temperature: Not applicable.
Flash Points: Not applicable.
Flammable Limits: Not applicable.
Products of Combustion: Not available.
Fire Hazards in Presence of Various Substances: Not applicable.
Explosion Hazards in Presence of Various Substances:
Risks of explosion of the product in presence of mechanical impact: Not available. Risks of explosion of the product in presence of static discharge: Not

available.
Fire Fighting Media and Instructions: Not applicable.
Special Remarks on Fire Hazards: When heated to decomposition it emits toxic fumes.
Special Remarks on Explosion Hazards:
Electrolysis of sodium chloride in presence of nitrogenous compounds to produce chlorine may lead to formation of explosive nitrogen trichloride. Potentially explosive reaction with dichloromaleic anhydride + urea.

SECTION 6: ACCIDENTAL RELEASE MEASURES

Small Spill:
Use appropriate tools to put the spilled solid in a convenient waste disposal container. Finish cleaning by spreading water on the contaminated surface and dispose of according to local and regional authority requirements.

Large Spill:
Use a shovel to put the material into a convenient waste disposal container. Finish cleaning by spreading water on the contaminated surface and allow to evacuate through the sanitary system.

SECTION 7: HANDLING AND STORAGES

Precautions:
Keep locked up.. Do not ingest. Do not breathe dust. Avoid contact with eyes. Wear suitable protective clothing. If ingested, seek medical advice immediately

and show the container or the label. Keep away from incompatibles such as oxidizing agents, acids.
Storage: Keep container tightly closed. Keep container in a cool, well-ventilated area. Hygroscopic

SECTION 8: EXPOSURE CONTROLS/PERSONAL PROTECTION

Engineering Controls:
Use process enclosures, local exhaust ventilation, or other engineering controls to keep airborne levels below recommended exposure limits. If user operations generate dust, fume or mist, use ventilation to keep exposure to airborne contaminants below the exposure limit.
Personal Protection:
Splash goggles. Lab coat. Dust respirator. Be sure to use an approved/certified respirator or equivalent. Gloves.

Personal Protection in Case of a Large Spill:
Splash goggles. Full suit. Dust respirator. Boots. Gloves. A self contained breathing apparatus should be used to avoid inhalation of the product. Suggested protective clothing might not be sufficient; consult a specialist BEFORE handling this product.
Exposure Limits: Not available.

SECTION 9: PHYSICAL AND CHEMICAL PROPERTIES

Physical state and appearance: Solid. (Solid crystalline powder.)
Odor: Slight.
Taste: Saline.
Molecular Weight: 58.44 g/mole
Color: White.
pH (1% soln/water): 7 [Neutral.]
Boiling Point: 1413°C (2575.4°F)
Melting Point: 801°C (1473.8°F)

Critical Temperature: Not available.
Specific Gravity: 2.165 (Water = 1)
Vapor Pressure: Not applicable.
Vapor Density: Not available.
Volatility: Not available.
Odor Threshold: Not available.
p. 3
Water/Oil Dist. Coeff.: Not available.
Ionicity (in Water): Not available.

SECTION 9: PHYSICAL AND CHEMICAL PROPERTIES (CONTINUED)

Dispersion Properties: See solubility in water.
Solubility:
Easily soluble in cold water, hot water.
Soluble in glycerol, and ammonia.
Very slightly soluble in alcohol.
Insoluble in Hydrochloric Acid.

SECTION 10: STABILITY AND REACTIVITY DATA

Stability: The product is stable.
Instability Temperature: Not available.
Conditions of Instability: Incompatible materials, high temperatures.
Incompatibility with various substances: Reactive with oxidizing agents, metals, acids.
Corrosivity: Not considered to be corrosive for metals and glass.

Special Remarks on Reactivity:
Hygroscopic.
Reacts with most nonnoble metals such as iron or steel, building materials (such as cement) Sodium chloride is rapidly attacked by bromine trifluoride.
Violent reaction with lithium.
Special Remarks on Corrosivity: Not available.
Polymerization: Will not occur.

SECTION 11: TOXICOLOGICAL INFORMATION

Routes of Entry: Inhalation. Ingestion.
Toxicity to Animals:
WARNING: THE LC50 VALUES HEREUNDER ARE ESTIMATED ON THE BASIS OF A 4-HOUR EXPOSURE.
Acute oral toxicity (LD50): 3000 mg/kg [Rat.].
Acute dermal toxicity (LD50): >10000 mg/kg [Rabbit].
Acute toxicity of the dust (LC50): >42000 mg/m3 1 hours [Rat].
Chronic Effects on Humans: MUTAGENIC EFFECTS: Mutagenic for mammalian somatic cells. Mutagenic for bacteria and/or yeast.
Other Toxic Effects on Humans: Slightly hazardous in case of skin contact (irritant), of ingestion, of inhalation.
Special Remarks on Toxicity to Animals: Lowest Published Lethal Dose (LDL) [Man] - Route: Oral; Dose: 1000 mg/kg
Special Remarks on Chronic Effects on Humans:
Causes adverse reproductive effects in humans (fetotoxicity, abortion,) by intraplacental route.
High intake of sodium chloride, whether from occupational exposure or in the diet, may increase risk of TOXEMIA OF PREGNANCY in susceptible women (Bishop, 1978). Hypertonic sodium chloride solutions have been used to induce abortion in late pregnancy by direct infusion into the uterus (Brown et al, 1972), but this route of administration is not relevant to occupational exposures.
May cause adverse reproductive effects and birth defects in animals, particularly rats and mice (fetotoxicity, abortion, musculoskeletal abnormalities, and maternal effects (effects on ovaries, fallopian tubes) by oral, intraperitoneal, intraplacental, intrauterine, parenteral, and subcutaneous routes. While sodium chloride has been used as a negative control n some reproductive studies, it has also been used as an example that almost any chemical can cause birth defects in experimental animals if studied under the right conditions (Nishimura & Miyamoto, 1969). In experimental animals, sodium chloride has caused delayed effects on newborns, has been fetotoxic, and has caused birth defects and abortions in rats and mice (RTECS, 1997).
May affect genetic material (mutagenic)
Special Remarks on other Toxic Effects on Humans:
Acute Potential Health Effects:
Skin: May cause skin irritation.
Eyes: Causes eye irritation.
Ingestion: Ingestion of large quantities can irritate the stomach (as in overuse of salt tablets) with nausea and vomiting. May affect behavior (muscle spasicity/contraction, somnolence), sense organs, metabolism, and cardiovascular system. Continued exposure may produce dehydration, internal organ congestion, and coma.
Inhalation: Material is irritating to mucous membranes and upper respiratory tract.

SECTION 12: ECOLOGICAL INFORMATION

Ecotoxicity: Not available.
BOD5 and COD: Not available.
Products of Biodegradation:
Possibly hazardous short term degradation products are not likely. However, long term degradation products may arise.

Toxicity of the Products of Biodegradation: The product itself and its products of degradation are not toxic.
Special Remarks on the Products of Biodegradation: Not available

SECTION 13: DISPOSAL CONSIDERATIONS

Waste Disposal:
Waste must be disposed of in accordance with federal, state and local environmental control regulations.

SECTION 14: TRANSPORT INFORMATION

DOT Classification: Not a DOT controlled material (United States).
Identification: Not applicable.
Special Provisions for Transport: Not applicable

SECTION 15: OTHER REGULATORY INFORMATION

Federal and State Regulations: TSCA 8(b) inventory: Sodium chloride
Other Regulations: EINECS: This product is on the European Inventory of Existing Commercial Chemical Substances.
Other Classifications:
WHMIS (Canada): Not controlled under WHMIS (Canada).
DSCL (EEC):
R40- Possible risks of irreversible effects.
S24/25- Avoid contact with skin and eyes.
HMIS (U.S.A.):
Health Hazard: 1

Fire Hazard: 0
Reactivity: 0
Personal Protection: E
National Fire Protection Association (U.S.A.):
Health: 1
Flammability: 0
Reactivity: 0
Specific hazard:
Protective Equipment:
Gloves. Lab coat. Dust respirator. (Be sure to use an approved/certified respirator or equivalent.) Splash goggles.

SODIUM BICARBONATE

SECTION 1: CHEMICAL PRODUCT IDENTIFICATION

Product Name: Sodium bicarbonate
Catalog Codes: SLS3241, SLS2446, SLS3868
CAS#: 144-55-8
RTECS: VZ0950000
TSCA: TSCA 8(b) inventory: Sodium bicarbonate
CI#: Not available.

Synonym: Baking Soda; Bicarbonate of soda; Sodium acid
carbonate; Monosodium carbonate; Sodium hydrogen
carbonate; Carbonic acid monosodium salt
Chemical Name: Sodium Bicarbonate
Chemical Formula: NaHCO3

SECTION 2: COMPOSITION AND INFORMATION ON INGREDIENTS

Composition:

Name	CAS #	% by Weight
Sodium Bicarbonate	144-55-8	100

Toxicological Data on Ingredients: Not applicable.

SECTION 3: HAZARDS IDENTIFICATION

Potential Acute Health Effects: Slightly hazardous in case of skin contact (irritant), of eye contact (irritant), of
ingestion, of inhalation.
Potential Chronic Health Effects:
CARCINOGENIC EFFECTS: Not available.
MUTAGENIC EFFECTS: Not available.
TERATOGENIC EFFECTS: Not available.
DEVELOPMENTAL TOXICITY: Not available.
Repeated or prolonged exposure is not known to aggravate medical condition.

SECTION 4: FIRST AID MEASURES

Eye Contact:
Check for and remove any contact lenses. In case of
contact, immediately flush eyes with plenty of water for
at least 15 minutes. Cold water may be used. Get
medical attention if irritation occurs.
Skin Contact:
Wash with soap and water. Cover the irritated skin with
an emollient. Get medical attention if irritation develops.
Cold water may be used.
Serious Skin Contact: Not available.
Inhalation:
If inhaled, remove to fresh air. If not breathing, give

artificial respiration. If breathing is difficult, give oxygen.
Get medical attention.
Serious Inhalation: Not available.
Ingestion:
Do NOT induce vomiting unless directed to do so by
medical personnel. Never give anything by mouth to an
unconscious person. Loosen tight clothing such as a
collar, tie, belt or waistband. Get medical attention if
symptoms appear.
Serious Ingestion: Not available.

SECTION 5: FIRE AND EXPLOSION DATA

Flammability of the Product: Non-flammable.
Auto-Ignition Temperature: Not applicable.
Flash Points: Not applicable.
Flammable Limits: Not applicable.
Products of Combustion: Not available.
Fire Hazards in Presence of Various Substances:
Not applicable.
**Explosion Hazards in Presence of Various
Substances:**

Risks of explosion of the product in presence of
mechanical impact: Not available.
Risks of explosion of the product in presence of static
discharge: Not available.
Fire Fighting Media and Instructions: Not applicable.
Special Remarks on Fire Hazards: When heated to
decomposition it emits acrid smoke and irritating fumes.
Special Remarks on Explosion Hazards: Not
available.

SECTION 6: ACCIDENTAL RELEASE MEASURES

Small Spill:
Use appropriate tools to put the spilled solid in a convenient waste disposal container. Finish cleaning by spreading water on the contaminated surface and dispose of according to local and regional authority requirements.

Large Spill:
Use a shovel to put the material into a convenient waste disposal container. Finish cleaning by spreading water on the contaminated surface and allow to evacuate through the sanitary system.

SECTION 7: HANDLING AND STORAGES

Precautions:
Do not ingest. Do not breathe dust. If ingested, seek medical advice immediately and show the container or the label. Keep away from incompatibles such as acids.

Storage: Keep container tightly closed. Keep container in a cool, well-ventilated area.

SECTION 8: EXPOSURE CONTROLS/PERSONAL PROTECTION

Engineering Controls:
Use process enclosures, local exhaust ventilation, or other engineering controls to keep airborne levels below recommended exposure limits. If user operations generate dust, fume or mist, use ventilation to keep exposure to airborne contaminants below the exposure limit.
Personal Protection: Safety glasses. Lab coat. Dust respirator. Be sure to use an approved/certified respirator or equivalent. Gloves.

Personal Protection in Case of a Large Spill:
Splash goggles. Full suit. Dust respirator. Boots. Gloves. A self contained breathing apparatus should be used to avoid inhalation of the product. Suggested protective clothing might not be sufficient; consult a specialist BEFORE handling this product.
Exposure Limits: Not available.

SECTION 9: PHYSICAL AND CHEMICAL PROPERTIES

Physical state and appearance: Solid.
Odor: Odorless.
Taste: Saline. Alkaline.
Molecular Weight: 84.01g/mole
Color: White.
pH (1% soln/water): Not available.
Boiling Point: Not available.
Melting Point: Not available.
Critical Temperature: Not available.
Specific Gravity: Density: 2.159 (Water = 1)
Vapor Pressure: Not applicable.
Vapor Density: Not available.
Volatility: Not available.

Odor Threshold: Not available.
Water/Oil Dist. Coeff.: Not available.
Ionicity (in Water): Not available.
Dispersion Properties: See solubility in water.
Solubility:
Soluble in cold water.
Slightly soluble in alcohol.
Solubility in Water: 6.4, 7.6, 8.7, 10.0, 11.3, 12.7, 14.2, 16.5, 19.1 g/100 solution at 0, 10, 20, 30, 40, 50, 60, 80, adn 100 deg. C, respectively.
Solubility in Water: 6.9, 8,2, 9.6, 11.1, 12.7, 14.5, 16.5, 19.7, and 23.6 g/100g water at 0, 10, 20, 30, 40, 50, 60, 80, 100 deg. C, respectively.

SECTION 10: STABILITY AND REACTIVITY DATA

Stability: The product is stable.
Instability Temperature: Not available.
Conditions of Instability: Incompatible materials, Moisture. Stable in dry air, but slowly decomposes in moist air.
Incompatibility with various substances: Reactive with acids.

Corrosivity: Non-corrosive in presence of glass.
Special Remarks on Reactivity:
Reacts with acids to form carbon dioxide.
Dangerous reaction with monoammonium phosphate or a sodium-potassium alloy.
Special Remarks on Corrosivity: Not available.
Polymerization: Will not occur.

SECTION 11: TOXICOLOGICAL INFORMATION

Routes of Entry: Inhalation. Ingestion.
Toxicity to Animals: Acute oral toxicity (LD50): 3360 mg/kg [Mouse].
Chronic Effects on Humans: Not available.
Other Toxic Effects on Humans: Slightly hazardous in case of skin contact (irritant), of ingestion, of inhalation.
Special Remarks on Toxicity to Animals: Not available.
Special Remarks on Chronic Effects on Humans: Sodium Bicarbonate as produced genetic effects in rats (unscheduled DNA synthesis). However, no affects have been found in humans.
Special Remarks on other Toxic Effects on Humans:
Acute Potential Health Effects:
Skin: May cause mild skin irritation.
Eyes: May cause mild eye irritation.
Inhalation: May cause respiratory tract irritation. Symptoms may include coughing and sneezing.
Ingestion: Symptoms of overexposure to Sodium Bicarbonate include thirst, abdominal pain, gastroenteritis, and inflammation of the digestive tract.
Chronic Potential Health Effects:
Skin: Repeated or prolonged skin contact may cause irritation, drying or cracking of the skin.
Ingestion and Inhalation: Chronic toxicity usually occurs within 4 to 10 days following ingestion of very large amounts. Repeated or prolonged ingestion or inhalation of large amounts may cause metabolic abnormalities, and sodium retention. Metabolic abnormalities such as acidosis, hypernatremia, hypochloremia, alkalosis, hypocalcemia, or sodium retention may affect the blood, kidneys, respiration (cyanosis, apnea secondary to metabolic acidosis or pulmonary edema), and cardiovascular system (tachycardia, hypotension). Severe toxicity may also affect behavior/central nervous system/nervous system. Neurological changes may result from metabolic abnormalities. These may include fatigue, irritability, dizziness, mental confusion, paresthesia, seizures, tetany, cerebral edema
Medical Conditions Aggravated by Exposure: Persons with pre-existing skin conditions might have increased sensitivity. Predisposing conditions that contribute to a mild alkali syndrome include, renal disease, dehydration, adn electrolyte imbalance, hypertension, sarcoidosis, congestive heart failure, edema, or other sodium retaining conditions.

SECTION 12: ECOLOGICAL INFORMATION

Ecotoxicity: Not available.
BOD5 and COD: Not available.
Products of Biodegradation:
Possibly hazardous short term degradation products are not likely. However, long term degradation products may arise.
Toxicity of the Products of Biodegradation: The product itself and its products of degradation are not toxic.
Special Remarks on the Products of Biodegradation: Not available.

SECTION 13: DISPOSAL CONSIDERATIONS

Waste Disposal:
Waste must be disposed of in accordance with federal, state and local environmental control regulations.

SECTION 14: TRANSPORT INFORMATION

DOT Classification: Not a DOT controlled material (United States).
Identification: Not applicable.
Special Provisions for Transport: Not applicable.

SECTION 15: OTHER REGULATORY INFORMATION

Federal and State Regulations: TSCA 8(b) inventory: Sodium bicarbonate
Other Regulations: Not available.
Other Classifications:
WHMIS (Canada): Not controlled under WHMIS (Canada).
DSCL (EEC): This product is not classified according to the EU regulations. Not applicable.
HMIS (U.S.A.):
Health Hazard: 1
Fire Hazard: 0
Reactivity:
Personal Protection: E
National Fire Protection Association (U.S.A.):
Health: 1
Flammability: 0
Reactivity: 0
Specific hazard:
Protective Equipment:
Gloves. Lab coat. Dust respirator. (Be sure to use an approved/certified respirator or equivalent.) Safety glasses.

POTASSIUM CARBONATE

SECTION 1: CHEMICAL PRODUCT IDENTIFICATION

Product Name: Potassium carbonate, anhydrous
Catalog Codes: SLP4780, SLP1951, SLP3760, SLP5575
CAS#: 584-08-7
RTECS: TS7750000
TSCA: TSCA 8(b) inventory: Potassium carbonate,

anhydrous
CI#: Not available.
Synonym: Salt of Tartar
Chemical Name: Potassium Carbonate
Chemical Formula: K2CO3

SECTION 2: COMPOSITION AND INFORMATION ON INGREDIENTS

Composition:

Name	CAS #	% by Weight
Potassium Carbonate	584-08-7	100

Toxicological Data on Ingredients: Potassium

carbonate, anhydrous: ORAL (LD50): Acute: 1870 mg/kg [Rat].

SECTION 3: HAZARDS IDENTIFICATION

Potential Acute Health Effects:
Hazardous in case of skin contact (irritant), of eye contact (irritant), of ingestion, of inhalation. Slightly hazardous in case of eye contact (corrosive).
Potential Chronic Health Effects:
CARCINOGENIC EFFECTS: Not available.
MUTAGENIC EFFECTS: Not available.

TERATOGENIC EFFECTS: Not available.
DEVELOPMENTAL TOXICITY: Not available.
The substance is toxic to mucous membranes.
The substance may be toxic to skin, eyes.
Repeated or prolonged exposure to the substance can produce target organs damage.

SECTION 4: FIRST AID MEASURES

Eye Contact:
Check for and remove any contact lenses. In case of contact, immediately flush eyes with plenty of water for at least 15 minutes. Cold water may be used. Get medical attention immediately.
Skin Contact:
In case of contact, immediately flush skin with plenty of water. Cover the irritated skin with an emollient. Remove contaminated clothing and shoes. Cold water may be used.Wash clothing before reuse. Thoroughly clean shoes before reuse. Get medical attention.
Serious Skin Contact:
Wash with a disinfectant soap and cover the

contaminated skin with an anti-bacterial cream. Seek immediate medical attention.
Inhalation:
If inhaled, remove to fresh air. If not breathing, give artificial respiration. If breathing is difficult, give oxygen. Get medical attention.
Serious Inhalation: Not available.
Ingestion:
Do NOT induce vomiting unless directed to do so by medical personnel. Never give anything by mouth to an unconscious person. If large quantities of this material are swallowed, call a physician immediately. Loosen tight clothing such as a collar, tie, belt or waistband.

SECTION 5: FIRE AND EXPLOSION DATA

Flammability of the Product: Non-flammable.
Auto-Ignition Temperature: Not applicable.
Flash Points: Not applicable.
Flammable Limits: Not applicable.
Products of Combustion: Not available.
Fire Hazards in Presence of Various Substances: Not applicable.
Explosion Hazards in Presence of Various Substances:

Risks of explosion of the product in presence of mechanical impact: Not available.
Risks of explosion of the product in presence of static discharge: Not available.
Fire Fighting Media and Instructions: Not applicable.
Special Remarks on Fire Hazards: Not available.
Special Remarks on Explosion Hazards: Not available.

SECTION 6: ACCIDENTAL RELEASE MEASURES

Small Spill:
Use appropriate tools to put the spilled solid in a convenient waste disposal container. Finish cleaning by spreading water on the contaminated surface and dispose of according to local and regional authority requirements.

Large Spill:
Use a shovel to put the material into a convenient waste disposal container. Finish cleaning by spreading water on the contaminated surface and allow to evacuate through the sanitary system.

SECTION 7: HANDLING AND STORAGES

Precautions:
Keep container dry. Do not ingest. Do not breathe dust. Never add water to this product. In case of insufficient ventilation, wear suitable respiratory equipment. If ingested, seek medical advice immediately and show the container or the label. Avoid contact with skin and eyes. Keep away from incompatibles such as oxidizing agents, metals, acids.

Storage:
Hygroscopic. Keep container tightly closed. Keep container in a cool, well-ventilated area. Do not store above 25°C (77°F).

SECTION 8: EXPOSURE CONTROLS/PERSONAL PROTECTION

Engineering Controls:
Use process enclosures, local exhaust ventilation, or other engineering controls to keep airborne levels below recommended exposure limits. If user operations generate dust, fume or mist, use ventilation to keep exposure to airborne contaminants below the exposure limit.

Personal Protection:
Splash goggles. Lab coat. Dust respirator. Be sure to use an approved/certified respirator or equivalent. Gloves.

Personal Protection in Case of a Large Spill:
Splash goggles. Full suit. Dust respirator. Boots. Gloves. A self contained breathing apparatus should be used to avoid inhalation of the product. Suggested protective clothing might not be sufficient; consult a specialist BEFORE handling this product.

Exposure Limits: Not available.

SECTION 9: PHYSICAL AND CHEMICAL PROPERTIES

Physical state and appearance: Solid. (Powdered solid. Deliquescent solid.)
Odor: Odorless.
Taste: Not available.
Molecular Weight: 138.21 g/mole
Color: White.
pH (1% soln/water): Not available.
Boiling Point: Decomposes.
Melting Point: 891°C (1635.8°F)
Critical Temperature: Not available.

Specific Gravity: 2.29 (Water = 1)
Vapor Pressure: Not applicable.
Vapor Density: Not available.
Volatility: Not available.
Odor Threshold: Not available.
Water/Oil Dist. Coeff.: Not available.
Ionicity (in Water): Not available.
Dispersion Properties: See solubility in water.
Solubility: Soluble in cold water.

SECTION 10: STABILITY AND REACTIVITY DATA

Stability: The product is stable.
Instability Temperature: Not available.
Conditions of Instability: Dust generation, moist air, water, incompatible materials
Incompatibility with various substances:
Reactive with oxidizing agents, metals, acids. Slightly reactive to reactive with moisture.
Corrosivity: Non-corrosive in presence of glass.

Special Remarks on Reactivity:
Hygroscopic.
Reacts with water to evolve heat.
Incompatible with KCO, chlorine trifluoride, calcium oxide, and magnesium.
Special Remarks on Corrosivity: Not available.
Polymerization: Will not occur.

SECTION 11: TOXICOLOGICAL INFORMATION

Routes of Entry: Eye contact. Inhalation. Ingestion.
Toxicity to Animals: Acute oral toxicity (LD50): 1870 mg/kg [Rat].
Chronic Effects on Humans:
Causes damage to the following organs: mucous membranes.
May cause damage to the following organs: skin, eyes.
Other Toxic Effects on Humans:
Hazardous in case of skin contact (irritant), of ingestion, of inhalation.
Slightly hazardous in case of eye contact (corrosive).
Special Remarks on Toxicity to Animals: Not available.
Special Remarks on Chronic Effects on Humans: Not available.
Special Remarks on other Toxic Effects on Humans:

Acute Potential Health Effects:
Skin: Causes severe skin irritation.
Eyes: It is severely irritating to the eyes and its mucous membranes. It may cause corneal injury. It may cause burns and loss of vision. It may cause permanent damage. The amount of tissue damage depends on the length of contact.
Ingestion: It causes gastrointestinal irritation with nausea, vomiting, abdominal pain, swollen glottis, increased respiration, and possible burns to the lips, tongue, oral mucosa, hypopharynx, stomach, or esophagus. It may affect the cardiovascular system(circulatory collapse), urinary system, and metabolism.
Inhalation: Causes respiratory tract and mucous membrane irritation. Exposure can cause coughing, chest pains, and difficulty breathing (dyspnea).

SECTION 12: ECOLOGICAL INFORMATION

Ecotoxicity: Not available.
BOD5 and COD: Not available.
Products of Biodegradation: Possibly hazardous short term degradation products are not likely. However, long term degradation products may arise.

Toxicity of the Products of Biodegradation: The products of degradation are less toxic than the product itself.
Special Remarks on the Products of Biodegradation: Not available.

SECTION 13: DISPOSAL CONSIDERATIONS

Waste Disposal:
Waste must be disposed of in accordance with federal, state and local environmental control regulations.

SECTION 14: TRANSPORT INFORMATION

DOT Classification: Not a DOT controlled material (United States).
Identification: Not applicable.
Special Provisions for Transport: Not applicable.

SECTION 15: OTHER REGULATORY INFORMATION

Federal and State Regulations: TSCA 8(b) inventory: Potassium carbonate, anhydrous
Other Regulations:
OSHA: Hazardous by definition of Hazard Communication Standard (29 CFR 1910.1200).
EINECS: This product is on the European Inventory of Existing Commercial Chemical Substances.
Other Classifications:
WHMIS (Canada):
CLASS D-2B: Material causing other toxic effects (TOXIC).
CLASS E: Corrosive solid.

DSCL (EEC):
R22- Harmful if swallowed.
R37/38- Irritating to respiratory system and skin.
R41- Risk of serious damage to eyes.
S2- Keep out of the reach of children.
S26- In case of contact with eyes, rinse immediately with plenty of water and seek medical advice.

SODIUM HYDROXIDE

SECTION 1: CHEMICAL PRODUCT IDENTIFICATION

Product Name: Sodium Hydroxide, 20%
Catalog Codes: SLS2788
CAS#: Mixture.
RTECS: Not applicable.
TSCA: TSCA 8(b) inventory: Sodium hydroxide; Water

CI#: Not applicable.
Synonym:
Chemical Name: Not applicable.
Chemical Formula: Not applicable.

SECTION 2: COMPOSITION AND INFORMATION ON INGREDIENTS

Composition:

Name	CAS #	% by Weight
Potassium Carbonate	1310-73-2	20
Water	7732-18-5	80

Toxicological Data on Ingredients: Sodium hydroxide LD50: Not available. LC50: Not available.

SECTION 3: HAZARDS IDENTIFICATION

Potential Acute Health Effects:
Very hazardous in case of skin contact (corrosive, irritant), of eye contact (irritant), of ingestion. Hazardous in case of inhalation. Liquid or spray mist may produce tissue damage particularly on mucous membranes of eyes, mouth and respiratory tract. Skin contact may produce burns. Inhalation of the spray mist may produce severe irritation of respiratory tract, characterized by coughing, choking, or shortness of breath. Inflammation of the eye is characterized by redness, watering, and itching. Skin inflammation is characterized by itching, scaling, reddening, or, occasionally, blistering.
Potential Chronic Health Effects:
Non-corrosive for skin. Non-irritant for skin. Non-

sensitizer for skin. Non-permeator by skin. Non-irritating to the eyes. Non-hazardous in case of ingestion. Non-hazardous in case of inhalation. CARCINOGENIC EFFECTS: Not available. MUTAGENIC EFFECTS: Not available. TERATOGENIC EFFECTS: Not available. DEVELOPMENTAL TOXICITY: Not available. The substance is toxic to lungs, mucous membranes. Repeated or prolonged exposure to the substance can produce target organs damage. Repeated or prolonged contact with spray mist may produce chronic eye irritation and severe skin irritation. Repeated or prolonged exposure to spray mist may produce respiratory tract irritation leading to frequent attacks of bronchial infection.

SECTION 4: FIRST AID MEASURES

Eye Contact:
Check for and remove any contact lenses. Immediately flush eyes with running water for at least 15 minutes, keeping eyelids open. Finish by rinsing thoroughly with running water to avoid a possible infection. Cold water may be used.
Skin Contact: If the chemical got onto the clothed portion of the body, remove the contaminated clothes as quickly as possible, protecting your own hands and body. Place the victim under a deluge shower. If the chemical got on the victim's exposed skin, such as the hands : Gently and thoroughly wash the contaminated skin with running water and non-abrasive soap. Be particularly careful to clean folds, crevices, creases and groin. Cold water may be used. If irritation persists, seek medical attention. Wash contaminated clothing before reusing.
Serious Skin Contact:
Wash with a disinfectant soap and cover the contaminated skin with an anti-bacterial cream. Seek

medical attention.
Inhalation: Allow the victim to rest in a well ventilated area. Seek immediate medical attention.
Serious Inhalation:
Evacuate the victim to a safe area as soon as possible. Loosen tight clothing such as a collar, tie, belt or waistband. If breathing is difficult, administer oxygen. If the victim is not breathing, perform mouth-to-mouth resuscitation. WARNING: It may be hazardous to the person providing aid to give mouth-to-mouth resuscitation when the inhaled material is toxic, infectious or corrosive. Seek immediate medical attention.
Ingestion:
Do not induce vomiting. Loosen tight clothing such as a collar, tie, belt or waistband. If the victim is not breathing, perform mouth-to-mouth resuscitation. Seek immediate medical attention.
Serious Ingestion: Not available.

SECTION 5: FIRE AND EXPLOSION DATA

Flammability of the Product: Non-flammable.
Auto-Ignition Temperature: Not applicable.
Flash Points: Not applicable.
Flammable Limits: Not applicable.
Products of Combustion: Not available.
Fire Hazards in Presence of Various Substances: Not applicable.
Explosion Hazards in Presence of Various

Substances:
Risks of explosion of the product in presence of mechanical impact: Not available.
Risks of explosion of the product in presence of static discharge: Not available.
Fire Fighting Media and Instructions: Not applicable.
Special Remarks on Fire Hazards: Not available.
Special Remarks on Explosion Hazards: Not available.

SECTION 6: ACCIDENTAL RELEASE MEASURES

Small Spill:
Dilute with water and mop up, or absorb with an inert dry material and place in an appropriate waste disposal container. If necessary: Neutralize the residue with a dilute solution of acetic acid.
Large Spill:
Corrosive liquid.
Stop leak if without risk. Absorb with DRY earth, sand or

other non-combustible material. Do not get water inside container. Do not touch spilled material. Use water spray curtain to divert vapor drift. Prevent entry into sewers, basements or confined areas; dike if needed. Call for assistance on disposal. Neutralize the residue with a dilute solution of acetic acid. Be careful that the product is not present at a concentration level above TLV. Check TLV on the MSDS and with local authorities.

SECTION 7: HANDLING AND STORAGES

Precautions:
Keep container dry. Do not breathe gas/fumes/vapour/spray. Never add water to this product In case of insufficient ventilation, wear suitable respiratory equipment If you feel unwell, seek medical attention and show the label when possible. Avoid contact with skin and

eyes Keep away from incompatibles such as moisture.
Storage:
Alkalis may be stored in heavy duty gauge steel containers. Corrosive materials should be stored in a separate safety storage cabinet or room.

SECTION 8: EXPOSURE CONTROLS/PERSONAL PROTECTION

Engineering Controls:
Provide exhaust ventilation or other engineering controls to keep the airborne concentrations of vapors below their respective threshold limit value.
Personal Protection:
Face shield Lab Coat Vapor respirator. Be sure to use an approved/certified respirator or equivalent. Gloves. Boots.
Personal Protection in Case of a Large Spill:

Splash goggles. Full suit. Vapor respirator. Boots. Gloves. A self contained breathing apparatus should be used to avoid inhalation of the product. Suggested protective clothing might not be sufficient; consult a specialist BEFORE handling this product.
Exposure Limits:
Sodium hydroxide CEIL: 2 (mg/m3) from ACGIH [1995]
Consult local authorities for acceptable exposure limits.

SECTION 9: PHYSICAL AND CHEMICAL PROPERTIES

Physical state and appearance: Liquid.
Odor: Odorless.
Taste: Not available.
Molecular Weight: Not applicable.
Color: Clear Colorless.
pH (1% soln/water): Basic.
Boiling Point: The lowest known value is 100°C (212°F) (Water).
Melting Point: Not available.
Critical Temperature: Not available.
Specific Gravity: Weighted average: 1.12 (Water = 1)

Vapor Pressure: The highest known value is 17.535 mm of Hg (@ 20°C) (Water).
Vapor Density: The highest known value is 0.62 (Air = 1) (Water).
Volatility: Not available.
Odor Threshold: Not available.
Water/Oil Dist. Coeff.: Not available.
Ionicity (in Water): Not available.
Dispersion Properties: See solubility in water.
Solubility: Easily soluble in cold water, hot water.

SECTION 10: STABILITY AND REACTIVITY DATA

Stability: The product is stable.
Instability Temperature: Not available.
Conditions of Instability: Not available.
Incompatibility with various substances: Not available.

Corrosivity: Slightly corrosive to corrosive in presence of glass.
Special Remarks on Reactivity: Not available.
Special Remarks on Corrosivity: Not available.
Polymerization: No.

SECTION 11: TOXICOLOGICAL INFORMATION

Routes of Entry: Absorbed through skin. Dermal contact. Eye contact. Inhalation. Ingestion.
Toxicity to Animals:
LD50: Not available.
LC50: Not available.
Chronic Effects on Humans: The substance is toxic to lungs, mucous membranes.
Other Toxic Effects on Humans:

Very hazardous in case of skin contact (corrosive, irritant), of ingestion. Hazardous in case of inhalation.
Special Remarks on Toxicity to Animals: Not available.
Special Remarks on Chronic Effects on Humans: Not available.
Special Remarks on other Toxic Effects on Humans: Not available.

SECTION 12: ECOLOGICAL INFORMATION

Ecotoxicity: Not available.
BOD5 and COD: Not available.
Products of Biodegradation:
Possibly hazardous short term degradation products are not likely. However, long term degradation products may arise.

Toxicity of the Products of Biodegradation: The product itself and its products of degradation are not toxic.
Special Remarks on the Products of Biodegradation: Not available.

SECTION 13: DISPOSAL CONSIDERATIONS

Waste Disposal:
Waste must be disposed of in accordance with federal, state and local environmental control regulations.

SECTION 14: TRANSPORT INFORMATION

DOT Classification: CLASS 8: Corrosive liquid.
Identification: : Sodium hydroxide, solution (Sodium hydroxide) : UN1824 PG: II
Special Provisions for Transport: Not available.

SECTION 15: OTHER REGULATORY INFORMATION

Federal and State Regulations: TSCA 8(b) inventory:
Pota**Federal and State Regulations:**
Pennsylvania RTK: Sodium hydroxide
Massachusetts RTK: Sodium hydroxide
TSCA 8(b) inventory: Sodium hydroxide; Water
Other Regulations: OSHA: Hazardous by definition of Hazard Communication Standard (29 CFR 1910.1200).
Other Classifications:
WHMIS (Canada):
CLASS D-2A: Material causing other toxic effects (VERY TOXIC).
CLASS E: Corrosive liquid.
DSCL (EEC): R35- Causes severe burns.
HMIS (U.S.A.):

Health Hazard: 3
Fire Hazard: 0
Reactivity: 0
Personal Protection:
National Fire Protection Association (U.S.A.):
Health: 2
Flammability: 0
Reactivity: 0
Specific hazard:
Protective Equipment:
Gloves. Lab coat. Vapor respirator. (Be sure to use an approved/certified respirator or equivalent.) Wear appropriate respirator when ventilation is inadequate. Face shield.

OXYGEN

SECTION 1: CHEMICAL PRODUCT IDENTIFICATION

Product Name: Oxygen
CAS: 7782-44-7
Oxygen; Oxygen, compressed (D.O.T.)
DOT I.D No.: UN 1072

Chemical Name and Synonyms: Oxygen
DOT Hazard Class: Division 2.2
Formula: O2 **Chemical Family:** Oxidizer

SECTION 2: COMPOSITION AND INFORMATION ON INGREDIENTS

Composition:

Name	CAS #	% by Weight
Potassium Carbonate	7782-44-7	100

Toxicological Data on Ingredients: Not available.

SECTION 3: HAZARDS IDENTIFICATION

Time Weighted Average Exposure Limit:
None established (ACGIH 1994-1995). Oxygen is the "vital element" in the atmosphere in which we live and breathe.
Symptoms of Exposure:
Breathing high concentrations (greater than 75 molar percent) causes symptoms of hyperoxia which includes cramps, nausea, dizziness, hypothermia, amblyopia, respiratory difficulties, bradycardia, fainting spells, and convulsions capable of leading to death. For additional information on hyperoxia, see Compressed Gas Association's Pamphlet P-14.

SECTION 4: FIRST AID MEASURES

Recommended First Aid Treatment:
Prompt medical attention is mandatory in all cases of overexposure to oxygen. Rescue personnel should be cognizant of extreme fire hazard associated with oxygen-rich atmosphere. Conscious persons should be assisted to an uncontaminated area and breathe fresh air. They should be kept warm and quiet. The physician should be informed that the victim is experiencing hyperoxia.
Unconscious persons should be moved to an uncontaminated area and given assisted respiration. When breathing has been restored, treatment should be as above. Continues treatment should be symptomatic and supportive.

SECTION 5: FIRE AND EXPLOSION DATA

Flash Point (Method used):
N/A Gas
Auto Ignition Temperature:
N/A
Flammable Limits % by Volume: LEL N/A
UEL N/A
Extinguishing Media: Copious quantities of water for fires with oxygen as the oxidizer.

Electrical Classification:
Nonhazardous
Special Fire fighting Procedures: If possible, stop the flow of oxygen, which is supporting the fire. If cylinders are involved in a fire, safely relocate or keep cool with water spray.
Unusual Fire and Explosion Hazards: Vigorously accelerates combustion.

SECTION 6: ACCIDENTAL RELEASE MEASURES

Steps to be taken in case material is released or spilled:
Evacuate all personnel from affected area. Use appropriate protective equipment. If leak is in user's equipment, be certain to purge piping with an inert gas to attempting repairs. If leak is in container or container valve, contact your closest supplier location or call the emergency telephone number listed herein.

SECTION 7: HANDLING AND STORAGES

Special Handling Recommendation:
Use only in well-ventilated areas. Valve protection caps and valve outlet threaded plugs must remain in place unless container is secured with valve outlet piped to use point. Do not drag, slide or roll cylinders. Use a suitable hand truck for cylinder movement. Use a pressure-reducing regulator when connecting cylinder to lower pressure (<3,000 psig) piping or systems. Do not heat cylinder by any means to increase the discharge rate of product from the cylinder. Use a check valve or trap in the discharge line to prevent hazardous back flow into the cylinder. For additional handling recommendations, consult Compressed Gas Association's Pamphlets P-1, P-14, and G-4.

Special Storage Recommendations:
Protect cylinders from physical damage. Store in cool, dry, well-ventilated area away from heavily trafficked areas and emergency exits and away from full or empty stored cylinders which contain flammable products. Do not allow the temperature where cylinders are stored to exceed 125F (52C). Cylinders should be stored upright and firmly secured to prevent falling or being knocked over. Full and empty cylinders should be segregated. Use a "first in -first out" inventory system to prevent full cylinders being stored for excessive periods of time. For additional storage recommendations, consult Compressed Gas Association's Pamphlets P-1, P-i4, and G-4.

Special Packaging Recommendations:
Carbon steels and low alloy steels are acceptable for use at lower pressures. For high pressure applications use stainless steels, copper and its alloys, nickel and its alloys, brass, bronze, silicon alloys, Monel®, Inconel®, or beryllium. Lead and silver or lead and tin alloys are good gasketing materials. Teflon® and Kel-F® are the preferred nonmetal gaskets. Special Note: It should be recognized that the ignition temperature of metals and nonmetals in pure oxygen service decreases with increasing oxygen pressure.

SECTION 8: EXPOSURE CONTROLS/PERSONAL PROTECTION

Respiratory Protection (Specify type): Positive pressure air line with mask or selfcontained breathing apparatus should be available for emergency use.
Ventilation: See Local Exhaust
Local Exhaust: To prevent accumulation above 25 molar percent.
Protective Gloves: As required; any material
Eye Protection: Safety goggles or glasses
Other Protective Equipment: Safety shoes, safety shower

SECTION 9: PHYSICAL AND CHEMICAL PROPERTIES

Hazardous Mixtures of other Liquids, Solids or Gases:
Oxygen vigorously accelerates combustion. Contact with all flammable materials should be avoided. Some materials that are not flammable in air will burn in pure oxygen or oxygen-enriched atmospheres.
Boiling Point: -297.3°F (-182.9°C)
Liquid Density at Boiling Point: 71.23 lb/ft3 (1141 kg/m3)

Vapor Pressure @ 70°F (21.1°C) = Above the critical temperature of -181.1°F (-118.4°C)
Gas Density at 70°F. 1 atm .0725 lb/ft3 (1.161 kq/m3)
Solubility in Water: Slightly
Freezing Point: -361.8°F (-218.8°C)
Evaporation Rate: N/A (Gas)
Specific Gravity (AIR=1) @ 70°F (21.1°C) = 1.11
Appearance and Odor: Colorless, odorless gas

SECTION 10: STABILITY AND REACTIVITY DATA

Stability: Stable
Incompatibility (Materials to Avoid): None
Hazardous Decomposition Products: All flammable materials
Hazardous Polymerization: Will not occur
Conditions to Avoid: None

SECTION 11: TOXICOLOGICAL INFORMATION

Toxicological Properties:
• The property is that hyperoxia which leads to pneumonia. Concentrations between 25 and 75 molar percent present a risk of inflammation of organic matte in the body.

• Oxygen is not listed in the LARC, NTP or by OSHA as a carcinogen or potential carcinogen.
• Persons in ill health where such illness would be aggravated by exposure to oxygen should not be allowed to work with or handle this product.

SECTION 12: ECOLOGICAL INFORMATION

None

SECTION 13: DISPOSAL CONSIDERATIONS

Waste disposal methods:
Do not attempt to dispose of waste or unused quantities. Return in the shipping container properly labeled, with any valve outlet plugs or caps secured and valve protection cap in place to your supplier. For emergency disposal assistance, contact your closest supplier location or call the emergency telephone number listed herein.

SECTION 14: TRANSPORT INFORMATION

Special Labeling Information:
DOT Shipping Name: Oxygen, Compressed
DOT Hazard Class: Division 2.2
DOT Shipping Label: Nonflammable Gas
I.D. No.: UN 1072

SECTION 15: OTHER REGULATORY INFORMATION

Other Recommendations or Precautions:
Oxygen should not be used as a substitute for compressed air in pneumatic equipment since this type generally contains flammable lubricants. Equipment to contain oxygen must be "cleaned for oxygen service." See Compressed Gas Association Pamphlet G-4.1. Compressed gas cylinders should not be refilled except by qualified producers of compressed gases.
Respiratory Protection (Specify type): Positive pressure air line with mask or self-contained breathing apparatus should be available for emergency use.
Ventilation: See Local Exhaust
Local Exhaust: To prevent accumulation above 25 molar percent.
Protective Gloves: As required; any material
Eye Protection: Safety goggles or glasses
Other Protective Equipment: Safety shoes, safety shower.

HYDROGEN

SECTION 1: CHEMICAL PRODUCT IDENTIFICATION

Product Name: Hydrogen
CAS: 1333-74-0
Hydrogen, Compressed (D.O.T); Water Gas
DOT I.D No.: UN 1049
Chemical Name and Synonyms: Hydrogen, Normal

Hydrogen
DOT Hazard Class: Division 2.1
Formula: H2
Chemical Family: Inorganic Flammable Gas

SECTION 2: COMPOSITION AND INFORMATION ON INGREDIENTS

Composition:

Name	CAS #	% by Weight
Hydrogen	1333-74-0	100

Toxicological Data on Ingredients: Not available.

SECTION 3: HAZARDS IDENTIFICATION

Time Weighted Average Exposure Limit:
Hydrogen is defined as a simple asphyxiant (ACGIH 1994-1995); OSHA 1993 PEL (8 Hr. TWA) = No Listing
Symptoms of Exposure:

Inhalation: High concentrations of hydrogen so as to exclude an adequate supply of oxygen to the lungs causes dizziness, deeper breathing due to air hunger, possible nausea and eventual unconsciousness.

SECTION 4: FIRST AID MEASURES

Conscious persons should be assisted to an uncontaminated area and breathe fresh air. They should be kept warm and quiet.
Unconscious persons should be moved to an

uncontaminated area and given assisted respiration. When breathing has been restored, treatment should be as above. Continues treatment should be symptomatic and supportive.

SECTION 5: FIRE AND EXPLOSION DATA

Flash Point (Method used):
N/A Gas
Auto Ignition Temperature:
1058°F (570°C)
Flammable Limits %
by Volume: LEL 4 UEL
74.5
Extinguishing Media: Water, carbon dioxide, dry chemical
Electrical
Classification: Class 1,

Group B
Special Fire fighting Procedures: If possible, stop the flow of hydrogen. Cool surrounding containers with water spray. Hydrogen burns with an almost invisible flame of relatively low thermal radiation.
Unusual Fire and Explosion Hazards: Hydrogen is very light and rises very rapidly in air. Should a hydrogen fire be extinguished and the flow of gas continue, increase ventilation to prevent an explosion hazard, particularly in the upper portions. Hydrogen is flammable over a very wide range in air.

SECTION 6: ACCIDENTAL RELEASE MEASURES

Steps to be taken in case material is released or spilled:
Evacuate all personnel from affected area. Use appropriate protective equipment. If leak is in user's

equipment, be certain to purge piping with an inert gas prior to attempting repairs. If leak is in container or container valve, contact your closest supplier location or call the emergency telephone number listed herein.

SECTION 7: HANDLING AND STORAGES

Special Handling Recommendation:
Use only in well-ventilated areas. Valve protection caps must remain in place unless container is secured with valve outlet piped to use point. Do not drag, slide or roll cylinders. Use a suitable hand truck for cylinder ovement. Use a pressure reducing regulator when connecting cylinder to lower pressure (<3,000 psig) piping or systems. Do not heat cylinder by any means to increase the discharge rate of product from the cylinder. Use a check valve or trap in the discharge line to prevent hazardous back flow into the cylinder. For additional handling recommendations, consult Compressed Gas Association's Pamphlets G-5, P-1, P-14, and Safety Bulletin SB-2.
Special Storage Recommendations:

Protect cylinders from physical damage. Store in cool, dry, well-ventilated area of noncombustible construction away from heavily trafficked areas and emergency exits. Do not allow the temperature where cylinders are stored to exceed 125F (52C). Cylinders should be stored upright and firmly secured to prevent falling or being knocked over. Full and empty cylinders should be segregated. Use a "first in -first out" inventory system to prevent full cylinders being stored for excessive periods of time. Post "No Smoking or Open Flames" signs in the storage or use area. There should be no sources of ignition in the storage or use area. For additional storage recommendations, consult Compressed Gas Association's Pamphlets G-5, P-1, P-14, and Safety Bulletin SB-2.

SECTION 8: EXPOSURE CONTROLS/PERSONAL PROTECTION

Respiratory Protection (Specify type): Positive pressure air line with mask or selfcontained breathing apparatus should be available for emergency use.
Ventilation: Hood with forced ventilation
Local Exhaust: To prevent accumulation above the

LEL
Mechanical (Gen.): In accordance with electrical codes
Protective Gloves: Plastic or rubber
Eye Protection: Safety goggles or glasses
Other Protective Equipment: Safety shoes, safety shower

SECTION 9: PHYSICAL AND CHEMICAL PROPERTIES

Boiling Point: -423°F (-252.8°C) **Liquid Density at Boiling Point:**
4.43 lb/ft3 (70.96 kg/m3)
Vapor Pressure @ 70°F (21.1°C) = Above the critical temperature of 399.8°F (-239.9°C) **Gas Density at 70°F. 1 atm** .0052

Solubility in Water: Very slightly **Freezing Point:** -434.6°F (-259.2°C)
Evaporation Rate: N/A (Gas) **Specific Gravity (AIR=1)** @ 70°F
(21.1°C) = .069
Appearance and Odor: Colorless, odorless gas

SECTION 10: STABILITY AND REACTIVITY DATA

Stability: Stable
Incompatibility (Materials to Avoid): Oxidizers
Hazardous Decomposition Products: None

Hazardous Polymerization: Will not occur
Conditions to Avoid: None

SECTION 11: TOXICOLOGICAL INFORMATION

Toxicological Properties:
• Hydrogen is inactive biologically and essentially nontoxic; therefore, the major property is the exclusion of an adequate supply of oxygen to the lungs.
• Hydrogen is not listed in the IARC, NTP or by OSHA

as a carcinogen or potential carcinogen.
• Persons in ill health where such illness would be aggravated by exposure to hydrogen should not be allowed to work with or handle this product.

SECTION 12: ECOLOGICAL INFORMATION

None

SECTION 13: DISPOSAL CONSIDERATIONS

Waste disposal methods:
Do not attempt to dispose of waste or unused quantities. Return in the shipping container properly labeled, with any valve outlet plugs or caps secured and valve protection cap in place to your supplier. For emergency disposal assistance, contact your closest supplier location or call the emergency telephone number listed herein.

SECTION 14: TRANSPORT INFORMATION

Special Labeling Information:
DOT Shipping Name: Hydrogen, Compressed
DOT Hazard Class: Division 2.1

DOT Shipping Label: Flammable Gas
I.D. No.: UN 1049

SECTION 15: OTHER REGULATORY INFORMATION

Other Recommendations or Precautions:
Earth-ground and bond all lines and equipment associated with the hydrogen system. Electrical equipment should be non-sparking or explosion proof. Compressed gas cylinders should not be refilled except by qualified producers of compressed gases. Shipment of a compressed gas cylinder which has not been filled by the owner or with his (written) consent is a violation of Federal Law (49CFR).

Special Packaging Recommendations:
Hydrogen is non-corrosive and may be used with any common structural material.

Respiratory Protection (Specify type): Positive pressure air line with mask or self-contained breathing apparatus should be available for emergency use.
Ventilation: Hood with forced ventilation
Local Exhaust: To prevent accumulation above the LEL
Mechanical (Gen.): In accordance with electrical codes
Protective Gloves: Plastic or rubber
Eye Protection: Safety goggles or glasses
Other Protective Equipment: Safety shoes, safety shower

Glossary

A

AC generator A device that rotates a coil within a magnetic field, which produces motional emfs in both sides of the coil which add. The component of the velocity perpendicular to the magnetic field changes sinusoidally with the rotation, generating sinusoidal voltage, or AC.

AC voltage function A function of a multimeter whereby the commercial power being supplied to a power outlet, or applied to a power supply unit can be measured. In addition to selecting the correct measurement range, additional caution is called for when making measurements of potentially lethal voltage levels.

active solar A solar power application involving the use of technologies to capture and convert solar energy into other energy forms, particularly as a source of clean electrons. The primary active solar technologies in use today include Stirling engines and photovoltaic devices.

active trackers PV solar mounts featuring optical sensors that drive horizontal and vertical positioning motors tracking the sun's path across the sky.

alkaline fuel cell (AFC) A highly developed fuel cell technology that employs an electrolyte of potassium hydroxide. It provides excellent performance, but is sensitive to the presence of carbon monoxide (CO). It requires a very high level of purity in the hydrogen and oxygen it uses.

alternating current (AC) The type of electrical power supplied by utilities, or created by running a generator. This form of electricity reverses its direction at regular intervals. For example, 120Vac 60Hz electric power reverses its flow direction 60 times a second.

alternator *(See AC generator)*

American Wire Gauge (AWG) A system of units used to express conductor sizes in the NEC, as required in Article 110.6. AWG is a convenient system that uses whole numbers with clear relationships to each other. Wire diameters are specified in a descending relationship, whereby larger AWG gauge numbers represent smaller wire diameters.

Amp/Hour (AH) A battery rating that specifies the length of time a specified battery can apply its specified level of power. This rating also indicates that the output of the battery is only useful until it falls off to 87.5% of its stated AH value.

ampacity The current-carrying capacity (the RMS electric current) which a specified wire or device can continuously carry, while remaining within its temperature rating. The ampacity of a specified cable depends on its insulation temperature rating, its electrical properties for current flow, its ability to dissipate heat, its surroundings, and the ambient temperature.

ampere (Amp) A measure of electric current, specifically how many electrons are moving past a given point each second. One ampere equals 6.24×10^{18} electrons passing a single point in one second. In electronic terms, one amp is equal to the electric force of one volt acting across the resistance of one ohm.

anode An electrode through which electric charge flows into a polarized electrical device, such as a fuel cell.

apparent power The calculated power produced by a specified AC circuit using the $P = V \times I$ power equation, and expressed in terms of Volt-Amperes (VA).

atmospheric pressure The force per unit area exerted against a surface by the weight of air above that surface at any given point in the Earth's atmosphere. When a difference in atmospheric pressure exists between two geographical points, the air molecules move from the area of high pressure to the area of low pressure.

B

batteries Batteries, or voltaic cells, are the most widely recognized examples of DC voltage sources. They consist of combinations of one or more electrochemical galvanic cells, which store chemical energy, and create a voltage difference between the terminals of the battery. When an external electrical circuit connects to the batteries, they drive an electric current through the circuit to perform electrical work.

battery disconnect switch For turbine systems, this switch disconnects the output of the wind turbine from the storage battery, grid, or inverter circuitry, so that these elements can be serviced safely, without power that is being generated by the wind turbine. In PV panels, this switch disconnects the output of the PV panels from the storage battery, grid, or inverter circuitry, so that these elements can be serviced safely, without power that is being generated by the PV array.

Bernoulli's principle Applied to the theory of air flow, the relative flow parallel to the top surface of an aircraft wing or a turbine blade is faster than along the bottom surface. Bernoulli's principle states that the pressure on the surfaces of the wing or rotor blade will be lower above than below, and this pressure difference results in an upwards lift force. If the relative air flows across the top and bottom surfaces of a blade are known, then lift forces can be calculated (to a good approximation) using Bernoulli's equations.

blade assembly The wind turbine component fundamentally responsible for converting wind energy into another usable source of energy.

British Thermal Units (BTUs) Units of energy used in the power, steam generation, heating and air conditioning industries. In North America, the term *BTU* is used to describe the heat value (energy content) of fuels, and also to describe the power of heating and cooling systems, such as furnaces, stoves, barbecue grills, and air conditioners.

bubbler tubes An arrangement whereby the production of gases can be visually monitored. When the tubes are filled with the specified gases, the associated fuel cells are ready to operate.

burning fuels Material such as wood or coal, which provided the necessary energy to heat water into steam, thereby operating the steam engine.

burns One of the dangers commonly associated with electrical current flow.

C

carbon dioxide (CO₂) One of the byproducts associated with the production of electricity from fossil fuels.

carbon monoxide (CO) One of the potentially dangerous gases produced when sodium bicarbonate is used as the electrolyte during the electrolysis process.

cathode The positive electrode in a fuel cell to which oxygen (or air) is introduced on one side of the cell.

caustic soda In the process of generating hydrogen and oxygen, the baking soda electrolyte solution in the electrolyzer is reduced to NaOH (Sodium Hydroxide, or lye), a caustic chemical, resulting from spent electrolyte from the electrolyzer.

circuit Created when an acceptable external pathway is provided for the movement of the electrons from the pushing end of the voltage source to the pulling end.

circuit breaker A device that senses the level of current flowing through it, and is designed to interrupt the path of current flow (open circuit) if the current level gets to a certain point (the fuse rating). A properly-sized fuse or circuit breaker is required in any line coming from an electrical source.

clean fuel Unlike dirty fossil fuels, clean fuel technologies such as wind, solar, hydrogen, hydro, geothermal, and nuclear power help to reduce the unacceptable impact on the environment, climate, and various geopolitical relationships.

climate change A rapidly approaching tipping point where the level of greenhouse gases accumulate in the atmosphere, causing irreversible changes in the environment, particularly in the area of climate. These gases (mainly carbon dioxide CO₂) act as an insulating layer, wrapping around the Earth, and holding in heat that would normally be radiated into space.

coal A popular burning fossil fuel (for devices such as steam engines), offering twice as much energy output potential as the same amount of wood.

cold fronts Air mass boundaries, denoted on a weather map with lines having small triangular pips on one side. They are associated with low-pressure areas and tend to move from west to east.

combustible Capable of igniting and burning, such as wood and paper, although a combustible materials can be either a solid or a liquid.

commercial power grid Power distribution lines energized by utility companies for delivery of electric power to utility company customers, from fuel sources such as coal, nuclear, hydroelectric, natural gas, and others.

commutator bars The slip rings of a dc generator, which are split to insure that the same polarity of electrical push is applied to the identical wires as the coils turn inside the magnets.

conductors Materials composed of atoms that have three or less electrons in their valence shell, and offer very little resistance to giving up electrons. When current passes through conductors, some energy is given off as heat. Heat is often a result of too much current flowing through an undersized conducting wire, or through a bad connection.

consumers People who have climbed the socioeconomic ladder to become users of more resources, in both variety and quantity. Seeking higher levels of comfort and security, they buy more commodities (things), which require more resources to create. These individuals also become direct consumers of energy.

continuity test A measure of resistance across an electrical circuit. Continuity checks are always conducted with the power removed from the system being tested, in order to prevent serious damage to the testing meter.

conventional current flow A engineering method of describing current flow as the movement of positive charges through an electric circuit.

Coriolis effect A result of the earth's rotation, whereby the direction of the wind moving between varying atmospheric pressures is forced to flow in a curved path between the pressure centers. Otherwise, the winds would travel more or less in a straight line.

covalent bonding The sharing of valence electrons, as with electrical insulators, which are usually composed of materials made up from different elements that have joined together to share these electrons.

crimp connections Electrical connections which involve crushing an insulated connector around bare lengths of wire. They require a relatively tight fitting between the sleeve of the connector and the wire. An effective crimp must create a solid path for current to flow between the wire and the connector's body.

crude oil Used in the industrial productive processes, and for residential and commercial heating. Crude oil originally replaced whale oil to provide heat and lighting. Its continued refinement eventually led to its use as fuel for engines used in industry and transportation.

current A flow of electrons, such as those moving through an electrical circuit. When a sufficient electromotive force is applied to all of the atoms between the two ends of the conductor, a flow of electrons (current) will move through the circuit.

current flow The movement of free electrons, providing a source of energy that can be used to perform work.

cycles per second A reference to the frequency of AC current or voltage, which is also called Hertz (Hz). In Europe this frequency is 50Hz, while in the United States, it is 60Hz.

D

daily cost of operation A mathematical calculation determined by multiplying the kilowatt-per-hour consumption rate for the specified electrical device by 24.

daisy-chain A series connection type for multiple DC sources such that their positive terminals are connected to the negative terminals of the next source. The voltage level provided to the external load is equal to the sum of all the individual DC source voltages.

DC voltage function A multimeter function in which a dc voltage reading is taken in a live circuit. The meter must be connected in parallel with the device being checked. The reference lead (black lead) is usually connected to a ground point, while the measuring lead (red lead) is connected to the specified test point.

DC voltage sources These include batteries, fuel cells, and photovoltaic (solar) cells.

deforestation The loss of green areas (forests and prairies) around the globe, such as huge areas in countries like Brazil and Indonesia. This has contributed more CO_2 to the atmosphere than all of the transportation devices in the world combined.

diesel fuel Any fuel used in diesel engines, the most common being a specific fractional distillate of petroleum fuel oil. Alternatives not derived from petroleum include biodiesel, biomass to liquid (BTL), or gas to liquid (GTL) diesel. To distinguish these types, petroleum-derived diesel is increasingly called petrodiesel. Ultra-Low Sulfur Diesel (ULSD) is a diesel fuel standard with substantially lowered sulfur contents.

differential heating The biggest reason for differing atmospheric pressure levels, where different levels of heating from the sun occur because some geographical areas receive or absorb more solar energy than others.

direct current (DC) The movement of electrons whereby their movement around the circuit, from atom to atom, is always in one constant direction.

direct methanol fuel cell (DMFC) A fuel cell type that employs a PEM membrane, and operating similar to other fuel cell types. However, the DMFC is designed to use methanol (CH_3OH) as a fuel instead of hydrogen. Its major drawback is that methanol is dangerous and corrosive to work with.

dirty A reference to cheap, abundant, and environmentally damaging fossil fuels (coal, oil, and gas) that have been used to provide power for industrialization and life-style advancements. However, the system that supports these fuels cannot continue due to the adverse impact to the environment, geopolitical relationships, and global climate.

diversion style regulator Also known as a load diverter, a device that monitors the voltage of the load battery and applies voltage to it whenever its voltage level falls below its stated fully charged value. However, when the battery is fully charged, the diverter shifts the current coming from the source to an alternate load.

DMMs (Digital MultiMeters) Electronic test instruments providing standard functions of current, voltage, and resistance measurement. Some DMM models contain built-in facilities to test transistors and diodes.

E

earth ground A grounding connection designed to protect an electronic system from environmental electrical discharges, such as lightning. It involves creating a grounding path between all system devices and a copper rod driven into the earth.

electricity A variety of phenomena resulting from the presence and flow of electric charge. This flow serves as an energy source used to generate heat and light, as well as to produce mechanical and motive forces. The demand for electricity has produced a world full of electrical generation plants.

electrolyzer A device used to perform electrolysis, which separates the elements of chemically bonded compounds from each other by passing an electric current through them.

electromagnetic induction An altered AC power relationship within inductive electrical loads whereby the resulting AC current flows at some time following (lags) the application of the voltage to the circuit. The lag time is based on the amount of inductance (henries) in the load device.

electromotive force (EMF) The amount of voltage existing between the different terminals of an electrical power source. It is a measurement of the potential electrical push and pull on both sides of a connected circuit or device.

electron current flow A method of describing current flow used by technicians, which depends on the movement of electrons throughout the electronic circuit.

electrons Basic atomic particles that orbit around an atom's nucleus in elliptical paths called shells. Atomic shells are organized in such a way as to accommodate only a certain number of electrons.

energy The amount (quantity) of work that can be performed by a specific force. Energy appears as kinetic, potential, or thermal.

equipment ground The grounding that provides a common reference point for all of the electrical components of a given system. It also provides protection to personnel that might come into contact with system components in the event of a short circuit.

explosive Describes any material that is chemically or otherwise energetically unstable enough to produce a sudden expansion of the material. This expansion (explosion) is usually accompanied by the production of heat, as well as large changes in pressure. Upon initiation, the explosion usually exhibits a bright flash, or a loud noise.

F

fire A danger associated with electrical current flow, whereby heat in a wiring system builds up as a result of too much current flowing through an undersized wire, or through a bad connection.

fossil fuels Fuels such as oil, natural gas, or coal that produce carbon dioxide (CO_2) as a byproduct of their use.

free electron A valence electron from an atom's outer shell that has been physically separated from the atom. In this condition, the electron is referred to as a free electron and represents a negative electrical charge.

front A boundary where air masses having different temperatures and densities meet, such as where dry cold air collides with warm moist air.

fuel cells Alternate energy generation systems used extensively with transportation and remote site power applications.

functions Facilities built into multimeters to test or measure standard electrical parameters of current, voltage, and resistance. Certain meters also contain built-in facilities to test transistors and diodes.

fuse A required safety device that is placed in the line of an electrical source to sense the level of current flowing through the line. It is designed to interrupt the path of current flow (open circuit) when the current level surpasses the fuse rating.

G

gasoline A petroleum-derived liquid mixture, primarily used as fuel in internal combustion engines. It also is used as a powerful solvent, similar to the way in which acetone is used.

gear sets Placed within the nacelle of a wind turbine, to mechanically amplify the force produced by the blades.

generators Common electro-mechanical devices used to produces DC electrical current flows by using rotational energy to create electrical energy.

green A collection of ideas that include generating electric power without producing carbon; limiting energy usage and conserving resources through behavior modification and technology; conserving energy through improved building techniques, materials, and technologies; creating transportation systems and techniques not dependent on carbon-based products.

greenhouse gases Large amounts of airborne pollutants accumulated in the atmosphere, due to industrialization, that absorb and emit radiation within the thermal infrared range. Common greenhouse gases in the Earth's atmosphere include water vapor, carbon dioxide, methane, nitrous oxide, ozone, in addition to chlorofluorocarbons.

ground (GND) The multimeter jack into which the black (GND) lead is inserted. The jack itself is often designated by being black in color.

grounding To protect both people and electrical systems, this is an important safety consideration for any electrical installation. It includes equipment grounding, and earth grounding for field installations.

H

Hertz A reference to the basic unit of frequency, or cycles per second, the term can be used to measure any periodic event. It is named after the German physicist Heinrich Hertz, who made important scientific contributions to electromagnetism.

high-pressure A reference to pressure areas in the atmosphere corresponding to cooler, dryer air.

horizontal axis wind turbine (HAWT) A type of wind turbine that features blades that are mounted vertical to the ground. The majority of wind turbines are of this type.

horse power Originally defined to allow the output of steam engines to be measured and compared with the power output of draft horses. The horsepower was widely adopted to measure the output of piston engines, turbines, electric motors, and other machinery.

hydrides Forms of hydrocarbon used with various fuel cell types, and featuring negative hydrogen ions.

hydroxide ions Negatively charged oxygen-hydrogen ions, which are attracted to the positive anode fuel cell terminal.

I

inductance The property in an electrical circuit where a change in the current flowing through that circuit induces an electromotive force (EMF) that opposes the change in current. The amount of difference between the application of the voltage (the push/pull on the circuit) and the actual flow of current is based on this.

industrial revolution Refers to the time period in the late 1700's, where older work methods began to be replaced by, and enhanced through the use of, machines. Largely agricultural societies in Europe and North America became machine-based manufacturing communities. Its long running era of economic growth and inventiveness depended on energy and power.

infrastructure The elements that make up an urban environment, including roads and streets, electrical supply, and sanitation systems, such as water, sewage, and garbage services.

insolation The measurement of radiation energy received on a given surface (such as the photovoltaic cell), and specified in terms of average irradiance in watts per square meter.

insulation Material that resists the flow of electric current. A large class of materials use rubber-like polymers and plastics to insulate electrical wiring and cables. These materials can serve as practical and safe insulators for low to moderate voltages (hundreds, or even thousands, of volts).

insulators Materials that possess more then three electrons in their outer shell insulators, and do not give up valence electrons easily. Common electrical insulators include rubber, plastics, paper, and glass.

internal combustion engine Developed towards the end of the 1800's (the late 19th century), this machine created a major shift in the transportation of goods and people.

ion An atom that has given up an electron and is now out of balance, exhibiting a positive electrical charge.

irradiance A term for the power of electromagnetic radiation at a surface, per unit area, when the electromagnetic radiation is incident on the surface.

isobar Line on a meteorological (weather) map connecting points having equal or constant atmospheric pressures.

K

kilowatt-hour (kWh) A measurement of energy consumption equal to one thousand watts of power consumed in one hour. Utility companies measure energy in terms of the kilowatt-hour (kWh), so that monthly electric utility bills are based on the base rate charged by the local utility per kilowatt-hour.

L

lift An aerodynamic force on the blade of a wind turbine, causing the blade assembly to rotate around the central shaft it is attached to. The blades are designed so that the striking wind is diverted around their opposite faces. One side of the blade is curved so that air passing over it takes longer to travel over the surface than the air passing over the opposite surface of the blade.

load diverter A device that monitors the voltage of the load battery, applying voltage if its voltage level falls below its stated fully charged value, and shifting the source current to an alternate load when the battery voltage reaches the fully charged level.

loads The collective name given to various devices that perform useful activities while attached to an electrical energy source.

low pressure An areas of atmospheric pressure associated with moist, warm air.

M

machines The devices that began to replace the manual labor methods (domesticated animals and waterpower). These older work methods were replaced by and enhanced through the use of machines during the industrial revolution.

mechanical work At the beginning of the industrial revolution, this was performed through the use of the steam engine. The steam engine was itself powered through the burning of wood or coal fuels.

megawatt (MW) Equal to one-million watts of electrical power.

meteorological map A common weather forecasting aid in determining wind movements. A meteorological (weather) map displays high-pressure and low-pressure centers across the areas of concern.

methane (CH₄) A colorless, odorless greenhouse gas produced by cattle as part of their digestive process.

middle class A group of people in contemporary society situated between the working class and upper class, including professionals, highly skilled workers, and lower and middle management. They share a set of cultural values, commonly associated with professionals.

molten carbonate fuel cell (MCFC) A type of fuel cell employing a molten mixture of alkali metal carbonates capable of working with alternative fuel sources such as natural gas, biogas and coal gas, in addition to hydrogen and oxygen/air.

monitoring and control circuitry Contained within a wind turbine's nacelle, and used to manage its output and safe operation.

motor A DC device that converts electrical energy into rotational mechanical force and operates according to the principles of magnetic retraction and repulsion. DC motors typically contain multiple commutator segments and armature coils.

multimeter A test instrument (analog or digital) that can be used to directly measure values of voltage (V), current in milliamperes (mA) or amperes (A), and resistance in ohms (Ω).

N

nacelle A housing that is generally mounted on the top of a wind turbine's tower, containing its electrical generation circuitry.

National Electrical Code (NEC) A document that describes recommended safe practice for the installation of all types of electrical equipment. Its stated purpose is for the "practical safeguarding of persons and property from hazards arising from the use of electricity."

National Fire Protection Association (NFPA) An insurance industry group under the official title of NFPA 70, which is responsible for publishing and maintaining the NEC.

natural gas Consisting primarily of methane and associated with fossil fuels, it is found primarily in coal beds, as methane clathrates, and is created by methanogenic organisms in marshes, bogs, and landfills. It is an important fuel source, a major feedstock for fertilizers, and a potent greenhouse gas.

negative electrical charge The charge state of an electron particle.

neutrons Atomic particles exhibiting no electrical charge whatsoever.

no utility-needs batteries Another name for inverters designed to work specifically with wind turbines installations requiring some type of battery-based storage system. These application types are referred to as off-grid inverters.

no-battery-grid intertie Another name for an on grid inverter designed for connection to the AC power system provided by the local electric utility company. It does not require any batteries.

north pole A magnetic reference that determines the direction of electron movement in a wire according to a moving magnet's polarity. This electron movement is opposite in direction to that caused by a south pole magnetic reference.

nucleus The cluster of protons and neutrons located in the center of an atom's structure.

O

Occupational Safety and Health Administration (OSHA) An agency of the United States Department of Labor, and created by Congress under the Occupational Safety and Health Act, on December 29, 1970. Its mission is to prevent work-related injuries, illnesses, and deaths by issuing and enforcing standards for workplace safety and health.

off grid inverters Battery-based storage systems for wind turbine or PV power installations that are not designed for connection to the commercial AC power grid.

Ohm's Law A mathematical formula expressing the relationship between voltage, resistance and current flow in an electrical circuit.

ohms Ohms (Ω) are the unit of electrical impedance according to the International System of Units (SI). In the direct current case, they symbolize the unit of electrical resistance, named after Georg Simon Ohm.

on grid inverters For wind turbine or PV power installations, they are designed for connection to the AC power system provided by the local electric utility company, and do not require any batteries.

on-grid/off-grid capable inverters Used with wind turbine or PV power installations, and designed for direct connection to the utility grid. They can also work with a battery storage system to provide backup power in case of a power outage.

open circuit With a voltage source pushing against the atoms in the internal wiring, an absence of current flow due to the lack of an external circuit path. Although voltage is present providing a push, no current flow exists.

open circuit regulator A device that monitors the balance of voltage in the charging system. When the battery voltage falls off to a predetermined level, the regulator closes the circuit to begin charging the batteries to the PV array. As long as light is present, the PV array will continue to produce energy whether the regulator is opened or closed. The energy generated while the regulator is in the open circuit condition is simply wasted.

open-circuit An open-circuit condition provides no path for current flow. The Marcraft wind turbine is not designed to operate in an open-circuit condition for extended periods of time.

overcharge When power is continually applied to charged storage batteries, they can be overcharged. This creates a potentially dangerous situation because overcharged batteries can overheat and possibly explode.

overflow tubes Used to collect any liquid solution that escapes from the electrolyzer, thus avoiding contamination of the hydrogen and oxygen storage containers.

P

parallel A method of connecting identical voltage sources together (positive terminals are connected to positive terminals) such that the total voltage level is identical to that of an individual voltage source. However the current delivery capability is equal to the sum of the currents produced by each individual source.

parts per million (PPM) A method for describing the safe level of some potentially dangerous airborne or waterborne substance, when compared to the natural exposure of humans in the atmosphere or in a large body of water. For example, OSHA lists the safe levels of CO_2 gas in the atmosphere as 5,000 parts per million (PPM), or less. Its normal short term exposure limit is 15,000 ppm.

passive solar Solar energy applications that include designing homes and buildings to use the heat and light received directly from the sun for space heating, water heating, ventilation, distillation, and solar lighting.

passive trackers The sun's heat is used to move liquid from side to side inside the tracker, allowing gravity to turn it and follow the sun, so that no motors, no gears and no controls are used.

phosphoric acid fuel cell (PAFC) A fuel cell that uses phosphoric acid in order to work with alternative fuel sources. PAFCs tend to be very inefficient compared to other fuel cell types.

photosynthesis A process by which trees and plants take in CO_2 from the atmosphere, and produce oxygen.

photovoltaic (PV) Green technology and research related to the application of solar cells for energy, which convert sunlight directly into electricity. The manufacture of solar cells and photovoltaic arrays has greatly expanded in recent years.

photovoltaic (PV) cells Clean energy devices capable of converting solar energy (sun light) into electricity.

photovoltaic (PV) panels Modules composed of solar cells that have been connected together and mounted in a common frame.

photovoltaic array A grouping of multiple PV panels mounted together. Individual panels may be wired together in a series circuit to provide additional voltage capabilities, in parallel to provide greater current flow capabilities, or in a series-parallel combination to match the voltage and current requirements of a given load device.

photovoltaic devices The most common active solar devices used to generate electricity from solar energy, accomplished through a process known as the photovoltaic effect. Semiconductor material that absorbs light (such as silicon) is used in order to produce free electrons that can be channeled into an electrical current flow.

photovoltaic panels Used in an alternate energy generation system to provide residential and commercial power generation and cogeneration applications.

pitch The angle at which the wind strikes the blades of a wind turbine, thereby determining the rotational direction of the turbine's blade assembly.

polarity The determination as to which side of a voltage cell exhibits a positive charge, while the other side exhibits a negative charge.

population increase This increase in the next forty to fifty years is expected to equal to the total population that was present on the earth just fifty years ago, and expected to climb to 9.2 billion by 2050.

positioning motors Driven horizontally and vertically by optical sensors, and used to guide active trackers.

positive electrical charge The charge state of a proton.

potassium carbonate (K_2CO_3) Used in an electrolyte solution to make the water more conductive for carrying electrical current.

power The amount of work that can be done in a given unit of time, or the amount of energy that can be transferred in a given unit of time. It is measured in watts.

power factor A cosine trigonometric function relating the phase shift between the current and voltage waveforms.

primary cells A battery type for which the recharging option is not available. Applying a reverse voltage to non-rechargeable battery types can cause them to overheat and possibly explode.

propellers A blade assembly structure used as a source of propulsion in aircraft and watercraft, where mechanical energy is applied to the blade assembly to turn it.

protons Atomic particles from the nucleus possessing a positive electrical charge.

pulse width modulation (PWM) A high-frequency switching technique used to convert incoming DC battery voltage into a high DC voltage.

Q

quality of life The degree to which a person enjoys the important possibilities of his/her life. Possibilities result from the opportunities and limitations each person has in his/her life, and reflect the interaction of personal and environmental factors.

R

reactance An AC circuit parameter in which the load poses an opposition to the changing current push being applied. This is opposition to AC current flow from inductance or capacitance, instead of resistance.

real power Also referred to as true power, expressed in Watts, and calculated using the formula Real Power (watts) = cosine (phase) x Apparent Power (VA). Real power varies with the value of the cosine function of the phase difference between the voltage and current waveforms.

recharges The repeated restoration of the original chemical configuration inside a battery. The recharge rate depends on the battery's chemical configuration, and the amount of reverse current flowing through it. The reverse current depends on the voltage difference between the battery and the recharging source.

rectifier A device used to convert a generated AC output to DC current, such as the operation of an automotive alternator.

regulation mode An operational mode whereby a wind turbine automatically shuts off to prevent the batteries from being overcharged. The turbine enters regulation mode when the battery voltage level rises above the set point.

resistance The opposition to the flow of current by a circuit or component. When checking resistance with a multimeter, always check to be sure that power is first removed from the system, circuit, and component being measured.

resistivity The resistance of a specified element to giving up a valence electron. To free an electron from its atom, enough energy must be applied to the electron to overcome this resistance. Each element has its own resistivity level.

rms Refers to the measurement of AC voltage with a standard multimeter, with the result being expressed as volt-amperes (VA), rather than watts.

rotor A wind turbine structure containing a set of magnets, which turns inside a collection of coiled wires (field coils) called the stator. As the magnets turn past the field coils, their magnetic fields push on the atoms in the coil's causing them to give up outer shell electrons.

S

schematic diagram A symbolic wiring diagram depicted the technical details of an electric or electronic circuit.

secondary cells Storage battery types that can be recharged by applying a reverse current to them, at a level slightly higher than its terminal voltage. The reverse current is forced to flow back into the battery and its internal chemical process is reversed.

semiconductor A material having a resistivity value between that of a conductor and an insulator. The conductivity of a semiconductor material can be varied using an external electrical field.

series The connection of batteries, solar panels, or other DC power sources in such a way as to attach positive terminals to negative terminals in a daisy-chain configuration.

set point An intelligent, internal regulator circuit that continually monitors the battery voltage and compares it to a preset internal regulation set point. When the battery voltage level rises above the set point, the turbine enters regulation mode, automatically shutting off to prevent the batteries from being overcharged.

short circuit A condition whereby a wire or conductor is placed across the power terminals in the absence of a suitable load. Current flow through the circuit and inside the power source (battery) moves as quickly as the internal process can generate more free electrons. The acceleration of current causes the power source to heat up, which in turn can cause it to overheat. If the power source is a battery, it may explode.

Side of Pole Mounts A method of installing pole mounted PV arrays such that the pole continues upward past the point at which the array is attached.

Single Pole, Double Throw (SPDT) A stop switch control mechanism having one pole and two possible connection points. It is capable of connecting either of two terminals to a common terminal.

Single Pole, Single Throw (SPST) A simple on-off switch, where the two terminals are either connected together, or not connected to anything.

sized Circuit breakers and fuses must be properly sized to safely handle the maximum amount of current that the system is designed to carry. They break (open) the circuit (interrupt the current flow) to protect wiring, devices, and personnel from damage and injury whenever an over current condition is detected.

smart grids Smart grids deliver electricity from suppliers to consumers using digital technology to save energy, reduce cost, and increase reliability. Many governments promote these modernized electricity networks as a way of addressing energy independence and global warming issues.

sodium chloride (NaCl) Also known as table salt, its electrolyte solution produces chlorine gas along with the hydrogen and oxygen. Because chlorine gas is very dangerous, this electrolyte solution is not recommended for use in creating hydrogen through electrolysis.

sodium hydroxide (NaOH) Also known as caustic soda or lye, this caustic chemical is a byproduct in the generation of hydrogen and oxygen from a baking soda electrolyte solution. Therefore, care should be taken when removing the spent electrolyte from the electrolyzer.

solar array A construct of multiple PV panels that are mounted and wired together (in series, parallel, or series-parallel), and combined to match the voltage and current requirements of a given load device.

solar cells Also referred to as photovoltaic (PV) cells, are devices that are designed to convert solar energy (sun light) into electricity.

solar energy Radiated energy received from the sun in the form of light and heat.

solar farms Large commercial solar energy constructs that combine the outputs of multiple PV panels to provide hundreds of megawatts (MWs) of electric power. This power is applied directly to the commercial power grid.

solar panels Also known as photovoltaic (PV) panels, and composed of multiple solar cells, connected together and mounted in a common frame.

solid oxygen fuel cells (SOFCs) Fuel cells based on the exchange of oxygen ions (rather than hydrogen ions) through a conductive membrane. The oxygen ions are permitted to migrate across the cell, while the resulting electrons are forced to pass through the external circuit.

south pole A magnetic reference that determines the direction of electron movement in a wire according to a moving magnet's polarity. This electron movement is opposite in direction to that caused by a north pole magnetic reference.

stator A collection of coiled wires (field coils).

steam engine A heat engine that uses boiling water to produce mechanical motion. It became a major source of mechanical power over the last 300 years, enabling the industrial revolution.

Stirling engine An engine that uses mirrors to collect and focus sunlight at one end. The difference of temperature on the opposite end of the engine causes a piston inside the engine to move. This mechanical movement is then converted into electric energy through generator action.

stop switch An SPDT switch that routes the current flow from the Positive (red) lead of a wind turbine to the ammeter, the breaker, and the disconnect switch. In its STOP setting, the switch creates a short circuit between the turbine's (red) lead and its Negative (black) lead. This causes a breaking action to occur within the turbine's circuitry, which protects the turbine in times of excess wind speeds.

storage The ability of a secondary cell to hold a recharge by having a reverse current applied to it.

storage batteries Battery types (secondary cells) that can be recharged by applying a reverse current to them. The charging source must provide a voltage level slightly higher than the battery's terminal voltage. A reverse current is forced to flow back into the battery, reversing its internal chemical process. During recharge, a storage battery becomes a load, rather than a source.

storage tubes During electrolysis, the hydrogen and oxygen gases pass through the overflow tubes, and are routed into a pair of these tubes, which are filled with water. As the gases fill these tubes, the water is forced out and into the bubbler tubes above them.

Suns A term used to express the amount of insolation, or radiation energy received on a given surface. A Sun is equal to 1000 watts per square meter (1000 w/m$_2$).

T

The grid Another name for the electrical power delivered by the power company, or the commercial AC power system.

Top of Pole Mounts A method of installing pole mounted PV arrays such that the array attaches to the very top of the pole.

true power *(See real power)*

V

valence electrons Residing in the outer atomic shell, these are the only electrons capable of being separated from an atom to become free electrons.

vertical axis wind turbine (VAWT) A type of wind turbine design that mounts the blades horizontally.

voltage (V) The electromotive force (EMF) that places the electrical push and pull on the different terminals of a power source. In live DC circuits, a multimeter's DC voltage function is used to take measurements of these electrical values.

Volt-Ampere (VA) The unit of apparent power for an AC circuit, using the $P = V \times I$ power equation.

volt The value of potential difference across a conductor when a current of one ampere dissipates one watt of power in the conductor. It is also equal to one joule of energy per coulomb of charge.

VOM (Volt-Ohm-Milliammeter) An analog multimeter capable of directly measuring values of voltage (V), current (mA) or (A), and resistance (Ω).

W

warm fronts Weather boundaries associated with high-pressure areas, and tending to move toward the Earth's north and south poles.

watts An expression of electrical power, governed by the power formula for Ohms Law, $P = V \times I$, where P is power in watts, I is current in amperes, and V is voltage in volts.

wind The movement (or flow) of air, or other atmospheric gas molecules from one place to another. Wind is created on Earth when a difference in atmospheric pressure exists between two geographical points.

wind farms Large commercial wind turbine constructs that combine the outputs of multiple turbines to provide hundreds of megawatts (MWs) of electric power. This power is applied directly to the commercial power grid.

wind loading A major concern when selecting the mounting brackets for solar arrays. The installation must be sturdy enough so that conditions associated with thunder and wind storms cannot dislodge the array.

wind turbines Rotating machines capable of converting the kinetic energy of the wind into mechanical energy.

wood One of the fuels used for the operation of early steam engines.

work The amount of energy transferred by a force, or from system to another, in order to provide heat, light, or driving an electric motor.

Y

YAW shaft A freely turning shaft connection that securely fastens the body of a wind turbine to its mounting mast.

Acronyms

A	Amperes
AC	Alternating current
AFC	Alkaline fuel cells
AH	Amp/hour
AWG	American Wire Gauge
BTL	Biomass to liquid
BTUs	British Thermal Units
C	Carbon
CH_3OH	Methanol
CH_4	Methane
CO	Carbon monoxide
CO_2	Carbon dioxide
CompTIA	Computing Technology Industry Association
DC	Direct current
DMFC	Direct methanol fuel cells
DMM	Digital MultiMeters
DOE	Department of Energy
DOT	Department of Transportation
EERC	Energy and Environmental Research Center
EMF	Electromotive force
ETA-I	Electronics Technicians Association – International
GND	Ground
GTL	Gas to liquid
H	Hydrogen
H_2O	Water molecule
HAWT	Horizontal axis wind turbine
Hz	Hertz or cycles per second
Imp	Rated Current
ISA	International Society for Automation
Isc	Short Circuit Current
K	Potassium
K_2CO_3	Potassium Carbonate
kWh	Kilowatt-hour
mA	Milliamperes
MCFC	Molten carbonate fuel cell
MW	Megawatts or million Watts
Na	Sodium
NaCL	Sodium Chloride
NaOH	Sodium hydroxide
NEC	National Electrical Code
NFPA	National Fire Protection Association
NREL	National Renewable Energy Laboratory
O	Oxygen
O_2	Oxygen molecule
OSHA	Occupational Safety and Health Administration
PAFC	Phosphoric acid fuel cell
PEM	Proton exchange membrane
PPM	Parts per million
PSI	Pounds per square inch
PV	Photovoltaic
PWM	Pulse width modulation
rms	Root mean square
SI	International System of Units
SOFC	Solid oxygen fuel cells
SPDT	Single Pole, Double Throw
SPST	Single Pole, Single Throw
TIA	Telecommunications Industry Association
UND	University of North Dakota
ULSD	Ultra-Low Sulfur Diesel
V	Voltage
VA	Volt-Amperes
VAWT	Vertical axis wind turbine
Vmp	Rated Voltage
Voc	Open Circuit Voltage
VOM	Volt-Ohm-Milliammeter

Index

A

AC generator, 53
AC voltage function, 30
Active solar, 113
Active trackers, 121
Alkaline fuel cells (AFC), 186
Alternating current (AC), 18, 50
Alternator, 50, 53
American Wire Gauge (AWG), 25, 55, 122
Amp/hour (AH), 90, 159
Ampacity, 25, 55, 122
Ampere, 19, 20, 118
Anode, 183
Apparent power, 23
Atmospheric pressure, 47

B

Batteries, 31
Battery Disconnect switch, 63, 132
Bernoulli's Principle, 49
Blade assembly, 49
British Thermal Units, 21
Bubbler tubes, 190
Burning fuels, 3
Burns, 24, 55, 122, 192

C

Carbon dioxide (CO_2), 4, 7, 193
Carbon monoxide (CO), 193
Cathode, 183
Caustic soda, 194
Circuit, 17, 51, 115
Circuit breaker, 26, 56, 63, 122
Clean fuel, 7
Climate change, 7
Coal, 3
Cold fronts, 48
Combustible, 192
Commercial power grid, 71, 142
Commutator bars, 53
Conductors, 16, 24, 55, 118, 122, 192
Consumers, 5
Continuity test, 37
Conventional current flow, 18
Coriolis effect, 47
Covalent bonding, 16
Crimp connections, 26
Crude oil, 3

Current, 17, 29, 115
Current flow, 114

D

Daily cost of operation, 23
Daisy-chain, 33
DC voltage function, 30
DC voltage sources, 31
Deforestation, 7
Diesel fuel, 3
Differential heating, 47
Direct current (DC), 18, 50, 115, 184
Direct methanol fuel cells (DMFCs), 186
Dirty, 7
Diversion style regulator, 145, 154
DMMs (Digital MultiMeters), 29

E

Earth Ground, 151
Electricity, 4
Electrolyzer, 188
Electromagnetic induction, 23
Electromotive force (EMF), 17, 51, 115, 184
Electron current flow, 18
Electrons, 15
Element, 15
Energy, 2
Equipment ground, 151
Explosive, 192

F

Fire, 24, 55, 122, 192
Fossil fuels, 4
Free electron, 16
Front, 48
Fuel Cells, 8
Functions, 30
Fuse, 26, 56, 122

G

Gasoline, 3
Gear sets, 54
Generators, 50
Green, 1
Greenhouse gases, 7
Ground, 198
Grounding, 151

H

Hertz, 90, 159
High-pressure, 47
Horizontal axis wind turbine (HAWT), 50
Horse power, 21
Hydrides, 187
Hydroxide ions, 189

I

Inductance, 23
Industrial Revolution, 2
Infrastructure, 4
Insolation, 114
Insulation, 26
Insulators, 16
Internal combustion engine, 3
Ion, 16
Irradiance, 114
Isobar, 47

K

Kilowatt-hour (kWh), 22

L

Lift, 49
Load diverter, 74, 85, 145, 146, 154
Loads, 18
Low-pressure, 47

M

Machines, 2
Mechanical work, 3
Megawatts (MW), 72, 142
Meteorological map, 47
Methane (CH_4), 7
Middle class, 5
Molten carbonate fuel cell (MCFC), 186
Monitoring and control circuitry, 54
Motor, 215
Multimeter, 29

N

Nacelle, 54
National Electrical Code (NEC), 25
National Fire Protection Association (NFPA), 25
Natural gas, 3
Negative electrical charge, 16
Neutrons, 15
No utility-needs batteries, 74
No-battery-grid intertie, 74
North pole, 52
Nucleus, 15

O

Occupational Safety and Health Administration (OSHA), 193
Off grid inverters, 74, 145
Ohm's Law, 19, 20, 118
On grid inverters, 74, 145
On-grid/Off-grid capable inverters, 74, 145
Open circuit, 19, 85, 118
Open circuit regulator, 145
Overcharge, 74, 145
Overflow tubes, 190

P

Parallel, 33, 129, 144
Parts per million (PPM), 193
Passive solar, 113
Passive trackers, 121
Phosphoric acid fuel cell (PAFC), 186
Photosynthesis, 7
Photovoltaic (PV), 123
Photovoltaic (PV) cells, 115
Photovoltaic (PV) panels, 117
Photovoltaic array, 117
Photovoltaic devices, 113
Photovoltaic Panels, 8
Pitch, 49
Polarity, 115
Population increase, 4
Positioning motors, 121
Positive electrical charge, 16
Potassium Carbonate (K2CO3), 188
Power, 2, 116, 119
Power factor, 23
Primary cells, 32, 73, 143
Propellers, 49
Protons, 15
Pulse width modulation (PWM), 90, 159

Q

Quality of life, 1

R

Reactance, 18
Real power, 23
Recharges, 32, 73, 143
Rectifier, 53
Regulation mode, 82
Regulation stall mode, 84
Resistance, 18, 29, 37
Resistivity, 16
Rms, 24
Rotor, 51

S

Schematic diagram, 131